P9-DGE-350

Algebra 1

A Reference Guide

Book Staff and Contributors
Harold Lawrence *Content Specialist*
Jill Tunick *Senior Text Editor*
Kay McCarthy *Text Editor*
Suzanne Montazer *Creative Director, Print and ePublishing*
Stephanie Shaw Williams *Senior Print Visual Designer, Cover Designer*
Carol Leigh *Print Visual Designer*
Meredith Condit, Charlotte Fullerton, Steve Mawyer *Media Editors*
Susan Raley *Senior Manager, Writers and Editors*
Abhilasha Parakh *Senior Project Manager*

Paul Thomas *Senior Director, Content and Assessment*
Kelly Engel *Director, Mathematics Content Specialists*
Michelle Kitt *Director, Instructional Design*
Jason Golomb *Senior Director, Program Management Product Development*
Christopher Frescholtz *Senior Director, Program Management*

Lisa Dimaio Iekel *Director, Print Production and Manufacturing*

About K12 Inc.
K12 Inc., a technology-based education company, is the nation's leading provider of proprietary curriculum and online education programs to students in grades K–12. K^{12} provides its curriculum and academic services to online schools, traditional classrooms, blended school programs, and directly to families. K12 Inc. also operates the K^{12} International Academy, an accredited, diploma-granting online private school serving students worldwide. K^{12}'s mission is to provide any child the curriculum and tools to maximize success in life, regardless of geographic, financial, or demographic circumstances. K12 Inc. is accredited by CITA. More information can be found at www.K12.com.

ISBN: 978-1-60153-509-2 (online book)
ISBN: 978-1-60153-503-0 (printed book)

Printed by Quad Graphics, Versailles, KY, USA, May 2016

Contents

Two-Variable Linear Equations and Inequalities

Introduction to Functions

Radicals and Exponents

Exponential Functions

Sequences and Modeling with Functions

Systems of Equations

Polynomials

Quadratic Equations

Quadratic Functions

Univariate Data

Bivariate Data

Appendices

K^{12} Summit Curriculum

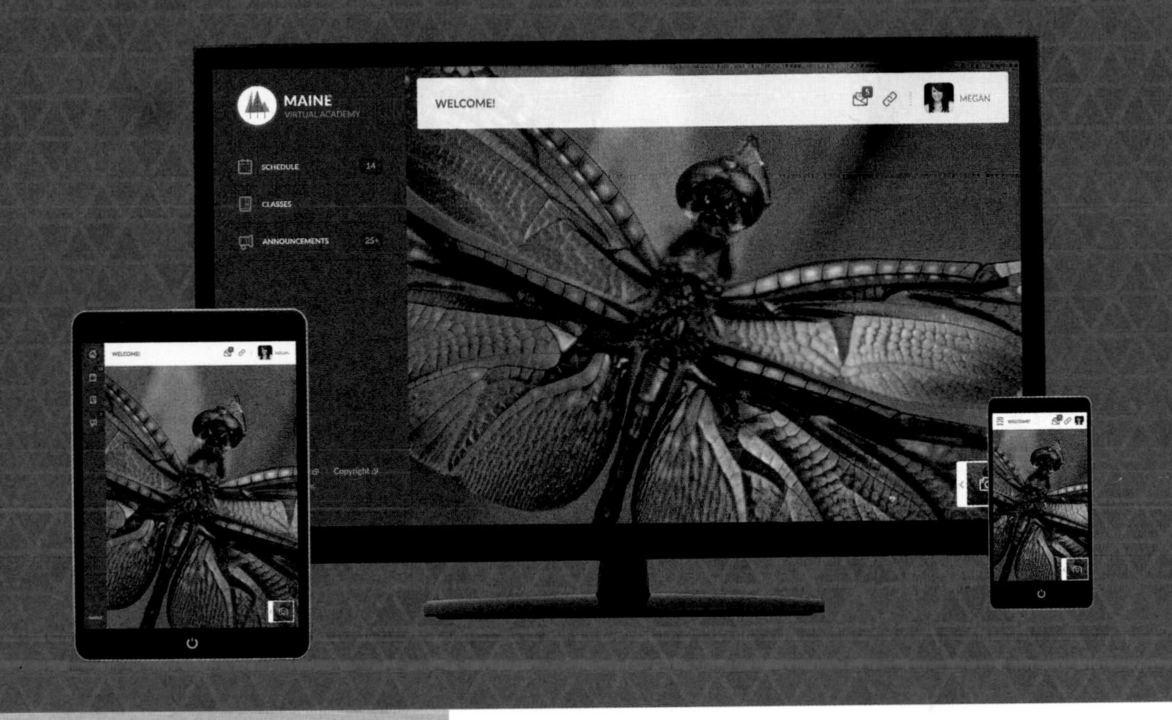

And remember: The pages in your book are also online!

Go to the online course to look for these digital resources in your lessons:

Videos will introduce you to each topic.

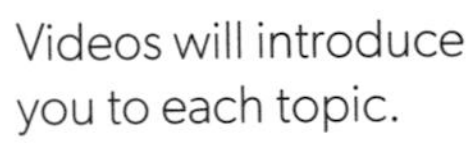

math CAST

Visual learning with animations and interaction will help you master key skills.

Solve problems with the help of stepped examples.

Use real-world examples to practice what you've learned.

Expressions and Problem Solving

Topic List

- Expressions
- Variables
- Equations
- Translating Words into Variable Expressions
- Translating Words into Equations
- Problem Solving
- Dimensional Analysis
- Structure and Meaning

The English word *algebra* and the Spanish word *algebrista* both come from an Arabic word meaning "restoration." Medieval barbers, sometimes called algebristas, fixed broken bones. Algebra can help you find solutions and "fix" problems.

Expressions

A **numerical expression** consists of numbers and one or more operations.

Here are some examples of numerical expressions:

$18 - 2$ $\quad 7 + 2 \cdot 3$ $\quad 4 + 2[3 - 4 \div (12 - 8)]$ $\quad \dfrac{(5+3)^2}{10 - 3(4-2)}$

▸ Think About It

NOTATION An exponent indicates repeated multiplication, so $8^2 = 8 \cdot 8$.

To find the value of a numerical expression, you need to simplify the expression or evaluate the expression. To simplify a numerical expression, perform the indicated operation(s).

Consider the expression $7 + 2 \cdot 3$. If you add and then multiply, you get the value 27. But if you multiply and then add, you get the value 13. Because an expression can have only one value, mathematicians have agreed on a process to follow so that everyone simplifies expressions the same way. This process is the order of operations.

Order of Operations

Step 1 Perform operations within grouping symbols. For nested grouping symbols, simplify in the innermost group first.

Step 2 Evaluate powers (as indicated by exponents).

Step 3 Multiply and divide from left to right.

Step 4 Add and subtract from left to right.

Think About It You can use "Please Excuse My Dear Aunt Sally" to remember the order of operations.

P: Parentheses
E: Exponents
M/D: Multiply and Divide
A/S: Add and Subtract

So the correct way to simplify $7 + 2 \cdot 3$ is to multiply and then add.

$$7 + 2 \cdot 3 = 7 + 6 = 13$$

The most common grouping symbols are parentheses ( ). Grouping symbols can affect the value of an expression. Nested grouping symbols (grouping symbols within grouping symbols) contain brackets [ ] and sometimes braces { }.

Simplifying Expressions With and Without Grouping Symbols

EXAMPLE 1

Simplify.

A $5 \cdot 2 + 7$

SOLUTION

$5 \cdot 2 + 7 = \mathbf{10} + 7$ Multiply.

$= 17$ Add.

B $5 \cdot (2 + 7)$

SOLUTION

$5 \cdot (2 + 7) = 5 \cdot \mathbf{(9)}$ Add first because addition appears inside parentheses.

$= 45$ Multiply. ■

Simplifying Expressions with Several Operations

EXAMPLE 2

Simplify.

A $3 \bullet 7 - 10 \div 2 \bullet 3$

SOLUTION

$3 \bullet 7 - 10 \div 2 \bullet 3 = \mathbf{21} - 10 \div 2 \bullet 3$	Multiply and divide in order from left to right.
$= 21 - \mathbf{5} \bullet 3$	
$= 21 - \mathbf{15}$	
$= 6$	Subtract.

B $4 + 2[3 - 4 \div (12 - 8)]$

SOLUTION

$4 + 2[3 - 4 \div (12 - 8)] = 4 + 2[3 - 4 \div \mathbf{4}]$	Parentheses are nested within brackets. Subtract.
$= 4 + 2[3 - \mathbf{1}]$	Divide inside the brackets.
$= 4 + 2[\mathbf{2}]$	Subtract inside the brackets.
$= 4 + \mathbf{4}$	Multiply.
$= 8$	Add. ■

Simplifying an Expression with a Fraction Bar

A fraction bar indicates division. It is also a grouping symbol, separating the numerator from the denominator.

EXAMPLE 3

Simplify.

$$\frac{(5+3)^2}{1+2^5-23}$$

▶ **Think About It** In Example 3, the expression can be written as follows:

$$(5+3)^2 \div (1+2^5-23)$$

SOLUTION

Treat the fraction bar as a grouping symbol. Simplify the numerator and denominator, and then divide.

$\frac{(5+3)^2}{1+2^5-23} = \frac{(\mathbf{8})^2}{1+2^5-23}$ Perform the operation inside the parentheses.

$= \frac{\mathbf{64}}{1+\mathbf{32}-23}$ Evaluate powers: $8^2 = 8 \cdot 8 = 64$ and $2^5 = 2 \cdot 2 \cdot 2 \cdot 2 \cdot 2 = 32$.

$= \frac{64}{\mathbf{10}}$ Add and subtract from left to right to simplify the denominator.

$= \frac{32}{5}$

$= 6.4$ Reduce the fraction or divide to simplify. ■

Placing Grouping Symbols to Get a Specified Value

You can get different values for an expression by changing the placement of grouping symbols.

EXAMPLE 4

Place grouping symbols in the expression $2 \bullet 8 + 2^3 \bullet 10$ to get expressions that have these values: 20,000 and 80,000.

SOLUTION

The method is trial and error. Some possible placements of grouping symbols are $2 \bullet (8 + 2)^3 \bullet 10$, $[2 \bullet (8 + 2)]^3 \bullet 10$, and $(2 \bullet 8 + 2)^3 \bullet 10$. Evaluate these expressions, and try other placements if necessary. The two correct expressions are shown.

First Expression

$2 \bullet (8 + 2)^3 \bullet 10 = 2 \bullet \mathbf{(10)}^3 \bullet 10$	Perform the operation inside the parentheses.
$= 2 \bullet \mathbf{1000} \bullet 10$	Evaluate the power: $10^3 = 10 \bullet 10 \bullet 10 = 1000$.
$= \mathbf{2000} \bullet 10$	Multiply from left to right.
$= 20{,}000$	Multiply.

Second Expression

$[2 \bullet (8 + 2)]^3 \bullet 10 = [2 \bullet \mathbf{(10)}]^3 \bullet 10$	Perform the operation inside the parentheses.
$= [\mathbf{20}]^3 \bullet 10$	Perform the operation inside the brackets.
$= \mathbf{8000} \bullet 10$	Evaluate the power: $20^3 = 20 \bullet 20 \bullet 20 = 8000$.
$= 80{,}000$	Multiply. ■

Variables

A **variable** is a symbol that represents a value.

Variables are usually represented by lowercase letters in italics. Most books use x, y, a, and n more than other letters. A variable expression is a combination of variables, numbers, and operations. Here are some examples of variable expressions:

$$x - 2 \qquad 5n + 7 \qquad \frac{c + 1}{d - 2} \qquad 2y - 21z + 6$$

▶ **Think About It** A variable expression can also be called an algebraic expression.

To evaluate variable expressions, substitute, or replace, numbers for the variables. So the value of a variable expression depends on the numbers chosen for the variable(s).

Evaluating Variable Expressions

To evaluate a variable expression, replace all the variables in the expression with numbers and simplify the resulting numerical expression.

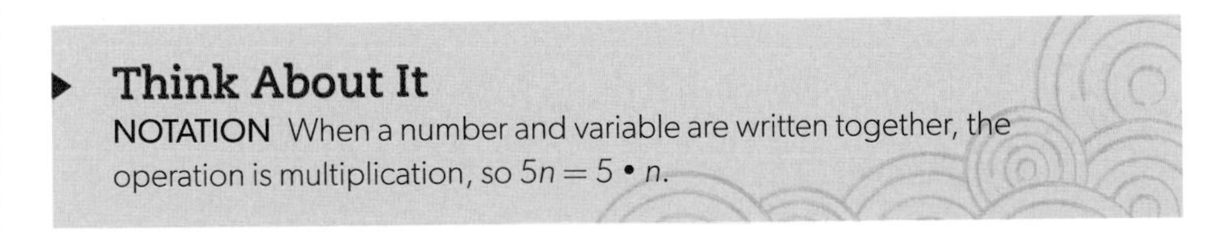

▶ **Think About It**

NOTATION When a number and variable are written together, the operation is multiplication, so $5n = 5 \cdot n$.

EXAMPLE 1

Evaluate.

A $5n + 7$ when $n = 8$

SOLUTION

$5n + 7 = 5 \cdot \mathbf{8} + 7$ Substitute 8 for n.

$= 40 + 7$ Multiply.

$= 47$ Add.

B $\frac{c + 1}{d - 2}$ when $c = 3$ and $d = 4$

SOLUTION

$\frac{c + 1}{d - 2} = \frac{\mathbf{3} + 1}{\mathbf{4} - 2}$ Substitute 3 for c and 4 for d.

$= \frac{4}{2}$ Simplify the numerator, and then the denominator.

$= 2$ Divide. ■

Identifying Terms

Variable expressions consist of terms. Terms are the parts of an expression that are added or subtracted. A term that has no variables is a constant.

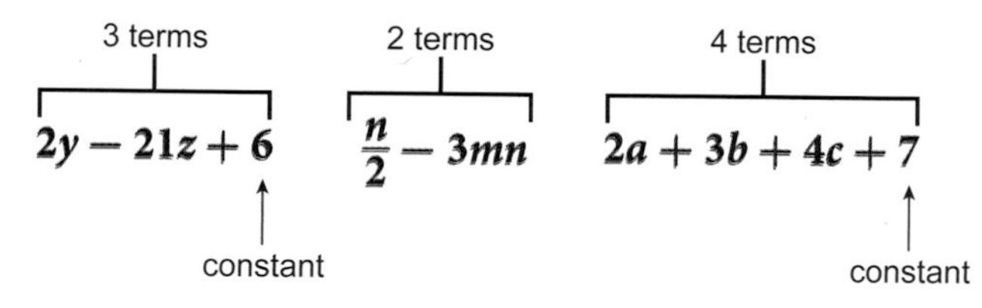

EXAMPLE 2

Identify the terms of the expression $3x + y + 23$.

SOLUTION

Each term is separated by a "+" sign. The terms are $3x$, y, and 23. The number 23 is a constant since there is no variable. ■

Identifying Coefficients and Factors

Terms can consist of two or more factors. The numerical part of a term is the coefficient. When the coefficient of a term is 1, it is usually not written.

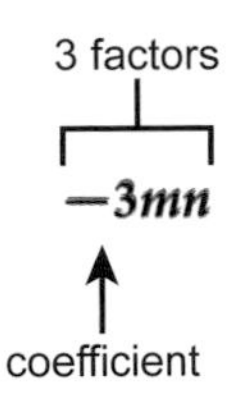

▶ **Remember** In $2 \cdot 3 = 6$, 2 and 3 are the factors and 6 is the product.

EXAMPLE 3

Identify the coefficient and factors of each term.

A $-mn$

SOLUTION

You can write the term $-mn$ as $-1 \cdot m \cdot n$. So the coefficient is -1. The factors are -1, m, and n.

B $\frac{n}{2}$

SOLUTION

You can write the term $\frac{n}{2}$ as $\frac{1}{2} \cdot n$. So the coefficient is $\frac{1}{2}$. The factors are $\frac{1}{2}$ and n. ■

Applications: Measurement and Distance Traveled

You can use expressions to solve many types of problems, including those involving measurement.

EXAMPLE 4

Identify the coefficient and factors of each term.

A Natalie jogged once around the perimeter of a football field, which has a length of 100 yd and a width of 60 yd. Find the total number of yards she jogged.

SOLUTION

Use the expression $2l + 2w$, where l is the length of the rectangle and w is the width of the rectangle, to find the perimeter. Evaluate $2l + 2w$ when $l = 100$ and $w = 60$.

$2l + 2w = 2 \cdot \mathbf{100} + 2 \cdot \mathbf{60}$	Substitute 100 for l and 60 for w.
$= 200 + 120$	Multiply.
$= 320$	Add.

Natalie jogged 320 yd.

B Find the area of the triangle.

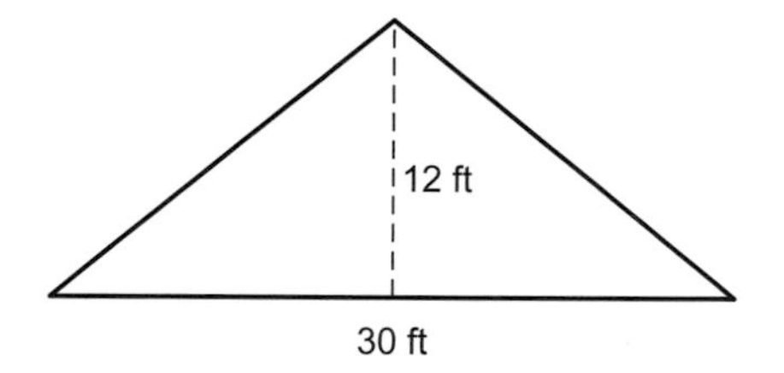

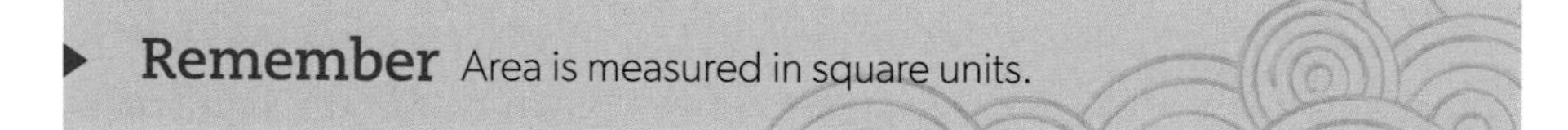

SOLUTION

Use the expression $\frac{1}{2}bh$, where b is the length of the base and h is the height of the triangle, to find the area. Evaluate $\frac{1}{2}bh$ when $b = 30$ and $h = 12$.

$\frac{1}{2}bh = \frac{1}{2} \cdot \mathbf{30} \cdot \mathbf{12}$	Substitute 30 for b and 12 for h.
$= 15 \cdot 12$	Multiply from left to right.
$= 180$	Multiply.

The area of the triangle is 180 ft^2.

C Find the number of miles the Perez family traveled if they drove nonstop for 2.5 h at a rate of 60 mph.

SOLUTION

Use the expression rt, where r is the rate of travel in miles per hour and t is the number of hours traveled, to find the number of miles the vehicle traveled. Evaluate rt when $r = 60$ and $t = 2.5$.

$rt = \mathbf{60} \cdot \mathbf{2.5}$	Substitute 60 for r and 2.5 for t.
$= 150$	Multiply.

The Perez family traveled 150 mi. ■

Equations

When you join two expressions with an equals sign, you create an equation.

The expressions $2 + 5$ and $1 + 6$ each simplify to the same value, 7. Because they have the same value, you can join them together with an equals sign to form an equation: $2 + 5 = 1 + 6$.

Definition

An **equation** is a number sentence that indicates that two expressions have the same value.

One way to distinguish between an equation and an expression is to look for an equals sign. Equations have an equals sign and expressions do not. Also, equations correspond to sentences, and expressions correspond to phrases.

Expression	Equation
$7 + 3$	$7 + 3 = 10$
phrase: the sum of seven and three	sentence: The sum of seven and three is ten.

Determining Whether Two Expressions Form an Equation

When two expressions are not equal, they do not form an equation. Instead of joining them with an equals sign, join them with the not-equal-to sign ($\neq$).

EXAMPLE 1

Write $=$ or $\neq$ to make a true statement.

A $5 \bullet 2 + 7 \blacksquare 5 \bullet (2 + 7)$

SOLUTION

Use the order of operations to simplify the expressions.

$$5 \bullet 2 + 7 = 10 + 7 \\ = 17$$

$$5 \bullet (2 + 7) = 5 \bullet (9) \\ = 45$$

The expression on the left has a different value than the expression on the right. So the expressions do not form an equation: $5 \bullet 2 + 7 \neq 5 \bullet (2 + 7)$.

B $3[5(2 + 1)] \blacksquare 100 - 5 \bullet 11$

SOLUTION

$$3[5(2 + 1)] = 3[5(3)] \\ = 3[15] \\ = 45$$

$$100 - 5 \bullet 11 = 100 - 55 \\ = 45$$

Both expressions have the same value. So the expressions form an equation: $3[5(2 + 1)] = 100 - 5 \bullet 11$. ■

Determining Whether a Given Value Makes an Open Sentence True

An equation that contains a variable is an open sentence. You do not know if the sentence is true or false until a value is substituted for the variable.

▶ **Think About It** Not all open sentences are equations. For instance, $3 + y \neq 5$ is an open sentence.

EXAMPLE 2

Determine whether the given value makes the open sentence true or false.

A $5a - 4 = 2; a = 2$

SOLUTION

Substitute the given value into each occurrence of the variable to see if the left and right sides of the equation are the same value.

$$\begin{aligned} 5a - 4 &= 2 \\ 5 \cdot \mathbf{2} - 4 &\stackrel{?}{=} 2 \\ 10 - 4 &\stackrel{?}{=} 2 \\ 6 &\neq 2 \end{aligned}$$

The sentence is false when $a = 2$.

B $10 = 0.5x; x = 40$

SOLUTION

$$\begin{aligned} 10 &= 0.5x \\ 10 &\stackrel{?}{=} 0.5 \cdot \mathbf{40} \\ 10 &\neq 20 \end{aligned}$$

The sentence is false when $x = 40$.

C $5n = 7n - 6; n = 3$

SOLUTION

$$\begin{aligned} 5n &= 7n - 6 \\ 5 \cdot \mathbf{3} &\stackrel{?}{=} 7 \cdot \mathbf{3} - 6 \\ 15 &\stackrel{?}{=} 21 - 6 \\ 15 &= 15 \checkmark \end{aligned}$$

The sentence is true when $n = 3$. ■

Application: Phone Plan

EXAMPLE 3

A phone company offers two monthly plans. The first plan costs \$25 per month plus 10¢ per minute. The second plan costs \$10 per month plus 25¢ per minute. Determine whether the monthly cost is the same when 100 min are used.

SOLUTION

To determine whether the cost is the same when 100 min are used, evaluate $25 + 0.10x = 10 + 0.25x$ when $x = 100$.

$$25 + 0.10x = 10 + 0.25x$$
$$25 + 0.10 \bullet \mathbf{100} \stackrel{?}{=} 10 + 0.25 \bullet \mathbf{100}$$
$$25 + 10 \stackrel{?}{=} 10 + 25$$
$$35 = 35 \checkmark$$

Yes, the monthly cost is the same when 100 min are used. ■

Translating Words into Variable Expressions

It is sometimes necessary to write a **variable expression** from words or phrases.

The table shows common words and phrases for each of the four basic operations.

Operation	Words and phrases
addition	plus, more than, increased by, sum
subtraction	minus, less than, decreased by, difference
multiplication	times, product
division	divided by, quotient

▶ **Think About It** The phrases "y less than x" and "x is decreased by y" are represented by the same expression: $x - y$.

The phrase "the quantity" indicates that grouping symbols should appear in the expression. For example, the expression $4x + 8$ represents the phrase "four times x plus eight," but the expression $4(x + 8)$ represents the phrase "four times the quantity x plus eight."

Translating Word Phrases into Variable Expressions

EXAMPLE 1

Translate the word phrase into a variable expression. Use n to represent "a number" in each expression.

> ▶ **Remember** Unless stated otherwise, you can choose any letter for the variable(s).

A twenty-five times a number

SOLUTION

$25n$

B six less than twice a number

SOLUTION

$2n - 6$

C twice the sum of nine and a number

SOLUTION

$2(9 + n)$

D the quotient of three and a number

SOLUTION

$\frac{3}{n}$ 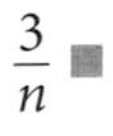

Using Only One Variable to Write a Variable Expression

Sometimes it is useful to write different quantities in terms of the same variable. For example, suppose you know the length of a rectangle is three times its width. Instead of using two variables, l and w, to represent the length and width, you can use w for width and $3w$ for length.

EXAMPLE 2

There are twelve more girls than boys in a classroom. Write expressions for the number of boys and the number of girls using the same variable, b.

SOLUTION

If b represents the number of boys, you can also represent the number of girls in terms of b.

$$\text{number of boys: } b$$
$$\text{number of girls: } b + 12$$

You can check your work by substituting a number for b. So if there are 8 boys, then the number of girls is $8 + 12$, or 20. ■

Application: Measurement

You can write a variable expression to help you convert from one unit of measure to another.

EXAMPLE 3

Find the number of feet in 2 yd, 5 yd, and y yd.

SOLUTION

There are 3 ft in 1 yd, so the number of feet is equal to the number of yards times 3.

Number of yards	Number of feet
2	$3 \cdot \mathbf{2} = 6$
5	$3 \cdot \mathbf{5} = 15$
y	$3 \cdot \boldsymbol{y} = 3y$

There are 6 ft in 2 yd, 15 ft in 5 yd, and $3y$ ft in y yd. ■

Application: Geometry

Geometric formulas are basically expressions that describe how to figure out values such as perimeter or area.

EXAMPLE 4

A Write and simplify an expression for the perimeter of the quadrilateral.

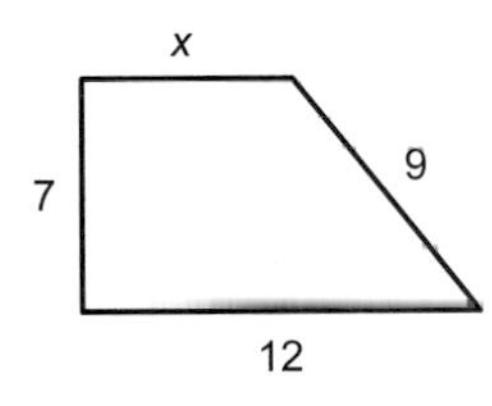

SOLUTION

Write an expression for the sum of all four sides, and then add the constant terms.

$$x + 7 + 12 + 9 = x + 28$$

The simplified expression for the perimeter is $x + 28$.

B Use the simplified expression to find the perimeter when $x = 5$.

SOLUTION

Evaluate $x + 28$ when $x = 5$. Substitute 5 for x, and then add.

$$x + 28 = \mathbf{5} + 28 = 33$$

When $x = 5$, the perimeter is 33 units. ■

Translating Words into Equations

Use the same words and phrases that allow you to translate word phrases into variable expressions to translate word sentences into equations.

Verbal sentences often use the word *is* and the phrase "is equal to." Represent each with an equals sign in an equation.

Translating Sentences into Equations

EXAMPLE 1

Translate the sentence into an equation.

A Two less than five times a number is equal to seven.

SOLUTION

$$\underbrace{\text{Two less than five times a number}}_{5n-2}\ \underbrace{\text{is equal to}}_{=}\ \underbrace{\text{seven.}}_{7}$$

The equation is $5n - 2 = 7$.

B The quotient of a number and four is the sum of six and the number.

SOLUTION

$$\underbrace{\text{The quotient of a number and four}}_{\frac{n}{4}}\ \underbrace{\text{is}}_{=}\ \underbrace{\text{the sum of six and the number.}}_{6+n}$$

The equation is $\frac{n}{4} = 6 + n$. ■

Finding True Statements

You may be asked to find the value of a variable that would make a verbal sentence true. Start by translating the sentence into an equation.

EXAMPLE 2

Find a value of the variable that makes the statement true.

A The product of six and a number is forty-two.

SOLUTION

$$\underbrace{\text{The product of six and a number}}_{6n}\ \underbrace{\text{is}}_{=}\ \underbrace{\text{forty-two.}}_{42}$$

The equation is $6n = 42$. Find the value of n by answering the question: What number times 6 equals 42? The answer is 7.

B Twelve less than a number is equal to nine.

SOLUTION

$$\underbrace{\text{Twelve less than a number}}_{n - 12}\ \underbrace{\text{is equal to}}_{=}\ \underbrace{\text{nine.}}_{9}$$

The equation is $n - 12 = 9$. Find the value of n by answering the question: What number reduced by 12 equals 9? The answer is 21. ■

Applications: Distance and Geometry

Equations can represent many real-world situations. These applications include problems involving distance traveled, as well as dimensions of common geometric shapes.

EXAMPLE 3

Carly rode her bicycle at a constant speed of 4 mph to her friend's house. Write an equation to represent the distance Carly rode.

SOLUTION

The formula for the distance traveled is $d = rt$, where d is the distance, r is the rate (or speed), and t is the time traveled. Since Carly's speed is 4 mph, $r = 4$. Substitute 4 for r to obtain the equation $d = 4t$. ■

EXAMPLE 4

A A rectangle is 2 m long, but the width is unknown. Write equations for the perimeter and area of the rectangle.

SOLUTION

The formula for the perimeter of a rectangle is $P = 2l + 2w$, and the formula for the area of a rectangle is $A = lw$. Substitute the known information into each formula and simplify as needed.

$P = 2l + 2w$ $\qquad$ $A = lw$

$P = 2 \cdot \mathbf{2} + 2w$ $\qquad$ $A = \mathbf{2}w$

$P = \mathbf{4} + 2w$

The equations are $P = 4 + 2w$ and $A = 2w$.

B Write an equation for the perimeter of the triangle.

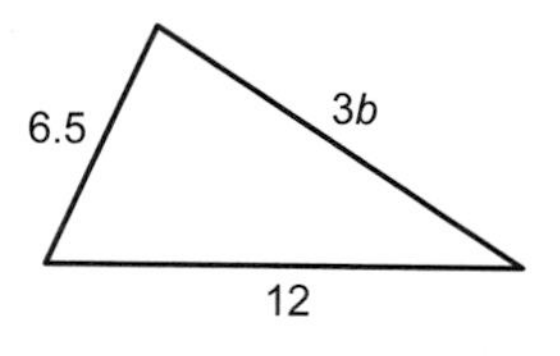

SOLUTION

The perimeter of a figure is the sum of the side lengths of the figure.

$$P = 12 + 6.5 + 3b$$
$$P = 18.5 + 3b$$

The equation is $P = 18.5 + 3b$. ■

Problem Solving

When using math to solve real-world problems, it can help to have a plan. The following suggested problem-solving strategy has five steps.

Problem-Solving Plan

Step 1 *Identify* Read the problem and identify the unknowns. What are you being asked to find? Write it down in words. If you can, estimate the answer.

Step 2 *Strategize* Select and define variables and variable expressions for all the unknowns.

Step 3 *Set Up* Write an equation, inequality, system of equations, or whatever other tools you need that model the problem that is being solved.

Step 4 *Solve* Solve the model (equation, inequality, system, and so on).

Step 5 *Check* Check your answer for reasonableness and accuracy with the original problem statement.

Application: Groups of People

EXAMPLE 1

The number of students is 7 more than 5 times the number of teachers. There are 12 teachers. How many students are there?

SOLUTION

Work through the five steps of the problem-solving plan.

Step 1 ***Identify*** List the known and the unknown information.

Known

number of teachers: 12

number of students: 7 more than 5 times the number of teachers

Unknown

number of students = ?

Step 2 ***Strategize*** Choose a variable for the unknown.

number of students = s

Step 3 ***Set Up*** Reread the problem. Write an equation to represent the relationship between the number of students and teachers.

$$\underbrace{\text{The number of students}}_{s}\ \underbrace{\text{is}}_{=}\ \underbrace{\text{7 more than 5 times the number of teachers.}}_{7 + 5 \bullet 12}$$

The equation is $s = 7 + 5 \bullet 12$.

Step 4 ***Solve*** Simplify the expression on the right side of the equation.

$$\begin{aligned} s &= 7 + 5 \bullet 12 \\ &= 7 + 60 \\ &= 67 \end{aligned}$$

Step 5 ***Check*** Check your results. Give your answer.

Five times the number of teachers is 60.

Seven more than 60 is 67.

The solution makes sense.

There are 67 students. ■

Applications: Perimeter and Area

You can also use the problem-solving plan to solve geometry problems.

EXAMPLE 2

The area of a rectangle is 70 units^2 and the width of the rectangle is 5 units. Find the perimeter of the rectangle.

SOLUTION

Use the problem-solving plan.

Step 1 ***Identify*** You are asked to find the perimeter. To find the perimeter, you must know both the length and width of the rectangle. The width is known, but the length is not known.

Step 2 ***Strategize*** Write and solve an equation for the area of a rectangle to find the value of the length. Then find the perimeter of the rectangle. Define the variables. Use w for width, l for length, A for area, and P for perimeter.

Step 3 ***Set Up*** Write an equation to represent the area.

$$A = lw$$
$$70 = l \cdot 5$$

Step 4 ***Solve*** Think: "What number times 5 equals 70?" You can guess and check, or divide: $70 \div 5 = 14$. The length is 14 units. To find the perimeter, substitute 5 and 14 into $P = 2l + 2w$.

$$\begin{aligned} P &= 2 \cdot \mathbf{14} + 2 \cdot \mathbf{5} \\ &= 28 + 10 \\ &= 38 \end{aligned}$$

▶ **Think About It** One way to check for accuracy is to use a different method than the one used to solve the problem. This check adds all four side lengths instead of finding the sum of twice the length and twice the width.

Step 5 ***Check*** Length times width equals area.

$$5 \cdot 14 = 70$$

The given area is 70, so the length is correct. The perimeter is the sum of the sides.

$$5 + 14 + 5 + 14 = 38$$

The answer is correct. The perimeter is 38 units. ■

Application: Distance, Rate, and Time

EXAMPLE 3

LeAnn drove 315 mi at a rate of 45 mph. How long did it take her to drive this distance?

SOLUTION

Step 1 ***Identify*** You are given the distance and rate and are asked to find the time.

Step 2 ***Strategize*** Use d for distance, r for rate, and t for time.

Step 3 ***Set Up*** Distance is the product of the rate and the time, or $d = rt$. Substitute the known information into the general equation.

$$315 = 45t$$

Step 4 ***Solve*** The equation states that 315 is the product of 45 and t. So to find t, divide 315 by 45.

$$315 \div 45 = 7$$

Step 5 ***Check*** Multiply the rate by the time.

$$45 \cdot 7 = 315$$

The distance is correct. It took LeAnn 7 h to drive 315 mi. ■

Dimensional Analysis

If you can multiply fractions, then you can convert units of measure.

▸ **Think About It** A conversion factor has a value of 1.

There are 12 in. in 1 ft. You can write this relationship as an equation.

$$12 \text{ in.} = 1 \text{ ft}$$

You can also write it as a conversion factor.

$$\frac{12 \text{ in.}}{1 \text{ft}}$$

In a **conversion factor**, the numerator and denominator are the same quantity written in different units.

Writing Conversion Factors

For any pair of units, there are two related conversion factors because you can switch the numerator and denominator.

EXAMPLE 1

Write two related conversion factors for the units.

A days and weeks

SOLUTION
There are 7 days in 1 week. The conversion factors are $\frac{7 \text{ days}}{1 \text{ week}}$ and $\frac{1 \text{ week}}{7 \text{ days}}$.

B meters and kilometers

SOLUTION

There are 1000 m in 1 km. The conversion factors are $\frac{1000 \text{ m}}{1 \text{ km}}$ and $\frac{1 \text{ km}}{1000 \text{ m}}$. ■

To convert between units, you can use a process called dimensional analysis. **Dimensional analysis** is the process of multiplying by conversion factors and dividing out common units. Dividing out common units is similar to dividing out common factors.

$$\frac{3}{\cancel{5}} \cdot \frac{\cancel{5}}{7} = \frac{3}{7} \qquad \frac{\text{ft}}{\cancel{\text{h}}} \cdot \frac{\cancel{\text{h}}}{\text{min}} = \frac{\text{ft}}{\text{min}}$$

Some conversions require multiplying by only one conversion factor. Others require multiplying by several conversion factors. To determine which of two related conversion factors to multiply by, think about how the units will divide out. Choose the factor that divides out the unit you no longer want.

Converting Measures

EXAMPLE 2

How many yards are in 162 ft?

SOLUTION

The conversion factors for converting from feet to yards are $\frac{3 \text{ ft}}{1 \text{ yd}}$ and $\frac{1 \text{ yd}}{3 \text{ ft}}$. Use the factor $\frac{1 \text{ yd}}{3 \text{ ft}}$ because the unit of feet is in the denominator, and it will divide out with the unit of feet in 162 ft.

$$162 \cancel{\text{ft}} \cdot \frac{1 \text{ yd}}{3 \cancel{\text{ft}}} = 54 \text{ yd}$$

There are 54 yd in 162 ft. ■

EXAMPLE 3

How many minutes are in 15 days?

SOLUTION

There are 24 h in 1 day and 60 min in 1 h. Use the conversion factors that will divide out the number of days and the number of hours.

$$15 \cancel{\text{days}} \bullet \frac{24 \cancel{\text{h}}}{1 \cancel{\text{day}}} \bullet \frac{60 \text{ min}}{1 \cancel{\text{h}}} = 21{,}600 \text{ min}$$

There are 21,600 min in 15 days. ■

You can also use dimensional analysis to convert rates.

How to Convert Rates Using Dimensional Analysis

Step 1 Write the original rate as a fraction.

Step 2 Determine the conversion factor or factors that will divide out the units you no longer want.

Step 3 Multiply by the conversion factor or factors and simplify.

▶ **Remember** A rate is a ratio of quantities in different units, such as $\frac{35 \text{ ft}}{2 \text{ days}}$.

Converting Rates

EXAMPLE 4

A train travels 540 mi in 4.5 h. What is the train's rate in miles per minute?

SOLUTION

Step 1 Write the original rate as a fraction.

$$\frac{540 \text{ mi}}{4.5 \text{ h}}$$

Step 2 In the new rate, the first quantity will still be miles but the second quantity will be minutes. The conversion factor that will divide out the hours with the original rate is $\frac{1 \text{ h}}{60 \text{ min}}$ because the unit of hours is in the numerator.

Step 3 Multiply.

$$\frac{\overset{9}{\cancel{540}}\text{ mi}}{4.5\cancel{\text{h}}} \bullet \frac{1\cancel{\text{h}}}{\underset{1}{\cancel{60}}\text{ min}} = \frac{9\text{ mi}}{4.5\text{ min}} = \frac{2\text{ mi}}{1\text{ min}}$$

The train's rate is 2 mi/min. ■

EXAMPLE 5

A hose is leaking water at a rate of 2 oz/h.

A How many cups of water will leak out after 2 weeks?

SOLUTION

Convert the rate into cups per week.

Step 1 Write the original rate as a fraction.

$$\frac{2\text{ oz}}{1\text{h}}$$

Step 2 Both quantities in the rate will change. The factor that will convert ounces to cups is $\frac{1\text{ cup}}{8\text{ oz}}$. The factors that will convert hours to days, and then days to weeks, are $\frac{24\text{ h}}{1\text{ day}}$ and $\frac{7\text{ days}}{1\text{ week}}$.

Step 3 Multiply.

$$\frac{2\cancel{\text{oz}}}{1\cancel{\text{h}}} \bullet \frac{1\text{ cup}}{\underset{1}{\cancel{8}}\cancel{\text{oz}}} \bullet \frac{\overset{3}{\cancel{24}}\cancel{\text{h}}}{1\text{ day}} \bullet \frac{7\text{ days}}{1\text{ week}} = \frac{42\text{ cups}}{1\text{ week}} = 42\text{ cups per week}$$

The hose is leaking at a rate of 42 cups per week. Therefore, 2 • 42 cups, or 84 cups, of water will leak out after 2 weeks.

B How many gallons of water will leak out after 2 weeks?

SOLUTION

Convert 84 cups into gallons.

$$84\cancel{\text{ cups}} \bullet \frac{1\cancel{\text{pt}}}{2\cancel{\text{ cups}}} \bullet \frac{1\cancel{\text{qt}}}{2\cancel{\text{pt}}} \bullet \frac{1\text{ gal}}{4\cancel{\text{qt}}} = \frac{84\text{ gal}}{16} = 5.25\text{ gal}$$

After 2 weeks, 5.25 gal will have leaked out of the hose. ■

Structure and Meaning

You can use the parts of an expression to understand the real-world situation the expression represents.

Interpreting Parts of an Expression

EXAMPLE 1

Maci buys a karate uniform and pays a fee for each karate class she takes. The fee for each class is the same. The number of classes she takes is unknown. The expression $10c + 19.95$ represents the total Maci pays for her uniform and the classes.

A What does each factor in the first term represent?

SOLUTION

The first term is $10c$. The fee per class is always the same, but the number of classes taken can vary. The coefficient 10 represents the cost per class in dollars, and the variable c represents the number of classes taken.

▶ **Remember** Terms are the parts of the expression that are added or subtracted.

B What does the first term in the expression represent?

SOLUTION

The first term is the product of the fee per class and the number of classes taken. The first term represents the total amount Maci pays for her karate classes.

▸ **Remember** A constant is a term with no variables.

C What does the constant in the expression represent?

SOLUTION

The constant is 19.95. It is not a factor, so it represents a one-time purchase. The only thing that Maci bought one time was her uniform. The constant represents the cost of Maci's uniform: \$19.95. ■

Geometric Expressions

Sometimes expressions look complicated until you understand how they are built.

EXAMPLE 2

Consider the expression $2\pi rh + 2\pi r^2$, which gives the surface area of a cylinder with radius r and height h. Explain what each part of the expression means for the actual surfaces.

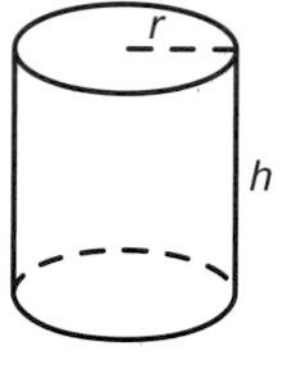

▸ **Think About It** Surface area is the sum of the areas of the outer surfaces of the solid.

SOLUTION

The area of the curved side that joins the top and bottom of the cylinder is given by the expression $2\pi rh$, which is the first term of the expression.

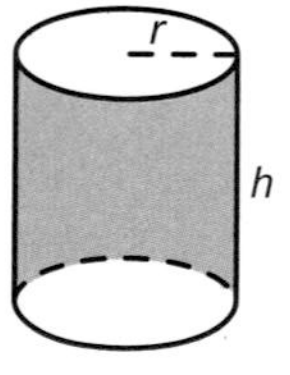

$$\mathbf{2\pi rh} + 2\pi r^2$$

▸ **Think About It** When "unfolded," the curved side is a rectangle with a length of $2\pi r$ and a width of h.

The area of the top circle is given by the expression πr^2. This quantity appears in the second term of the expression.

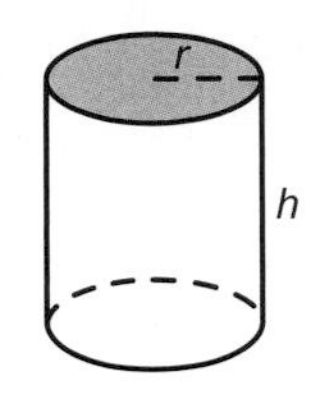

$$2\pi rh + 2\boldsymbol{\pi r^2}$$

There are two circles, each with the same area. So the expression for the area of a circle is multiplied by 2, and the second term represents the area of both the top and bottom of the cylinder.

$$2\pi rh + \mathbf{2}\pi r^2 \ ■$$

One-Variable Linear Equations and Inequalities

Topic List

- Addition and Subtraction Equations
- Multiplication and Division Equations
- Multiple Transformations
- Variables on Both Sides of an Equation
- Applications: Cost Problems
- Transforming Formulas
- Solving Inequalities
- Applications: Inequalities
- Reasoning with Solutions

The Greek mathematician Diophantus is often called "the father of algebra." His book *Arithmetica* collected solutions to math problems that had been found by Greeks, Egyptians, and Babylonians. Algebra has helped people solve real-world problems for centuries.

Addition and Subtraction Equations

Use properties of equality and what you know about inverse operations to solve addition and subtraction equations.

An **equation** is a number sentence indicating that two expressions have the same value. A **solution** of an equation is a value for the variable that makes the equation a true statement. To **solve** an equation, you need to find all the solutions of the equation. Some one-variable equations have more than one solution.

One way to solve an equation is to find a series of equivalent equations, each one simpler than the one before. **Equivalent equations** are equations with the same solution or solutions.

Properties of Equality

Addition Property of Equality If $a = b$, then $a + c = b + c$ and $c + a = c + b$.

Subtraction Property of Equality If $a = b$, then $a - c = b - c$.

Substitution Property of Equality If $a = b$, then a may be replaced with b in any expression or equation.

▶ **Think About It** Use the addition and subtraction properties to solve an equation. Use the substitution property to check your solution.

The addition property of equality tells you that you can add the same value to each side of an equation to create an equivalent equation. The subtraction property of equality tells you that you can subtract the same value from each side of an equation to create an equivalent equation.

Solving a Subtraction Equation

Remember that addition and subtraction are inverse operations, so use the addition property of equality to solve subtraction equations.

EXAMPLE 1

Solve $x - 12 = 8$.

SOLUTION

You need to isolate x. The expression $x - 12$ indicates that 12 is subtracted from x. To "undo" the subtraction, use the inverse operation, addition.

$x - 12 = 8$	
$x - 12 + \mathbf{12} = 8 + \mathbf{12}$	Add 12 to each side. (Addition Property of Equality)
$x = 20$	Simplify.

CHECK

$x - 12 = 8$	Write the original equation.
$\mathbf{20} - 12 \stackrel{?}{=} 8$	Substitute 20 for x. (Substitution Property of Equality)
$8 = 8$ ✓	The solution is correct because $8 = 8$ is a true statement. ■

▶ **Remember** The solution in Example 1 is 20, not 8.

Look back at Example 1. The equations $x - 12 = 8$ and $x = 20$ are equivalent equations. The equation $x = 20$ has the variable isolated on one side of the equals sign, so it names the solution, 20.

Solving an Addition Equation

Use the subtraction property of equality to solve addition equations.

EXAMPLE 2

Solve $21 = b + 9$.

SOLUTION

$21 = b + 9$	
$21 - \mathbf{9} = b + 9 - \mathbf{9}$	Subtract 9 from each side. (Subtraction Property of Equality)
$12 = b$	Simplify.

CHECK

$21 = b + 9$	Write the original equation.
$21 \stackrel{?}{=} \mathbf{12} + 9$	Substitute 12 for b. (Substitution Property of Equality)
$21 = 21$ ✓	The solution is correct because $21 = 21$ is a true statement. ■

Simplifying First

Sometimes it helps if you simplify each side of an equation before trying to solve it.

EXAMPLE 3

Solve.

A $5 + x - 14 = -15$

SOLUTION

$5 + x - 14 = -15$	
$x + 5 - 14 = -15$	Use the commutative property of addition to rewrite $5 + x$ as $x + 5$. Then simplify: $5 - 14 = -9$.
$x - 9 = -15$	
$x - 9 + \mathbf{9} = -15 + \mathbf{9}$	Add 9 to each side.
$x = -6$	Simplify.

CHECK

$5 + x - 14 = -15$	Write the original equation.
$5 + \mathbf{(-6)} - 14 \stackrel{?}{=} -15$	Substitute -6 for x.
$-15 = -15$ ✓	The solution is correct.

▶ **Think About It** In Example 3A, these are all equivalent equations:

$$5 + x - 14 = -15$$
$$x + 5 - 14 = -15$$
$$x - 9 = -15$$
$$x - 9 + 9 = -15 + 9$$
$$x = -6$$

The last one, $x = -6$, names the solution.

B $17 - (8 - q) = 10$

SOLUTION

$17 - (8 - q) = 10$	
$17 - 8 + q = 10$	Distributive Property
$9 + q = 10$	Simplify.
$9 - \mathbf{9} + q = 10 - \mathbf{9}$	Subtract 9 from each side.
$q = 1$	Simplify.

CHECK

$17 - (8 - q) = 10$	Write the original equation.
$17 - (8 - \mathbf{1}) \stackrel{?}{=} 10$	Substitute 1 for q.
$17 - 7 \stackrel{?}{=} 10$	Use the order of operations.
$10 = 10$ ✓	The solution is correct. ■

▶ **Think About It** In Example 3B, the distributive property is used as follows:

$$\begin{aligned} & 17 - (8 - q) \\ & = 17 + (-1)(8 - q) \\ & = 17 + (-1) \cdot 8 + (-1) \cdot (-q) \\ & = 17 - 8 + q \end{aligned}$$

Application: Change in Elevation

You can use an addition or subtraction equation to solve many real-world problems, including problems with changing altitude.

EXAMPLE 4

A hot-air balloon descended (went down) 150 ft to a height of 3500 ft. How high was the hot-air balloon before its descent?

SOLUTION

Step 1 Write an equation.

Let x represent the height of the balloon before its descent.

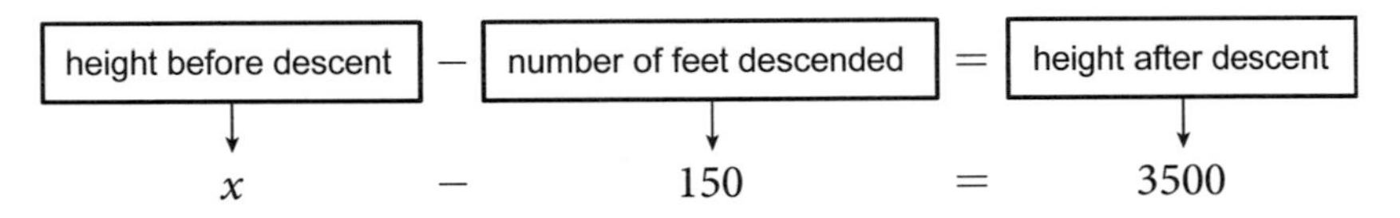

Step 2 Solve the equation.

$x - 150 = 3500$	
$x - 150 + \mathbf{150} = 3500 + \mathbf{150}$	Add 150 to each side.
$x = 3650$	Simplify.

Step 3 Check the solution.

$x - 150 = 3500$	Write the original equation.
$\mathbf{3650} - 150 \stackrel{?}{=} 3500$	Substitute 3650 for x.
$3500 = 3500$ ✓	Simplify.

The height of the hot-air balloon before its descent was 3650 ft. ■

Solving Absolute Value Equations

To solve equations involving absolute value, use the following property:
If $|x| = a$ for some positive number a, then $x = a$ or $x = -a$.

EXAMPLE 5

Solve.

A $|c| + 2 = 10$

SOLUTION

$\|c\| + 2 = 10$	
$\|c\| + 2 - \mathbf{2} = 10 - \mathbf{2}$	Subtract 2 from each side.
$\|c\| = 8$	Simplify.
$c = 8$ or $c = -8$	If $\|x\| = a$ for some positive number a, then $x = a$ or $x = -a$.

▶ **Think About It** If either 8 makes the equation true or −8 makes the equation true, then both numbers are solutions. That is, 8 and −8 are solutions. Of course, only one number at a time makes the equation true.

CHECK

$\|c\| + 2 = 10$	$\|c\| + 2 = 10$
$\|\mathbf{8}\| + 2 \stackrel{?}{=} 10$	$\|\mathbf{-8}\| + 2 \stackrel{?}{=} 10$
$8 + 2 \stackrel{?}{=} 10$	$8 + 2 \stackrel{?}{=} 10$
$10 = 10$ ✓	$10 = 10$ ✓

The solutions are 8 and −8, so the solution set is $\{-8, 8\}$.

B $-3 - |k| = -5$

SOLUTION

$-3 - \|k\| = -5$	
$-3 + \mathbf{3} - \|k\| = -5 + \mathbf{3}$	Add 3 to each side.
$-\|k\| = -2$	Simplify.
$\|k\| = 2$	$-\|k\|$ is the opposite of $\|k\|$, so if $-\|k\| = -2$, then $\|k\| = 2$.
$k = 2$ or $k = -2$	

CHECK

$$\begin{aligned} -3 - |k| &= -5 \\ -3 - |\mathbf{2}| &\stackrel{?}{=} -5 \\ -3 - 2 &\stackrel{?}{=} -5 \\ -5 &= -5 \checkmark \end{aligned} \qquad \begin{aligned} -3 - |k| &= -5 \\ -3 - |\mathbf{-2}| &\stackrel{?}{=} -5 \\ -3 - 2 &\stackrel{?}{=} -5 \\ -5 &= -5 \checkmark \end{aligned}$$

The solutions are 2 and -2, so the solution set is $\{-2, 2\}$. ■

Multiplication and Division Equations

You can use properties of equality to solve equations involving multiplication and division.

(More) Properties of Equality

Multiplication Property of Equality If $a = b$, then $ca = cb$ and $ac = bc$.

Division Property of Equality If $a = b$ and $c \neq 0$, then $\frac{a}{c} = \frac{b}{c}$.

The multiplication property of equality tells you that you can multiply each side of an equation by the same value to create an equivalent equation. The division property of equality tells you that you can divide each side of an equation by the same nonzero value to create an equivalent equation.

Solving a Division Equation

Recall that you use inverse operations to solve equations. So use the multiplication property of equality to solve division equations.

EXAMPLE 1

Solve $\frac{x}{4} = 8$.

SOLUTION

You need to isolate x. The expression $\frac{x}{4}$ indicates that x is divided by 4.

To "undo" the division, use the inverse operation, multiplication.

$$\frac{x}{4} = 8$$

$4 \cdot \frac{x}{4} = 4 \cdot 8$ Multiply each side by 4. (Multiplication Property of Equality)

$x = 32$ Simplify.

CHECK

$\frac{x}{4} = 8$ Write the original equation.

$\frac{32}{4} \stackrel{?}{=} 8$ Substitute 32 for x. (Substitution Property of Equality)

$8 = 8$ ✓ Simplify. The solution is correct because $8 = 8$ is a true statement.

The solution is 32. You can also say the solution set is $\{32\}$. ■

Solving a Multiplication Equation

Use the division property of equality to solve multiplication equations.

EXAMPLE 2

Solve $15 = -3n$.

SOLUTION

The expression $-3n$ indicates multiplication. Use division to "undo" the operation.

$15 = -3n$

$\frac{15}{-3} = \frac{-3n}{-3}$ Divide each side by -3. (Division Property of Equality)

$-5 = n$ Simplify. ■

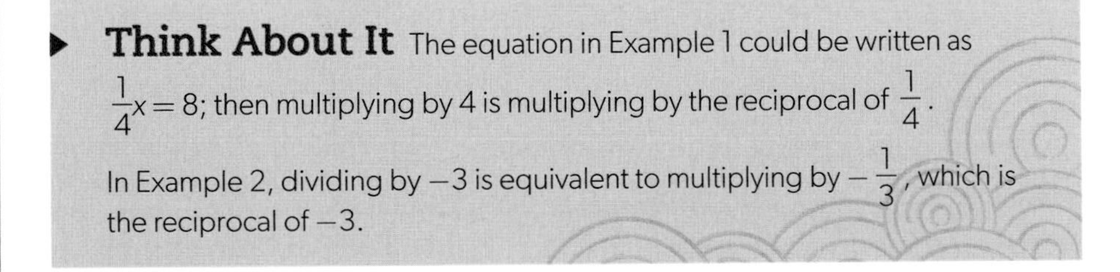

▶ **Think About It** The equation in Example 1 could be written as $\frac{1}{4}x = 8$; then multiplying by 4 is multiplying by the reciprocal of $\frac{1}{4}$.

In Example 2, dividing by -3 is equivalent to multiplying by $-\frac{1}{3}$, which is the reciprocal of -3.

Using a Reciprocal Property for Multiplication to Solve Equations

You don't really need the division property of equality. Instead of dividing, you could always multiply by the reciprocal. Still, the division property of equality can be convenient.

When an equation shows a variable multiplied by a fraction, use a reciprocal property for multiplication.

EXAMPLE 3

Solve.

A $\frac{1}{6}b = 12$

▶ **Remember** One of the reciprocal properties for multiplication says that for all $a \in \mathbb{R}$, $a \cdot \frac{1}{a} = 1$ if $a \neq 0$.

SOLUTION

$\frac{1}{6}b = 12$

$\mathbf{6} \cdot \frac{1}{6}b = \mathbf{6} \cdot 12$ Multiply each side by 6, which is the reciprocal of $\frac{1}{6}$.

$1 \cdot b = 72$ Simplify. $6 \cdot \frac{1}{6} = 1$ by a reciprocal property for multiplication.

$b = 72$ Simplify. $1 \cdot b = b$ by the multiplicative identity property.

B $\frac{2t}{5} = 14$

SOLUTION

$\frac{2t}{5} = 14$

$\frac{2}{5}t = 14$ Rewrite the equation as a multiplication equation.

$\mathbf{\frac{5}{2}} \cdot \frac{2}{5}t = \mathbf{\frac{5}{2}} \cdot 14$ Multiply each side by $\frac{5}{2}$, which is the reciprocal of $\frac{2}{5}$.

$t = 35$ Simplify. ■

Solving Absolute Value Equations

To solve equations that have an absolute value, keep in mind that if $|x| = a$ for some positive number a, then $x = a$ or $x = -a$.

EXAMPLE 4

Solve.

A $5|y| = 30$

SOLUTION

$$5|y| = 30$$

$$\frac{5|y|}{\mathbf{5}} = \frac{30}{\mathbf{5}}$$ Divide each side by 5.

$$5|y| = 6$$ Simplify.

$y = 6$ or $y = -6$ If $|x| = a$ for some positive number a, then $x = a$ or $x = -a$.

B $\frac{|x|}{15} = -3$

SOLUTION

$$\frac{|x|}{15} = -3$$

$$\mathbf{15} \bullet \frac{|x|}{15} = \mathbf{15} \bullet (-3)$$ Multiply each side by 15.

$$|x| = -45$$ Simplify.

no solution An absolute value is never negative.

The solution set is the empty set, represented by either $\{\ \}$ or $\varnothing$. ■

Application: Finding a Unit Price

Multiplication and division equations are useful for solving certain types of real-world problems such as unit price, which is a type of unit rate.

EXAMPLE 5

Mr. Boswell buys a package of 150 file folders for $6.00. What is the unit price per file folder?

SOLUTION

Step 1 Write an equation.

Let f represent the unit price per file folder in dollars.

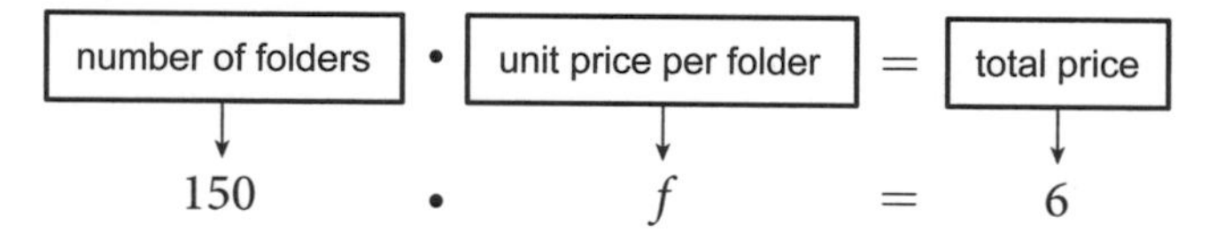

$$150 \cdot f = 6$$

Step 2 Solve the equation.

$150f = 6$

$\frac{150f}{\mathbf{150}} = \frac{6}{\mathbf{150}}$ Divide each side by 150.

$f = 0.04$ Simplify.

Step 3 Check the solution.

$150f = 6$ Write the original equation.

$150 \cdot \mathbf{0.04} \stackrel{?}{=} 6$ Substitute 0.04 for f.

$6 = 6$ ✓ Simplify. The solution is correct.

The unit price is 4¢ per folder. ■

Multiple Transformations

Solving an equation involves using the properties of equality and inverse operations to transform the original equation into a series of equivalent equations.

For example, $x - 12 = 8$ is transformed into $x = 20$ by the addition property of equality, and $\frac{x}{4} = 8$ is transformed into $x = 32$ by the multiplication property of equality.

Solving a Division–Subtraction Equation

To solve an equation such as $\frac{x}{4} - 12 = 8$, you need to make multiple transformations, using various properties and inverse operations.

EXAMPLE 1

Solve $\frac{x}{4} - 12 = 8$.

SOLUTION

Using the correct order of operations, take note of the order in which operations are applied to x.

$\frac{x}{4} - 12 = 8$ First, x is divided by 4. Second, 12 is subtracted from the quotient $\frac{x}{4}$.

Now use the properties of equality and inverse operations to "undo" these operations in reverse order.

$$\frac{x}{4} - 12 = 8$$

$\frac{x}{4} - 12 + \mathbf{12} = 8 + \mathbf{12}$	First, add 12 to each side to "undo" the subtraction. (Addition Property of Equality)
$\frac{x}{4} = 20$	Simplify.
$\mathbf{4} \cdot \frac{x}{4} = \mathbf{4} \cdot 20$	Second, multiply each side by 4 to "undo" the division. (Multiplication Property of Equality)
$x = 80$	Simplify.

CHECK

$\frac{x}{4} - 12 = 8$	Write the original equation.
$\frac{\mathbf{80}}{4} - 12 \stackrel{?}{=} 8$	Substitute 80 for x. (Substitution Property of Equality)
$20 - 12 \stackrel{?}{=} 8$	Use the order of operations to simplify.
$8 = 8$ ✓	The solution is correct.

The solution is 80, and the solution set is $\{80\}$. ■

Using Multiple Transformations to Solve an Equation

Multiple-transformation equations are not limited to subtraction and division, nor are they limited to two operations.

EXAMPLE 2

Solve.

A $3x + 18 = -39$

▶ **Think About It** To solve for a variable in an equation, use the reverse order of operations.

SOLUTION

Here x is multiplied by 3 and then 18 is added.

$$3x + 18 = -39$$

$3x + 18 - \mathbf{18} = -39 - \mathbf{18}$ Subtract 18 from each side. (Subtraction Property of Equality)

$3x = -57$ Simplify.

$\frac{3x}{\mathbf{3}} = \frac{-57}{\mathbf{3}}$ Divide each side by 3. (Division Property of Equality)

$x = -19$ Simplify.

B $3 = \frac{1 - 7n}{5}$

SOLUTION

Here n is multiplied by -7, 1 is added to the product, and then the sum is divided by 5.

$$3 = \frac{1 - 7n}{5}$$

$\mathbf{5} \bullet 3 = \mathbf{5} \bullet \frac{1 - 7n}{5}$ Multiply each side by 5.

$15 = 1 - 7n$ Simplify.

$15 - \mathbf{1} = 1 - 7n - \mathbf{1}$ Subtract 1 from each side.

$15 - 1 = (1 - 1) - 7n$ Combine like terms. (Commutative and Associative Properties of Addition)

$14 = -7n$ Simplify.

$\frac{14}{\mathbf{-7}} = \frac{-7n}{\mathbf{-7}}$ Divide each side by -7.

$-2 = n$ Simplify. ■

▶ **Think About It** If you prefer, use the commutative property of addition to rewrite the difference $1 - 7n$ as the sum $-7n + 1$.

Simplifying First

It is helpful to simplify each side of an equation before trying to solve it.

EXAMPLE 3

Solve $3(g-7)+g=3$.

SOLUTION

You can solve this equation in two ways.

Strategy 1

$3(g-7)+g=3$	
$3g-21+g=3$	Distribute.
$(3g+g)-21=3$	Combine like terms.
$4g-21=3$	Simplify.
$4g-21+\mathbf{21}=3+\mathbf{21}$	Add 21 to each side.
$\frac{4g}{\mathbf{4}}=\frac{24}{\mathbf{4}}$	Divide each side by 4.
$g=6$	Simplify.

Strategy 2

$3(g-7)+g=3$	
$\frac{3(g-7)+g}{\mathbf{3}}=\frac{3}{\mathbf{3}}$	Divide each side by 3.
$\frac{3(g-7)}{3}+\frac{g}{3}=\frac{3}{3}$	Simplify.
$g-7+\frac{1}{3}g=1$	Simplify.
$\left(g+\frac{1}{3}g\right)-7=1$	Combine like terms.
$\frac{4}{3}g-7=1$	Simplify.
$\frac{4}{3}g-7+\mathbf{7}=1+\mathbf{7}$	Add 7 to each side.
$\frac{4}{3}g=8$	Simplify.
$\frac{\mathbf{3}}{\mathbf{4}}\cdot\frac{4}{3}g=\frac{\mathbf{3}}{\mathbf{4}}\cdot 8$	Multiply each side by $\frac{3}{4}$, which is the reciprocal of $\frac{4}{3}$.
$g=6$	Simplify. ■

Simplifying first can make solving a complicated equation easier.

Application: Perimeter

EXAMPLE 4

The width of a rectangle is 2 in. less than its length. The perimeter of the rectangle is 40 in. What are the length and width of the rectangle?

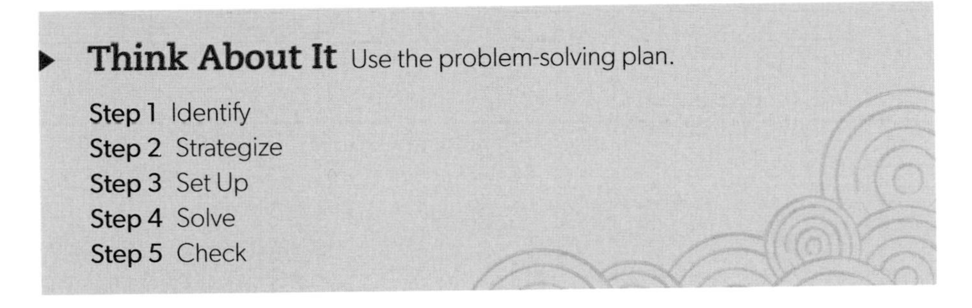

▸ **Think About It** Use the problem-solving plan.

Step 1 Identify
Step 2 Strategize
Step 3 Set Up
Step 4 Solve
Step 5 Check

SOLUTION

Step 1 ***Identify*** Find the length and width of the rectangle, given the perimeter.

Step 2 ***Strategize*** Let l represent the length in inches. The width is 2 in. less than the length, or $l - 2$.

Step 3 ***Set Up*** Write an equation.

$$2 \cdot \boxed{\text{length}} + 2 \cdot \boxed{\text{width}} = \boxed{\text{perimeter}}$$

$$2 \cdot l + 2 \cdot (l - 2) = 40$$

Step 4 ***Solve***

$2l + 2(l - 2) = 40$

$2l + 2l - 4 = 40$	Distribute.
$4l - 4 = 40$	Combine like terms.
$4l - 4 + \mathbf{4} = 40 + \mathbf{4}$	Add 4 to each side.
$\frac{4l}{\mathbf{4}} = \frac{44}{\mathbf{4}}$	Divide each side by 4.
$l = 11$	Simplify.

If $l = 11$, then the expression $l - 2 = 11 - 2 = 9$. The length of the rectangle is 11 in. and the width is 9 in.

▶ **Remember** Perimeter is the distance around a figure.

Step 5 ***Check*** An informal way to check your work is to sketch the rectangle and find its perimeter.

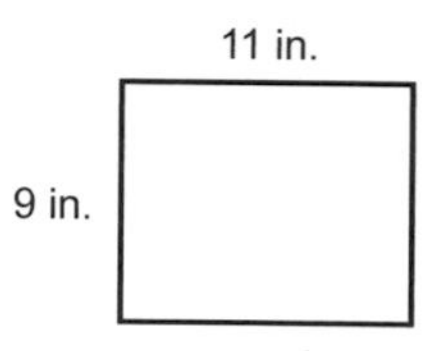

9 in. + 11 in. + 9 in. + 11 in. = 40 in. ✓

The solution works. ■

Variables on Both Sides of an Equation

Some equations have variable terms on both sides of the equals sign.

When an equation has variables on both sides of the equals sign, use the properties of equality and inverse operations to isolate the variable terms on one side of the equation and isolate the constant terms on the other side.

Collecting Variables on One Side

In general, it does not matter on which side you isolate the variable terms. However, these two guidelines can help make your solutions easier:

- If one side of the equation contains only a variable term, isolate the variable terms on that side.
- If both sides of the equation contain both variable and constant terms, isolate the variable terms on the side with the greater variable coefficient.

EXAMPLE 1

Solve.

A $5x = 3x - 18$

SOLUTION

Because $5x$ is already isolated on the left side, it is best to isolate all of the variable terms on the left and isolate the constants on the right. Use the subtraction property of equality to "undo" the $3x$ that is currently added to -18 on the right side.

$$5x = 3x - 18$$

$$5x - \mathbf{3x} = 3x - 18 - \mathbf{3x}$$ Subtract $3x$ from each side.

$$5x - 3x = (3x - 3x) - 18$$ Combine like terms.

$$2x = -18$$ Simplify.

$$\frac{2x}{\mathbf{2}} = \frac{-18}{\mathbf{2}}$$ Divide each side by 2.

$$x = -9$$ Simplify.

CHECK

$$5x = 3x - 18$$

$$5 \bullet (\mathbf{-9}) \stackrel{?}{=} 3 \bullet (\mathbf{-9}) - 18$$ Substitute -9 for each x in the original equation and simplify.

$$-45 \stackrel{?}{=} -27 - 18$$

$$-45 = -45 \checkmark$$

The solution set is $\{-9\}$.

B $n - 4 = \frac{5n + 1}{2}$

SOLUTION

$$n - 4 = \frac{5n + 1}{2}$$

$$\mathbf{2} \bullet (n - 4) = \mathbf{2} \bullet \frac{5n + 1}{2}$$ Multiply each side by 2.

$$2n - 8 = 5n + 1$$ Simplify.

$$2n - 8 - \mathbf{2n} = 5n + 1 - \mathbf{2n}$$ Subtract $2n$ from each side to isolate the variable terms on the right.

$$(2n - 2n) - 8 = (5n - 2n) + 1$$ Combine like terms.

$$-8 = 3n + 1$$ Simplify.

$$-8 - \mathbf{1} = 3n + 1 - \mathbf{1}$$ Subtract 1 from each side to isolate the constant terms on the left.

$$-9 = 3n$$ Simplify.

$$\frac{-9}{\mathbf{3}} = \frac{3n}{\mathbf{3}}$$ Divide each side by 3.

$$-3 = n$$ Simplify.

The solution set is $\{-3\}$. ■

Simplifying First

As with any equation, it helps if you simplify each side first.

> ▶ **Think About It** To shorten your solutions, you can combine consecutive steps of addition and subtraction or consecutive steps of multiplication and division.

EXAMPLE 2

Solve $8(d+2)-36=2+6(1-d)$.

SOLUTION

$8(d+2)-36=2+6(1-d)$	
$8d+16-36=2+6-6d$	Distribute.
$8d-20=8-6d$	Simplify.
$8d-20+\mathbf{6d}+\mathbf{20}=8-6d+\mathbf{6d}+\mathbf{20}$	Add $6d$ and 20 to each side.
$(8d+6d)+(-20+20)=(-6d+6d)+(8+20)$	Combine like terms.
$14d=28$	Simplify.
$\frac{14d}{\mathbf{14}}=\frac{28}{\mathbf{14}}$	Divide each side by 14.
$d=2$	Simplify.

The solution set is $\{2\}$. ■

Application: Number Problem

EXAMPLE 3

Twice a number is 5 more than 3 times the number. Find the number.

SOLUTION

Step 1 Write an equation.

Let n represent the number. Here, *more than* implies addition.

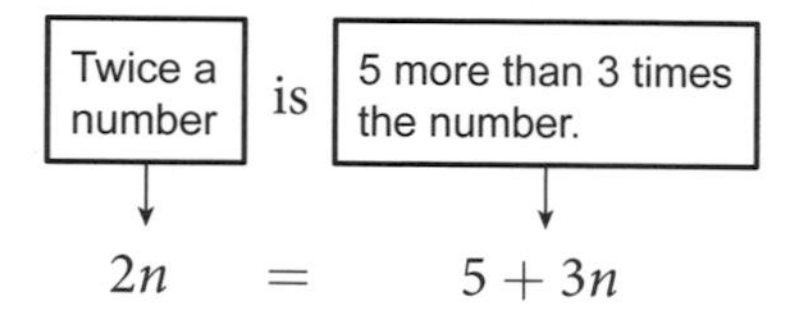

$$2n = 5 + 3n$$

Step 2 Solve the equation.

$2n = 5 + 3n$

$2n - \mathbf{3n} = 5 + 3n - \mathbf{3n}$ Subtract $3n$ from each side to isolate the variable terms on the left.

$\frac{-1n}{\mathbf{-1}} = \frac{5}{\mathbf{-1}}$ Divide each side by -1.

$n = -5$ Simplify.

Step 3 Check the solution.

$2n = 3n + 5$

$2 \cdot \mathbf{(-5)} \stackrel{?}{=} 3 \cdot \mathbf{(-5)} + 5$ Substitute -5 for each n in the original equation and simplify.

$-10 \stackrel{?}{=} -15 + 5$

$-10 = -10$ ✓

The number is -5. ■

Identifying Identities and Contradictions

Most of the equations that you have solved so far have had one or two solutions that make the equation true. But, it is possible for an equation to be true for any value of the variable or no value of the variable.

Definitions

An **identity** is an equation that is true for all values of the variable. An identity has infinitely many solutions, often represented as $\{x \mid x \in \mathbb{R}\}$.

A **contradiction** is an equation that is true for no values of the variable. A contradiction has no solutions, represented by the null set: $\{\ \}$ or $\varnothing$.

You can recognize identities and contradictions after solving a given equation because an identity has no variables and the same quantity of constants on both sides, and a contradiction has no variables and different quantities of constants on each side.

EXAMPLE 4

Identify whether the equation has zero, one, or infinitely many solutions.

A $5x + 3 = 2(x + 3) - 3(1 - x)$

SOLUTION

Simplify each side. Then compare variables and constants.

$5x + 3 = 2(x + 3) - 3(1 - x)$	
$5x + 3 = 2x + 6 - 3 + 3x$	Distributive Property
$5x + 3 = 5x + 3$	Combine like terms and simplify.
$3 = 3$	Subtract $5x$ from each side.

This equation is an identity. There are infinitely many solutions.

B $5x + 3 = 2(x + 3) - 3(2 - x)$

SOLUTION

$5x + 3 = 2(x + 3) - 3(2 - x)$

$5x + 3 = 2x + 6 - 6 + 3x$ Distributive Property

$5x + 3 = 5x$ Combine like terms and simplify.

$3 = 0$ Subtract $5x$ from each side.

This equation is a contradiction. There are zero solutions.

C $5x + 3 = 2(x + 3) - 3(2 - 2x)$

SOLUTION

$5x + 3 = 2(x + 3) - 3(2 - 2x)$

$5x + 3 = 2x + 6 - 6 + 6x$ Distributive Property

$5x + 3 = 8x$ Combine like terms and simplify.

$3 = 3x$ Subtract $5x$ from each side.

Both sides have different quantities of x. This equation has one solution. (If you finish the solution, you'll find $x = 1$.) ■

▶ **Think About It** Example 4C is often called a conditional equation because it is true only for the condition that x is 1.

Applications: Cost Problems

You can solve many applications involving unit prices and total cost by writing and solving an equation.

You have used multiplication and division equations to solve unit-price applications that involve one item. Now that you know how to solve equations with multiple transformations, you can solve more advanced cost problems that involve multiple items.

Mix of Products

In cost problems, your variable does not have to represent a unit price. It may represent the total cost or the quantity of an item.

EXAMPLE 1

Mrs. Rivera goes to a local grocery store to buy trail mix ingredients for a hiking trip she is planning. The store sells small bags of mixed nuts for $1.49 and small bags of dried fruit for $0.99. Her receipt shows that she bought 17 items for a total of $22.83. How many bags of mixed nuts and how many bags of dried fruit did Mrs. Rivera buy?

SOLUTION

Use the problem-solving plan to solve cost problems.

Step 1 ***Identify*** This problem involves two unknown quantities: the number of bags of mixed nuts and the number of bags of dried fruit.

Step 2 ***Strategize*** Use logic and algebra to define both quantities with just one variable.

Let m represent the number of bags of mixed nuts.

You know that Mrs. Rivera bought 17 items. So you can write an equation that helps you define the number of bags of dried fruit.

Step 3 ***Set Up*** Write a cost equation.

You can use the commutative property of multiplication to rewrite the equation as $1.49m + 0.99(17 - m) = 22.83$.

Step 4 ***Solve***

$1.49m + 0.99(17 - m) = 22.83$	
$1.49m + 16.83 - 0.99m = 22.83$	Distribute.
$(1.49m - 0.99m) + 16.83 = 22.83$	Combine like terms.
$0.50m + 16.83 = 22.83$	Simplify.
$0.50m + 16.83 - 16.83 = 22.83 - 16.83$	Subtract 16.83 from each side.
$0.50m = 6$	Simplify.
$\frac{0.50m}{0.50} = \frac{6}{0.50}$	Divide each side by 0.50.
$m = 12$	Simplify.

If $m = 12$, then $17 - m = 17 - 12 = 5$.

So Mrs. Rivera bought 12 bags of mixed nuts and 5 bags of dried fruit.

Step 5 ***Check***

$1.49m + 0.99(17 - m) = 22.83$	Write the original cost equation.
$1.49 \bullet \mathbf{12} + 0.99(17 - \mathbf{12}) \stackrel{?}{=} 22.83$	Substitute 12 for m.
$1.49 \bullet 12 + 0.99 \bullet 5 \stackrel{?}{=} 22.83$	Simplify. This step also confirms the quantity of 5.
$17.88 + 4.95 \stackrel{?}{=} 22.83$	Simplify.
$22.83 = 22.83$ ✓	The solution checks. ■

Different Wage Rates

To solve wage problems, use steps similar to those used to solve cost problems.

EXAMPLE 2

Bradley tutors students in mathematics and science. Last week he tutored 8 h in math and 15 h in science, and he earned \$200. If Bradley earns \$10 per hour for math tutoring, how much does he earn per hour for science tutoring?

SOLUTION

Step 1 ***Identify*** Find the dollar amount Bradley earns per hour tutoring science.

Step 2 ***Strategize*** Let s represent Bradley's charge per hour, in dollars, for science tutoring.

Step 3 ***Set Up*** Write an equation.

Step 4 ***Solve***

$$8 \bullet 10 + 15s = 200$$

$$80 + 15s = 200 \quad \text{Multiply to simplify the constant term on the left side.}$$

$$80 + 15s - 80 = 200 - 80 \quad \text{Subtract 80 from each side.}$$

$$15s + (80 - 80) = 200 - 80 \quad \text{Combine like terms.}$$

$$15s = 120 \quad \text{Simplify.}$$

$$\frac{15s}{15} = \frac{120}{15} \quad \text{Divide each side by 15.}$$

$$s = 8$$

Bradley earns \$8 per hour for science tutoring.

▶ **Think About It** It is also possible to set up and solve this equation with units included.

$$8\text{ h}\left(\frac{\$10}{1\text{ h}}\right) + s \bullet 15\text{ h} = \$200$$

$$\$80 + 15s\text{ h} = \$200$$

$$15s\text{ h} = \$120$$

$$s = \frac{\$8}{1\text{ h}}$$

Step 5 ***Check***

$8 \bullet 10 + 15s = 200$	Write the original equation.
$8 \bullet 10 + 15 \bullet \mathbf{8} \stackrel{?}{=} 200$	Substitute 8 for *s*.
$80 + 120 \stackrel{?}{=} 200$	Simplify.
$200 = 200$ ✓	The solution checks. ■

Estimating in a Cost Problem

Some cost problems may result in "messy" solutions. This happens because dollar amounts are usually rounded to the nearest cent. Apply your estimation skills in these situations.

EXAMPLE 3

Nectarines cost $2.99 per pound. Tenika buys a single nectarine for $0.75. How much does the nectarine weigh to the nearest hundredth of a pound?

SOLUTION

Step 1 ***Identify*** Find the weight of the nectarine.

Step 2 ***Strategize*** Let *w* represent the nectarine's weight in pounds.

Step 3 ***Set Up*** Write an equation. Total cost is the product of the unit price and the weight.

$$2.99w = 0.75$$

Step 4 ***Solve***

$2.99w = 0.75$	
$\frac{2.99w}{2.99} = \frac{0.75}{2.99}$	Divide each side by 2.99.
$w = 0.2508361204\ldots$	Use a calculator.
$w \approx 0.25$	Round to hundredths.

Tenika's nectarine weighs about 0.25 lb.

Step 5 ***Check*** If the nectarine weighs exactly 0.25 lb, the total cost would be $2.99 \bullet 0.25 = 0.7475$. The grocery store would round this number up to $0.75. ■

Transforming Formulas

A formula is an equation that describes the relationship between two or more real-world quantities.

A formula uses variables to represent real-world quantities. Sometimes you need to rearrange the formula to make it convenient to calculate what you need.

Rewriting a Formula with One Transformation

The formula $d = rt$ relates distance d, rate or speed r, and time t. The standard formula helps you calculate distance when you know the speed and time. But, if you need to calculate the amount of time it takes to travel a given distance at a given speed, you can solve the formula for t.

EXAMPLE 1

Solve the formula $d = rt$ for t.

SOLUTION

To solve for t, you need to isolate t. The expression rt indicates that t is multiplied by r. Use division to "undo" the multiplication.

$d = rt$

$\frac{d}{\mathbf{r}} = \frac{rt}{\mathbf{r}}$ Divide each side by r.

$\frac{d}{r} = t$ Simplify.

By the symmetric property, the transformed formula is $t = \frac{d}{r}$. ■

Rewriting a Formula with Multiple Transformations

Some formulas may require multiple transformations. For a rectangle, the formula $P = 2l + 2w$ relates the perimeter P, length l, and width w.

EXAMPLE 2

Solve the formula $P = 2l + 2w$ for w.

SOLUTION

In the expression $2l + 2w$, w is first multiplied by 2 and then $2l$ is added to the product. "Undo" these operations in reverse order.

$$P = 2l + 2w$$

$P - \mathbf{2l} = 2l + 2w - \mathbf{2l}$ Subtract $2l$ from each side.

$P - 2l = 2w$ Simplify.

$\frac{P - 2l}{\mathbf{2}} = \frac{2w}{\mathbf{2}}$ Divide each side by 2.

$\frac{P - 2l}{2} = w$ Simplify.

The transformed formula is $w = \frac{P - 2l}{2}$ or $w = \frac{P}{2} - l$. ■

Applications: Perimeter and Distance

You can apply a transformed formula to a real-world application.

EXAMPLE 3

A Find the time it takes to drive 195 mi at a speed of 65 mph.

SOLUTION

Use the transformed formula from Example 1.

$t = \frac{d}{r}$	Write the transformed formula.
$t = \frac{\mathbf{195}}{\mathbf{65}}$	Substitute 195 for d and 65 for r.
$t = 3$	Simplify.

It takes 3 h to drive 195 mi at 65 mph.

CHECK

Check your work by substituting the values into the original formula.

$d = rt$	Write the original formula.
$\mathbf{195} \stackrel{?}{=} \mathbf{65} \bullet \mathbf{3}$	Substitute 195 for d, 65 for r, and 3 for t.
$195 = 195$ ✓	The solution is correct.

B Find the width of a rectangle that has a perimeter of 49 in. and a length of 18 in.

SOLUTION

Use the transformed formula from Example 2.

$w = \frac{P - 2l}{2}$	Write the transformed formula.
$w = \frac{\mathbf{49} - 2 \bullet \mathbf{18}}{2}$	Substitute 49 for P and 18 for l.
$w = \frac{49 - 36}{2}$	Multiply.
$w = \frac{13}{2}$	Subtract.
$w = 6.5$	Divide.

The width of a rectangle is 6.5 in. when the perimeter is 49 in. and the length is 18 in.

CHECK

$P = 2l + 2w$	Write the original formula.
$\mathbf{49} \stackrel{?}{=} 2 \bullet \mathbf{18} + 2 \bullet \mathbf{6.5}$	Substitute 49 for P, 18 for l, and 6.5 for w.
$49 \stackrel{?}{=} 36 + 13$	Multiply.
$49 = 49$ ✓	The solution is correct. ■

You don't need to solve for the desired variable to use a formula. For instance, you can solve Example 2B by substituting the perimeter and length into the original formula and solving for w. Notice, however, that you will still subtract and then divide.

$$\begin{aligned} P &= 2l + 2w \\ \mathbf{49} &= 2 \bullet \mathbf{18} + 2w \\ 49 &= 36 + 2w \\ 49 - \mathbf{36} &= 36 + 2w - \mathbf{36} \\ 13 &= 2w \\ \frac{13}{\mathbf{2}} &= \frac{2w}{\mathbf{2}} \\ 6.5 &= w \end{aligned}$$

Using a transformed formula saves you from doing the same transformations over and over again.

Application: Unit Conversion

If you need to use a formula repeatedly to find the value of a particular variable, it is very helpful to solve for the desired variable first.

EXAMPLE 4

The Celsius and Fahrenheit temperature scales are related by the formula $C = \frac{5}{9}(F - 32)$, where C is a temperature in degrees Celsius and F is the corresponding temperature in degrees Fahrenheit. Use the formula to find the Fahrenheit temperatures that correspond to the Celsius temperatures 0°, 25°, 50°, 75°, and 100°.

SOLUTION

Step 1 Because you are computing several values in degrees Fahrenheit, transform the formula. To solve the formula for F, "undo" the operations on the original equation.

$C = \frac{5}{9}(F - 32)$

$\mathbf{\frac{9}{5}} \cdot C = \mathbf{\frac{9}{5}} \cdot \frac{5}{9}(F - 32)$ Multiply each side by $\frac{9}{5}$.

$\frac{9}{5}C = F - 32$ Simplify.

$\frac{9}{5}C + \mathbf{32} = F - 32 + \mathbf{32}$ Add 32 to each side.

$\frac{9}{5}C + 32 = F$ Simplify.

Step 2 Check the transformed formula. To check the transformed formula, substitute the new formula into the original. If the equation results in an identity, the formula is correct.

$C = \frac{5}{9}(F - 32)$ Write the original formula.

$C \stackrel{?}{=} \frac{5}{9}\left(\mathbf{\frac{9}{5}C + 32} - 32\right)$ Substitute $\frac{9}{5}C + 32$ for F.

$C \stackrel{?}{=} \frac{5}{9} \cdot \frac{9}{5}C$ Subtract.

$C = C$ ✓ Simplify.

Step 3 Use the transformed formula. A table helps organize your work.

Temperature (°C)	Substitute into the formula $F = \frac{9}{5}C + 32$ and simplify.	Temperature (°F)
0	$F = \frac{9}{5} \cdot \mathbf{0} + 32 = 0 + 32 = 32$	32
25	$F = \frac{9}{5} \cdot \mathbf{25} + 32 = 45 + 32 = 77$	77
50	$F = \frac{9}{5} \cdot \mathbf{50} + 32 = 90 + 32 = 122$	122
75	$F = \frac{9}{5} \cdot \mathbf{75} + 32 = 135 + 32 = 167$	167
100	$F = \frac{9}{5} \cdot \mathbf{100} + 32 = 180 + 32 = 212$	212

The temperatures 0°C, 25°C, 50°C, 75°C, and 100°C correspond to the temperatures 32°F, 77°F, 122°F, 167°F, and 212°F, respectively. ■

Solving Inequalities

Similar to solving an equation, you can solve an inequality by finding a series of equivalent inequalities.

Equivalent inequalities are inequalities with the same solutions. Because most inequalities tell you that one quantity is greater or less than another, you use properties of order that maintain the greater–lesser relationship between the two sides of the inequality.

Properties of Order

Note: These properties also hold for the inequality symbols $\geq$ and $\leq$.

Comparison Property of Order If $a > b$, then $b < a$.
If $a < b$, then $b > a$.

Transitive Property of Order If $a > b$ and $b > c$, then $a > c$.
If $a < b$ and $b < c$, then $a < c$.

Addition Property of Order If $a > b$, then $a + c > b + c$.
If $a < b$, then $a + c < b + c$.

Subtraction Property of Order If $a > b$, then $a - c > b - c$.
If $a < b$, then $a - c < b - c$.

Multiplication Properties of Order
Positive Multiplier If $a > b$ and $c > 0$, then $ca > cb$ and $ac > bc$.
If $a < b$ and $c > 0$, then $ca < cb$ and $ac < bc$.

Negative Multiplier If $a > b$ and $c < 0$, then $ca < cb$ and $ac < bc$.
If $a < b$ and $c < 0$, then $ca > cb$ and $ac > bc$.

Division Properties of Order
Positive Divisor If $a > b$ and $c > 0$, then $\frac{a}{c} > \frac{b}{c}$.
If $a < b$ and $c > 0$, then $\frac{a}{c} < \frac{b}{c}$.
Negative Divisor If $a > b$ and $c < 0$, then $\frac{a}{c} < \frac{b}{c}$.
If $a < b$ and $c < 0$, then $\frac{a}{c} > \frac{b}{c}$.

The properties of order are very similar to the properties of equality. But there is one major difference: if you multiply or divide each side of an inequality by a negative value, then you must reverse the inequality symbol.

Solving a One-Step Inequality

EXAMPLE 1

Solve the inequality.

A $x + 3 \leq 8$

SOLUTION

$x + 3 \leq 8$

$x + 3 - \mathbf{3} \leq 8 - \mathbf{3}$ Subtract 3 from each side. (Subtraction Property of Order)

$x \leq 5$ Simplify.

The solution is all real values less than or equal to 5. You can state the solution simply as $x \leq 5$ or display it with a graph of the inequality.

CHECK

Choose three values to check. A value to the left of the endpoint should make a true statement. The endpoint should make a true statement. Any value to the right should make a false statement.

$x = 0$	$x = 5$	$x = 10$
$x + 3 \leq 8$	$x + 3 \leq 8$	$x + 3 \leq 8$
$\mathbf{0} + 3 \overset{?}{\leq} 8$	$\mathbf{5} + 3 \overset{?}{\leq} 8$	$\mathbf{10} + 3 \overset{?}{\leq} 8$
$3 \leq 8$ ✓	$8 \leq 8$ ✓	$13 \nleq 8$

The solution is correct.

B $-2a > 6$

SOLUTION

$-2a > 6$

$\frac{-2a}{\mathbf{-2}} < \frac{6}{\mathbf{-2}}$ Divide each side by -2 and reverse the inequality symbol. (Division Property of Order, Negative Divisor)

$a < -3$ Simplify.

The solution is all real values less than -3.

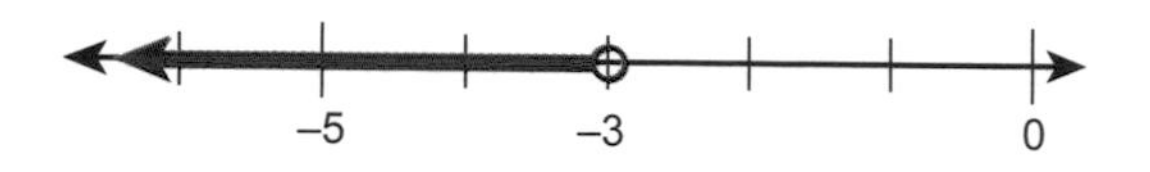

CHECK

The inequality does not include its endpoint, so substituting -3 for a should make the original inequality false. Values to the left should make the inequality true and values to the right should make it false.

$a = -4$	$a = -3$	$a = 0$
$-2a > 6$	$-2a > 6$	$-2a > 6$
$-2 \cdot \mathbf{(-4)} \overset{?}{>} 6$	$-2 \cdot \mathbf{(-3)} \overset{?}{>} 6$	$-2 \cdot \mathbf{0} \overset{?}{>} 6$
$8 > 6$ ✓	$6 \not> 6$	$0 \not> 6$

The solution is correct.

C $\frac{n}{4} \geq -3$

SOLUTION

$\frac{n}{4} \geq -3$

$\mathbf{4} \cdot \frac{n}{4} \geq \mathbf{4} \cdot (-3)$ Multiply each side by 4. (Multiplication Property of Order, Positive Multiplier)

$n \geq -12$ Simplify.

The solution is all real values greater than or equal to -12.

CHECK

$n = -16$	$n = -12$	$n = 0$
$\frac{n}{4} \geq -3$	$\frac{n}{4} \geq -3$	$\frac{n}{4} \geq -3$
$\frac{\mathbf{-16}}{4} \overset{?}{\geq} -3$	$\frac{\mathbf{-12}}{4} \overset{?}{\geq} -3$	$\frac{\mathbf{0}}{4} \overset{?}{\geq} -3$
$-4 \not\geq -3$	$-3 \geq -3$ ✓	$0 \geq -3$ ✓

The solution is correct. ■

Solving an Inequality with Multiple Transformations

EXAMPLE 2

Solve the inequality. Graph the solution on a number line.

A $-5 \geq \frac{x+1}{3}$

SOLUTION

$-5 \geq \frac{x+1}{3}$

$\mathbf{3} \cdot (-5) \geq \mathbf{3} \cdot x + \frac{1}{3}$ Multiply each side by 3. (Multiplication Property of Order, Positive Multiplier)

$-15 \geq x + 1$ Simplify.

$-15 - \mathbf{1} \geq x + 1 - \mathbf{1}$ Subtract 1 from each side. (Subtraction Property of Order)

$-16 \geq x$ Simplify.

$x \leq -16$ Reverse the entire inequality. (Comparison Property of Order)

The solution is all real values less than or equal to -16.

−16

−25 −20 −15 −10 −5 0

B $-5 - 3(g + 7) < g + 3$

SOLUTION

Whenever possible, you should simplify first.

$-5 - 3(g + 7) < g + 3$	
$-5 - 3g - 21 < g + 3$	Distribute.
$-3g - 26 < g + 3$	Combine like terms and simplify.
$-3g - 26 - \mathbf{g} < g + 3 - \mathbf{g}$	Subtract g from each side. (Subtraction Property of Order)
$-4g - 26 < 3$	Combine like terms and simplify.
$-4g - 26 + \mathbf{26} < 3 + \mathbf{26}$	Add 26 to each side. (Addition Property of Order)
$-4g < 29$	Simplify.
$\frac{-4g}{\mathbf{-4}} > \frac{29}{\mathbf{-4}}$	Divide each side by -4 and reverse the inequality symbol. (Division Property of Order, Negative Divisor)
$g > -7.25$	Simplify.

Applications: Inequalities

You can use inequalities to write mathematical models for many real-life situations.

Algebra is a tool for solving problems. You have learned how to solve many types of applications with equations. Now you can use inequalities to solve a wider variety of applications, particularly those that involve a range of possible solutions.

Maximum Cost

EXAMPLE 1

For a winter party, Noriko needs to buy a gift for one of her coworkers. According to the rules of the party, she can spend at most a total of $20, including tax. The rate of sales tax is 8%. How much can Noriko's gift cost before tax?

▶ **Think About It** The phrase ***at most*** tells you the largest possible value and is equivalent to ***less than or equal to***. The phrase ***at least*** tells you the smallest possible value and is equivalent to ***greater than or equal to.***

SOLUTION

Step 1 ***Identify*** Find the greatest possible price of the gift before tax.

Step 2 ***Strategize*** Let c represent the cost of the gift in dollars before tax. Note that Noriko can't spend negative money on the gift, so the domain of the problem is money values that are at least zero.

Step 3 ***Set Up*** Write an inequality.

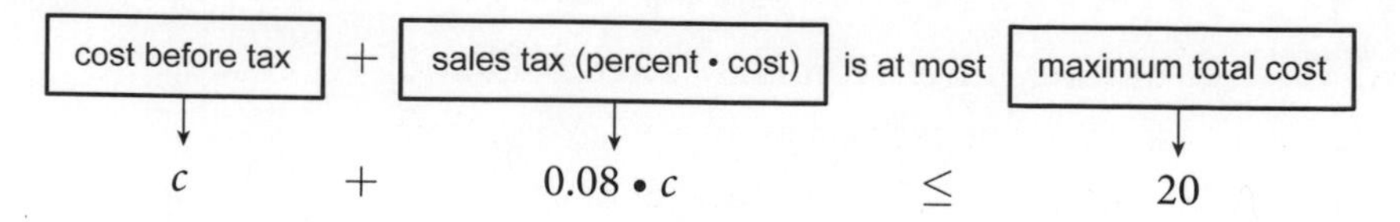

$$c \quad + \quad 0.08 \bullet c \quad \leq \quad 20$$

Step 4 ***Solve***

$c + 0.08c \leq 20$

$1.08c \leq 20$ Collect like terms. $c = 1c$

$\frac{1.08c}{\mathbf{1.08}} \leq \frac{20}{\mathbf{1.08}}$ Divide each side by 1.08.

$c \leq 18.5185185\ldots$

$c \leq \mathbf{18.51}$ Round down so Noriko won't go over budget.

Noriko's gift can cost at most \$18.51 before tax.

Step 5 ***Check*** Test prices greater than, less than, and equal to \$18.51.

$c = 16.99$	$c = 18.51$	$c = 18.52$
$c + 0.08c \leq 20$	$c + 0.08c \leq 20$	$c + 0.08c \leq 20$
$\mathbf{16.99} + 0.08 \bullet \mathbf{16.99} \overset{?}{\leq} 20$	$\mathbf{18.51} + 0.08 \bullet \mathbf{18.51} \overset{?}{\leq} 20$	$\mathbf{18.52} + 0.08 \bullet \mathbf{18.52} \overset{?}{\leq} 20$
$16.99 + 1.3592 \overset{?}{\leq} 20$	$18.51 + 1.4808 \overset{?}{\leq} 20$	$18.52 + 1.4816 \overset{?}{\leq} 20$
$18.3492 \leq 20$ ✓	$19.9908 \leq 20$ ✓	$20.0016 \nleq 20$

The solution checks. ■

Profit

In business, the money spent to run the business, manufacture items, or provide services is called cost. The money that is earned when items or services are sold is called revenue. A business makes profit when its revenue is greater than its cost.

EXAMPLE 2

Ygnacio starts a small business making video recordings of weddings and other events. His camcorder cost \$953. For each event, he spends another \$25 on media (tapes and DVDs). He earns \$85 per event that he records. When will Ygnacio begin to make a profit?

SOLUTION

Step 1 ***Identify*** Find the number of events Ygnacio must record to earn a profit.

Step 2 ***Strategize*** Let n represent the number of events that Ygnacio records. Assume that Ygnacio only records whole events, so the domain is restricted: $n \in \mathbb{W}$.

Step 3 ***Set Up*** Write an inequality.

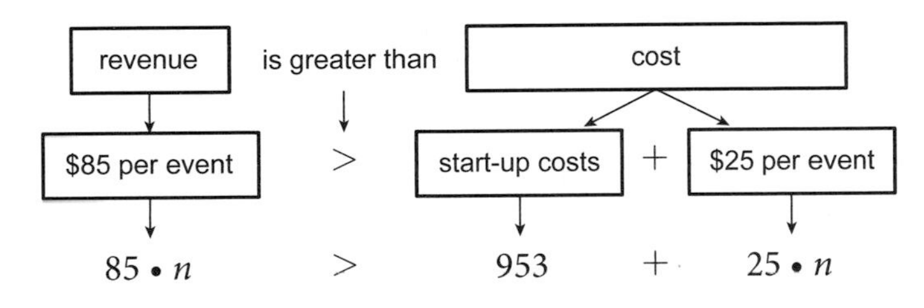

Step 4 ***Solve***

$$85n > 953 + 25n$$

$$85n - \mathbf{25n} > 953 + 25n - \mathbf{25n}$$ Subtract $25n$ to collect variables on one side.

$$60n > 953$$

$$\frac{60n}{\mathbf{60}} > \frac{953}{\mathbf{60}}$$ Divide each side by 60.

$$n > \frac{15.88}{3} \approx 15.9$$

▶ **Think About It** To find how much profit Ygnacio makes, subtract cost from revenue:

profit = revenue − cost.

For example, after his 20th event, Ygnacio's profit is \$1700 − \$1453, or \$247.

Now adjust the solution for the restricted domain. First graph $n > 15.9$ for all real numbers, and then adjust the endpoint and ray for whole-numbers.

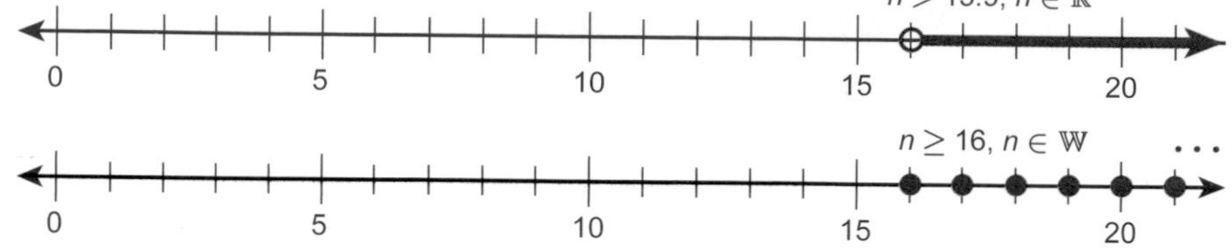

The solution is $n \geq 16$, where $n \in \mathbb{W}$. Ygnacio will make a profit with the 16th event that he records, and every event after that.

Step 5 ***Check***

$n = 15$	$n = 16$	$n = 20$
$85n > 953 + 25n$	$85n > 953 + 25n$	$85n > 953 + 25n$
$85 \bullet \mathbf{15} \overset{?}{>} 953 + 25 \bullet \mathbf{15}$	$85 \bullet \mathbf{16} \overset{?}{>} 953 + 25 \bullet \mathbf{16}$	$85 \bullet \mathbf{20} \overset{?}{>} 953 + 25 \bullet \mathbf{20}$
$1275 \overset{?}{>} 953 + 375$	$1360 \overset{?}{>} 953 + 400$	$1700 \overset{?}{>} 953 + 500$
$1275 \not> 1328$	$1360 > 1353$ ✓	$1700 > 1453$ ✓

The solution checks. ■

Minimum Grade

EXAMPLE 3

In Nico's math class, a student's overall average is the mean of the scores on four chapter exams and the final exam, which counts twice. A student who earns an overall average of at least 90 gets an A in the class.

Nico has scored 96, 82, 87, and 89 on the four chapter exams. He is now preparing for the final exam. What is the minimum score Nico needs to earn on the final exam to get an A in the class?

▸ **Remember** The mean is what most people commonly call the average. To find the mean, sum up the values and divide by the number of values.

SOLUTION

Step 1 ***Identify*** Find the score Nico must get on the final exam to earn an A in the class.

Step 2 ***Strategize*** Let f represent Nico's score on the final exam.

Step 3 ***Set Up*** Write an inequality.

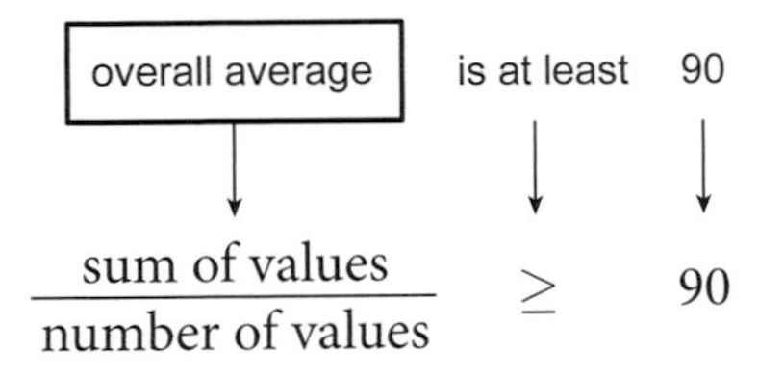

$$\frac{\text{sum of values}}{\text{number of values}} \geq 90$$

$$\frac{96 + 82 + 87 + 89 + f + f}{6} \geq 90$$ Remember to count the final exam score f twice.

$$\frac{354 + 2f}{6} \geq 90$$ Simplify the left side.

Step 4 ***Solve***

$$\mathbf{6} \bullet \frac{354 + 2f}{6} \geq \mathbf{6} \bullet 90$$ Multiply each side by 6.

$$354 + 2f \geq 540$$

$$354 + 2f - \mathbf{354} \geq 540 - \mathbf{354}$$ Subtract 354 from each side.

$$2f \geq 186$$

$$\frac{2f}{\mathbf{2}} \geq \frac{186}{\mathbf{2}}$$ Divide each side by 2.

$$f \geq 93$$

Nico needs to earn a minimum score of 93 on the final exam to get an A in the class.

Step 5 ***Check*** Test scores that are less than, equal to, and greater than 93.

Final exam score	Overall average	Is the grade an A?
$f = 92$	$\frac{96+82+87+89+\mathbf{92}+\mathbf{92}}{6} = \frac{538}{6} \approx 89.7$	No
$f = 93$	$\frac{96+82+87+89+\mathbf{93}+\mathbf{93}}{6} = \frac{540}{6} \approx 90$ ✓	Yes
$f = 94$	$\frac{96+82+87+89+\mathbf{94}+\mathbf{94}}{6} = \frac{542}{6} \approx 90.3$ ✓	Yes

The solution checks. ■

Reasoning with Solutions

When you solve an equation or inequality, you should be able to justify each step you make.

Justifying Steps when Solving an Equation

EXAMPLE 1

Justify each step in the solution.

Line 1 $4(x-3)+20=60$
Line 2 $4x-12+20=60$
Line 3 $4x+8=60$
Line 4 $4x=52$
Line 5 $x=13$

SOLUTION

Compare Line 2 to Line 1 The terms x and -3 were multiplied by 4. This step is an example of the distributive property of equality.

Compare Line 3 to Line 2 The left side was simplified. The numbers -12 and 20 were added.

Compare Line 4 to Line 3 The number 8 was subtracted from each side. This step is an example of the subtraction property of equality.

Compare Line 5 to Line 4 Each side was divided by 4. This step is an example of the division property of equality.

$4(x-3)+20=60$	
$4x-12+20=60$	Distributive Property of Equality
$4x+8=60$	Addition
$4x=52$	Subtraction Property of Equality
$x=13$	Division Property of Equality ■

▶ **Think About It** A complete list of the properties of equality and the properties of order are included in the Properties appendix.

EXAMPLE 2

Justify each step in the solution.

Line 1 $25 > -3m - 2$
Line 2 $27 > -3m$
Line 3 $-9 < m$
Line 4 $m > -9$

SOLUTION

Compare Line 2 to Line 1 The number 2 was added to each side. This step is an example of the addition property of order.

Compare Line 3 to Line 2 Both sides were divided by -3, and the direction of the inequality sign was changed. This step is an example of the division property of order.

Compare Line 4 to Line 3 The expressions on each side of the inequality were switched, and the direction of the inequality sign was changed. This step is an example of the comparison property of order.

$25 > -3m - 2$	
$27 > -3m$	Addition Property of Order
$-9 < m$	Division Property of Order
$m > -9$	Comparison Property of Order ■

Two-Variable Linear Equations and Inequalities

Topic List

- Graphs of Lines
- Forms of Linear Equations
- Writing Equations of Lines
- Applications: Linear Equations
- Graphing Linear Inequalities
- Systems of Linear Inequalities
- Constraints

Anything involving a constant rate can be described with a linear equation. You can find constant rates when driving a car, calculating a cost, or receiving an hourly wage.

Graphs of Lines

You can graph a line in the coordinate plane.

Graphing a Linear Equation

A **linear equation** is an equation whose graph in a coordinate plane is a line. You can graph a linear equation by plotting two ordered pairs that make the equation true, and then drawing a line through those points. But to guard against errors, it is best to plot three or more ordered pairs.

EXAMPLE 1

Graph the linear equation $y = -x + 6$.

SOLUTION

Use a table to find three ordered pairs that are solutions of the equation. Pick any three x-values and calculate the corresponding y-values.

x	y
0	6
2	4
5	1

How to calculate the y-value:

$$y = -x + 6$$
$$y = -\mathbf{0} + 6 = 6$$
$$y = -\mathbf{2} + 6 = 4$$
$$y = -\mathbf{5} + 6 = 1$$

Plot the points and draw a line through them. If all three points are not on the same line, double-check your calculations.

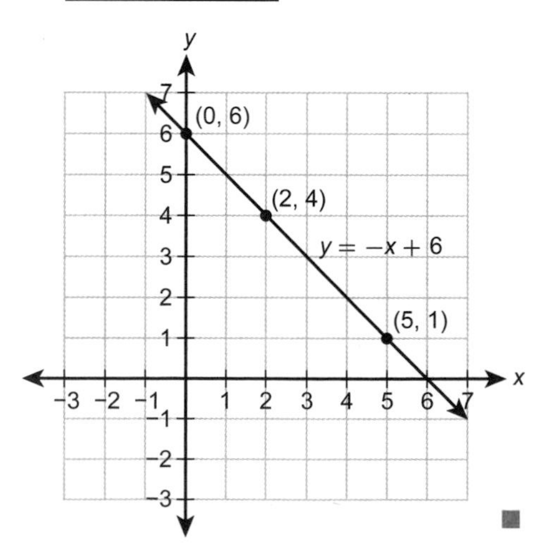

Determining Whether a Point Lies on a Line

The coordinates of any point on a line make the equation of that line true. The coordinates of any point not on a line make the equation of that line false.

EXAMPLE 2

Determine whether each point is on the line $y = -x + 6$.

A $(3, -1)$

SOLUTION

Substitute the x- and y-coordinates into the equation.

$$\begin{aligned} y &= -x + 6 \\ \mathbf{-1} &\stackrel{?}{=} \mathbf{-3} + 6 \\ -1 &\stackrel{?}{=} -3 + 6 \\ -1 &\neq 3 \end{aligned}$$

The point $(3, -1)$ is not on the line $y = -x + 6$. (See the graph in Example 1.)

B $(-8.25, 14.25)$

SOLUTION

Substitute the x- and y-coordinates into the equation.

$$\begin{aligned} y &= -x + 6 \\ \mathbf{14.25} &\stackrel{?}{=} -(\mathbf{-8.25}) + 6 \\ 14.25 &\stackrel{?}{=} 8.25 + 6 \\ 14.25 &= 14.25 \end{aligned}$$

The point $(-8.25, 14.25)$ is on the line $y = -x + 6$. ■

Using Intercepts to Graph a Linear Equation

Finding the points where a graph crosses the axes is often useful. When a graph is a diagonal line, it intersects each axis at no more than one point.

Definitions

An **x-intercept** is the *x*-coordinate of the point where a graph intersects the *x*-axis.

A **y-intercept** is the *y*-coordinate of the point where a graph intersects the *y*-axis.

EXAMPLE 3

Find the x- and y-intercepts of the equation $2x - 5y = 20$. Then graph the equation.

SOLUTION

The point that contains the x-intercept has a y-coordinate of zero, and the point that contains the y-intercept has an x-coordinate of zero.

To find the x-intercept, substitute 0 for y in the equation and solve for x.

$$\begin{aligned} 2x - 5y &= 20 \\ 2x - 5 \bullet \mathbf{0} &= 20 \\ 2x &= 20 \\ x &= 10 \end{aligned}$$

▶ **Remember** Every point on the *x*-axis has a *y*-coordinate of zero. Every point on the *y*-axis has an *x*-coordinate of zero.

The x-intercept is 10, so the point $(10, 0)$ is on the line.

To find the y-intercept, substitute 0 for x in the equation and solve for y.

$$\begin{aligned} 2x - 5y &= 20 \\ 2 \cdot \mathbf{0} - 5y &= 20 \\ -5y &= 20 \\ y &= -4 \end{aligned}$$

The y-intercept is -4, so the point $(0, -4)$ is on the line.

Plot the points $(10, 0)$ and $(0, -4)$, and then draw the line through them.

▶ **Think About It** To check your work, find a third ordered pair solution to the equation and make sure the graph of that ordered pair is a point on the line.

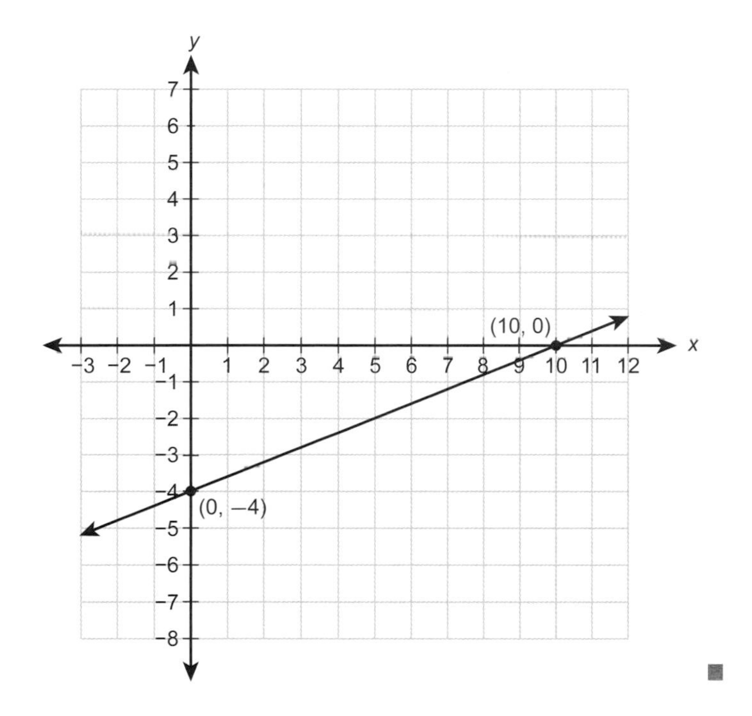

Simplifying and Graphing Linear Equations in One Variable

Some linear equations have just one variable. These special linear equations have graphs that are vertical or horizontal lines.

EXAMPLE 4

A Simplify and graph $2x = 10$.

SOLUTION

Divide both sides by 2 to get $x = 5$. To graph the equation, plot some points that have an x-coordinate of 5, such as $(5, 3)$, $(5, 1)$, and $(5, -2)$ as shown.

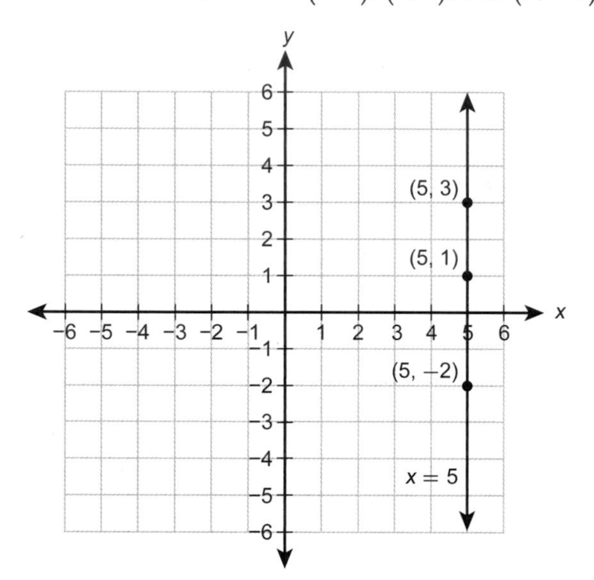

Any equation that can be written in the form $x = k$, where k is a constant, has a graph that is a vertical line.

B Simplify and graph $y + 5 = 2$.

SOLUTION

Subtract 5 from both sides to get $y = -3$. To graph the equation, plot some points that have a y-coordinate of -3, such as $(-4, -3)$, $(0, -3)$, and $(2, -3)$ as shown.

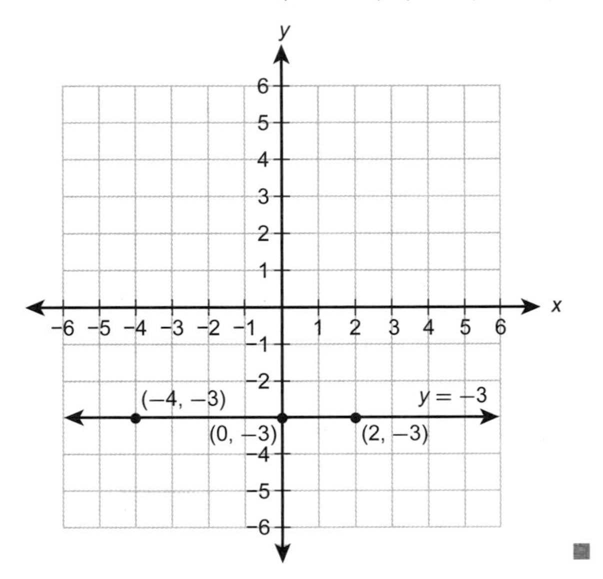

Any equation that can be written in the form $y = k$, where k is a constant, has a graph that is a horizontal line.

Calculating Slope from a Graph

Another useful skill is knowing how to describe the slant of a line: which direction it runs and how steep it is. You can determine this information by finding a line's slope.

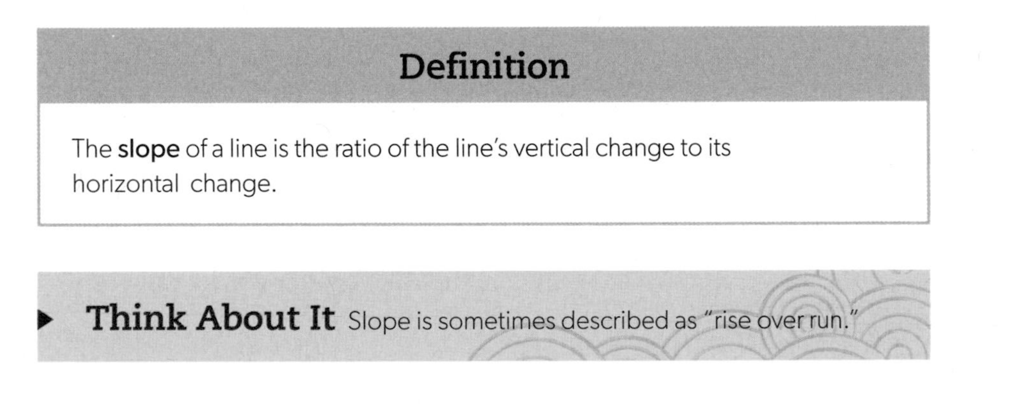

Definition

The **slope** of a line is the ratio of the line's vertical change to its horizontal change.

▶ **Think About It** Slope is sometimes described as "rise over run."

EXAMPLE 5

What is the slope of the graphed line?

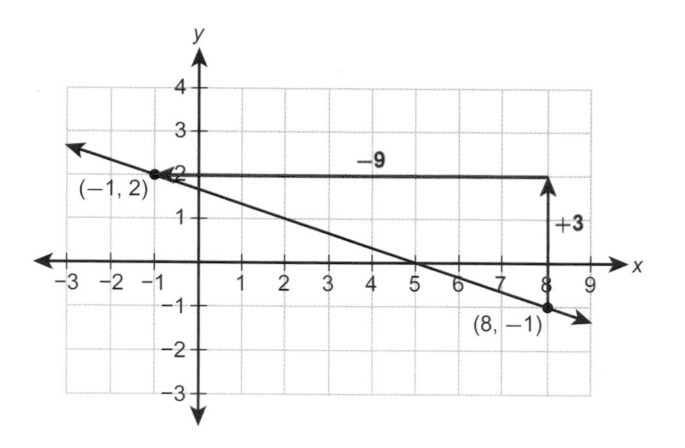

SOLUTION

Pick any two points on the line, for example $(8, -1)$ and $(-1, 2)$. Move from one point to the other by moving only vertically and horizontally. To move from $(8, -1)$ to $(-1, 2)$, you can move up 3 units and then left 9 units. Therefore, the vertical change is $+3$, and the horizontal change is -9. The slope of the line is $\frac{+3}{-9}$, which simplifies to $-\frac{1}{3}$. ■

Calculating Slope from a Linear Equation

The vertical change between any two points is the difference in the y-coordinates, and the horizontal change is the difference in the x-coordinates. So if you know the coordinates of two points on a line, you can calculate the slope without a graph.

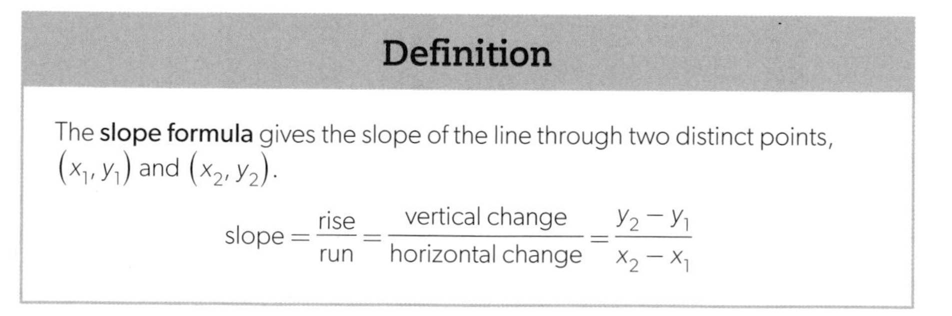

Definition

The **slope formula** gives the slope of the line through two distinct points, (x_1, y_1) and (x_2, y_2).

$$\text{slope} = \frac{\text{rise}}{\text{run}} = \frac{\text{vertical change}}{\text{horizontal change}} = \frac{y_2 - y_1}{x_2 - x_1}$$

EXAMPLE 6

Find the slope of the line passing through the points $(-3, 7)$ and $(1, 2)$.

SOLUTION

Use the slope formula. Choose either point to be (x_1, y_1).

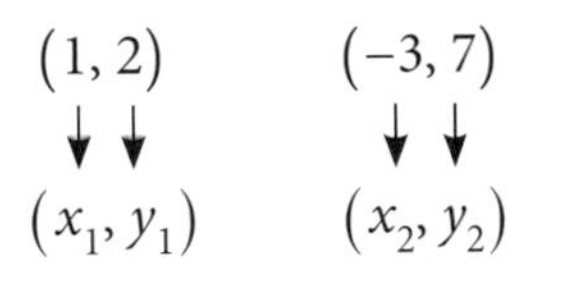

Substitute values into the slope formula for x_1, x_2, y_1, and y_2.

$$m = \frac{y_2 - y_1}{x_2 - x_1} = \frac{7 - 2}{-3 - 1} = \frac{5}{-4} = -\frac{5}{4}$$

The slope of the line is $-\frac{5}{4}$. ■

EXAMPLE 7

Calculate the slope of the line with equation $-3x + 4y = 24$.

SOLUTION

Find any two points on the line. In this case, it is easy to find the two points that contain the intercepts.

Substitute 0 for x.

$$-3 \bullet \mathbf{0} + 4y = 24 \Rightarrow y = 6$$

So the point $(0, 6)$ is on the line.

Substitute 0 for y.

$$-3x + 4 \bullet \mathbf{0} = 24 \Rightarrow x = -8$$

So the point $(-8, 0)$ is on the line.

Then substitute the coordinates of the two points into the slope formula. Let $(x_1, y_1) = (0, 6)$ and $(x_2, y_2) = (-8, 0)$.

$$\text{slope} = \frac{y_2 - y_1}{x_2 - x_1} = \frac{0 - 6}{(-8) - 0} = \frac{-6}{-8} = \frac{3}{4}$$

The slope of the line with equation $-3x + 4y = 24$ is $\frac{3}{4}$. ■

▸ **Think About It** It doesn't matter which point you use as (x_1, y_1) or (x_2, y_2). If you reverse the substitution of $(0, 6)$ and $(-8, 0)$, the signs change in the numerator and denominator, but you still get the same slope.

$$\frac{6-0}{0-(-8)} = \frac{6}{8} = \frac{3}{4}$$

Classifying of Lines by Slope

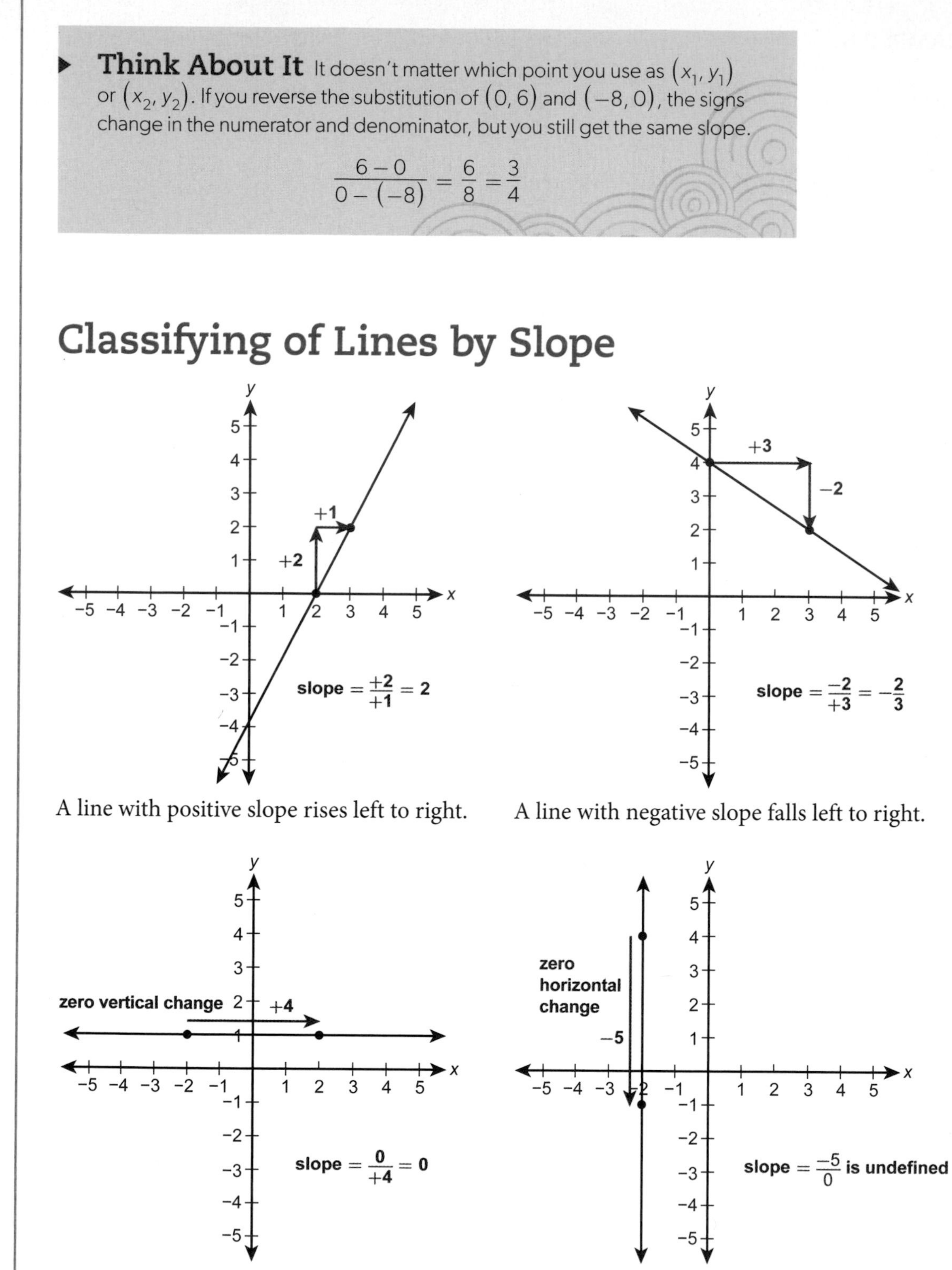

A line with positive slope rises left to right.

A line with negative slope falls left to right.

A line with zero slope is horizontal.

A line with undefined slope is vertical.

Forms of Linear Equations

You can write linear equations in different forms.

All linear equations have the following characteristics:

- There is no variable with an exponent other than 1 or 0.
- The variables are not multiplied together.
- It is possible to write the equation without any variable in the denominator of a fraction.
- The graph of the equation in a coordinate plane is a line.

Converting Between Forms of Linear Equations

Three forms of linear equations are most common.

Definitions

The **standard form** of a linear equation is $Ax + By = C$, where A, B, and C are integers, and A and B are not both zero.

The **slope-intercept form** of a linear equation is $y = mx + b$, where m is the slope and b is the y-intercept of the corresponding line.

The **point-slope form** of a linear equation is $y - y_1 = m(x - x_1)$, where m is the slope and (x_1, y_1) is a point on the corresponding line.

EXAMPLE 1

A Write the equation $4x + 3y = 15$ in slope-intercept form.

SOLUTION

To convert to slope-intercept form, solve the equation for y.

$4x + 3y = 15$	Original equation
$3y = -4x + 15$	Subtract $4x$ from both sides.
$y = -\frac{4}{3}x + 5$	Divide both sides by 3.

▶ **Think About It** To divide $-4x + 15$ by 3, divide each term by 3:

$$\frac{-4x + 15}{3} = -\frac{4x}{3} + \frac{15}{3}$$
$$= -\frac{4x}{3} + 5$$

B Write the equation $y - 4 = \frac{1}{5}(x + 7)$ in standard form.

SOLUTION

To convert to standard form, isolate the variables from the constants.

$y - 4 = \frac{1}{5}(x + 7)$	Original equation
$5y - 20 = x + 7$	Multiply both sides by 5 to clear the fraction.
$-x + 5y - 20 = 7$	Subtract x from both sides.
$-x + 5y = 27$	Add 20 to both sides.

▶ **Think About It** The final equation in Example 1B, $-x + 5y = 27$, is in standard form. An equivalent equation, also in standard form, is $x - 5y = -27$.

C Write the equation $y + 2 = 3(x - 4)$ in slope-intercept form.

SOLUTION

To convert to slope-intercept form, isolate the variable y.

$y + 2 = 3(x - 4)$	Original equation
$y + 2 = 3x - 12$	Distribute 3.
$y = 3x - 14$	Subtract 2 from both sides. ■

Graphing a Linear Equation in Slope-Intercept Form

EXAMPLE 2

Graph $y = \frac{1}{2}x - 3$.

SOLUTION

This equation is in the form $y = mx + b$.

$$y = \frac{1}{2}x + (-3)$$

The slope is $\frac{1}{2}$. The y-intercept is -3, so the point $(0, -3)$ is on the line.

Plot the y-intercept at $(0, -3)$. From that point, count the vertical and horizontal change in the slope ratio to plot another point on the line. Develop a good graphing habit by doing this several times, plotting several more points. Then draw a line through the points.

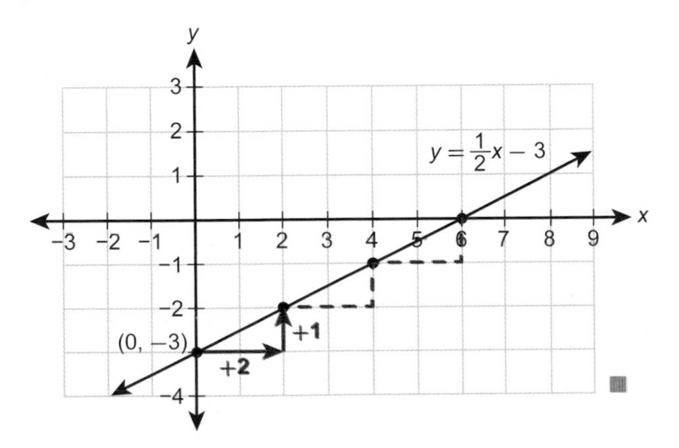

■

Graphing a Linear Equation in Standard Form

EXAMPLE 3

Graph $5x + 4y = 6$ using two different methods.

SOLUTION

Method 1 Convert the equation to slope-intercept form. Then use the graphing method shown in Example 2.

$5x + 4y = 6$

$4y = -5x + 6$ Subtract $5x$ from both sides.

$y = -\frac{5}{4}x + \frac{3}{2}$ Divide through by 4.

Plot the y-intercept at $\left(0, \frac{3}{2}\right)$. Then count, using the slope $-\frac{5}{4}$, to plot another point.

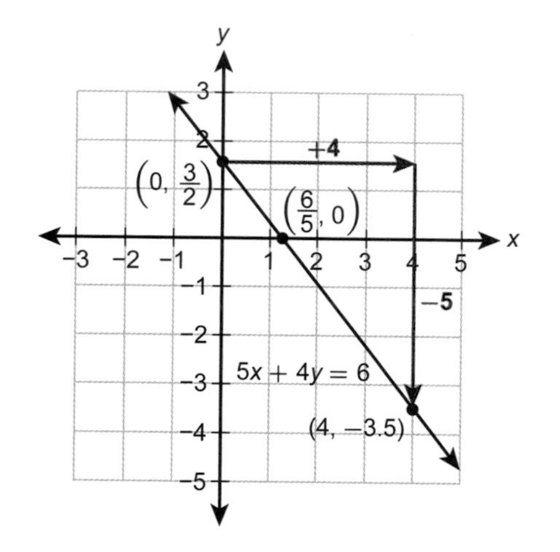

Method 2 Find both intercepts and use them to draw the line. Find the x-intercept.

$$5x + 4y = 6$$
$$5x + 4 \cdot \mathbf{0} = 6$$
$$5x = 6$$
$$x = \frac{6}{5}$$

Plot the point $\left(\frac{6}{5}, 0\right)$.

Find the y-intercept.

$$5x + 4y = 6$$
$$5 \bullet \mathbf{0} + 4y = 6$$
$$4y = 6$$
$$y = \frac{3}{2}$$

Plot the point $\left(0, \frac{3}{2}\right)$.

Draw the line through these points. The line is the same as in Method 1. ■

Graphing a Linear Equation in Point-Slope Form

EXAMPLE 4

Graph $y - 2 = 4(x + 3)$.

SOLUTION

The slope is 4 and $(-3, 2)$ is a point on the corresponding line.

Plot $(-3, 2)$. Then count, using the slope $\frac{4}{1}$, to plot another point. Another point on the line is $(-2, 6)$. Draw the line through the two points.

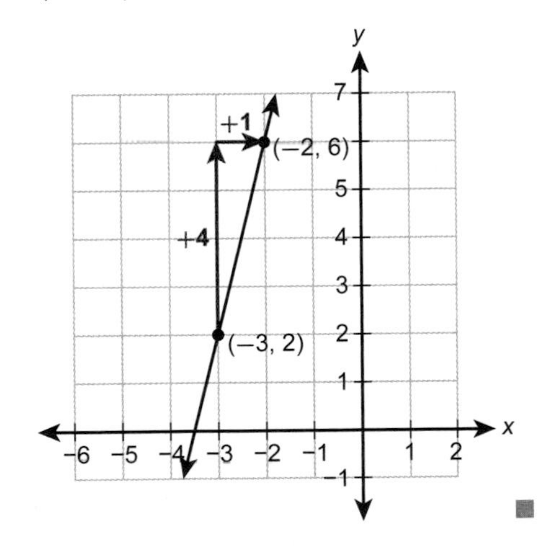

■

Linear Graph Family

Linear Graph Family: $y = mx + b$

Any changes to the parameters m and b in equations of the form $y = mx + b$ will change the graphs of the lines.

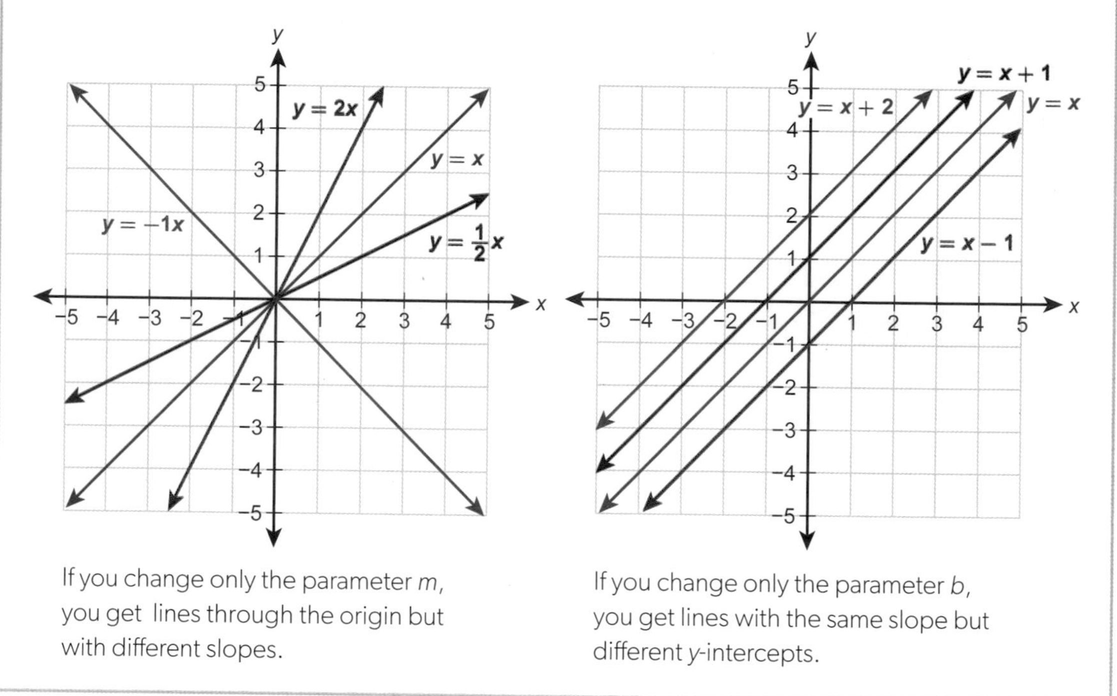

If you change only the parameter m, you get lines through the origin but with different slopes.

If you change only the parameter b, you get lines with the same slope but different y-intercepts.

Graphing a Linear Equation Not in a Common Form

You can graph a linear equation given in an uncommon form by finding the x- and y-intercepts and using them to draw the line.

EXAMPLE 5

Graph $x + 2y = -16$.

SOLUTION

Find the x- and y-intercepts. Plot these points, and use them to draw the line.

> **Remember** Substitute 0 for y to find the x-intercept, and substitute 0 for x to find the y-intercept.

Find the x-intercept.

$$
\begin{aligned}
x + 2y &= -16 \\
x + 2 \bullet \mathbf{0} &= -16 \\
x &= -16
\end{aligned}
$$

Plot the point $(-16, 0)$.

Find the y-intercept.

$$
\begin{aligned}
x + 2y &= -16 \\
\mathbf{0} + 2y &= -16 \\
2y &= -16 \\
y &= -8
\end{aligned}
$$

Plot the point $(0, -8)$.

Draw the line through these points.

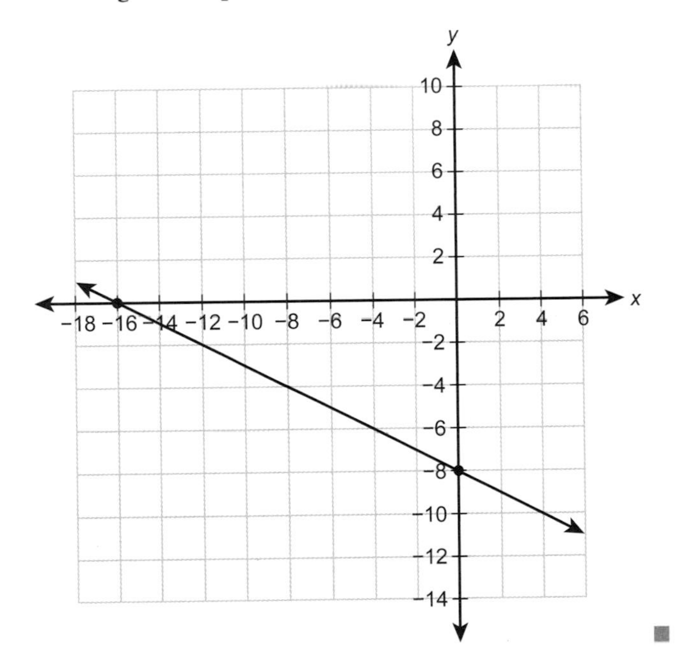

■

Writing Equations of Lines

You can use given information to write the equation of a line.

Finding a Linear Equation, Given the Slope and the y-Intercept

You can write an equation of a line if you know the slope and the y-intercept.

EXAMPLE 1

Find an equation of the line with a slope of $-\frac{2}{5}$ and a y-intercept of 6.

SOLUTION

The slope-intercept form of a linear equation is $y = mx + b$, where m is the slope and b is the y-intercept. So in this case, $m = -\frac{2}{5}$ and $b = 6$.

An equation of the line is $y = -\frac{2}{5}x + 6$. ■

▶ **Think About It** You can convert an equation in slope-intercept form to standard form.

$$y = -\frac{2}{5}x + 6$$
$$2x + 5y = 30$$

Finding a Linear Equation, Given the Slope and a Point on the Line

Given the slope and a point on the line, you can use the point-slope form of a linear equation to write an equation of the line.

EXAMPLE 2

Find an equation of the line that has a slope of 3 and passes through the point (1, −2). Write the equation in slope-intercept form.

SOLUTION

The point-slope form of a linear equation is $y - y_1 = m(x - x_1)$, where m is the slope and (x_1, y_1) is a point on the corresponding line.

$y - y_1 = m(x - x_1)$	Point-slope form
$y - (\mathbf{-2}) = \mathbf{3}(x - \mathbf{1})$	Substitute 3 for m, 1 for x_1, and −2 for y_1.
$y + 2 = 3(x - 1)$	Simplify the left side of the equation.
$y + 2 = 3x - 3$	Distribute 3 on the right side.
$y = 3x - 5$	Subtract 2 from both sides.

The equation of the line in slope-intercept form is $y = 3x - 5$. ■

Finding a Linear Equation, Given Two Points

You do not need to see a graph to find an equation of a line. If you know the coordinates of two points, or if you know the coordinates of one point and the slope, you have enough information to determine an equation.

EXAMPLE 3

Find an equation of the line that passes through the points $(1, 2)$ and $(2, 1)$. Write the equation in standard form.

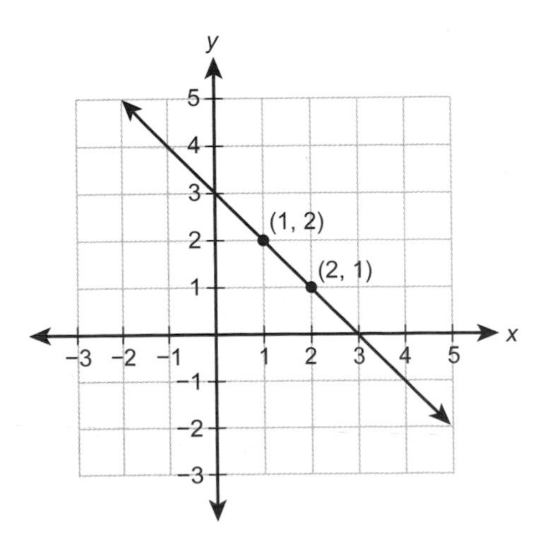

SOLUTION

Use the known points on the line, $(x_1, y_1) = (1, 2)$ and $(x_2, y_2) = (2, 1)$, to calculate the slope m between them.

$$m = \frac{y_2 - y_1}{x_2 - x_1} = \frac{1 - 2}{2 - 1} = \frac{-1}{1} = -1$$

(Count on the grid from one point to the other to verify the slope.)

Substitute the coordinates of one point and the slope into the point-slope form, and then convert the equation to standard form.

$y - y_1 = m(x - x_1)$	Point-slope form
$y - \mathbf{2} = \mathbf{-1}(x - \mathbf{1})$	Substitute for x_1, y_1, and m.
$y - 2 = -1x + 1$	Distribute.
$x + y = 3$	Isolate the variables from the constants.

An equation of the line in standard form is $x + y = 3$. ■

▶ **Think About It** In Example 3, the point $(1, 2)$ is substituted in the point-slope form for (x_1, y_1). But you can substitute any point that you know is on the line.

Determining Whether Two Lines Are Parallel, Perpendicular, or Neither

Parallel and Perpendicular Slope Properties

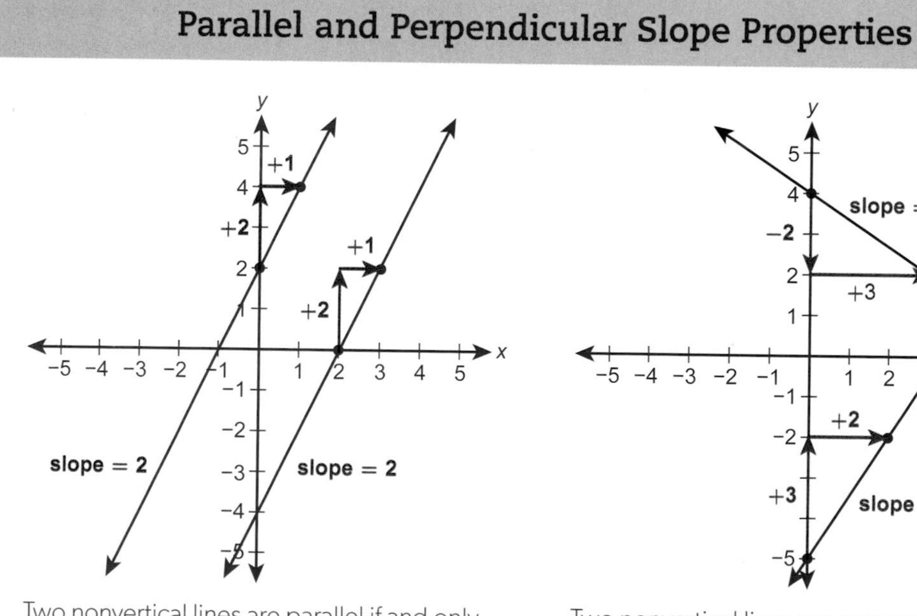

Two nonvertical lines are parallel if and only if they have equal slopes.

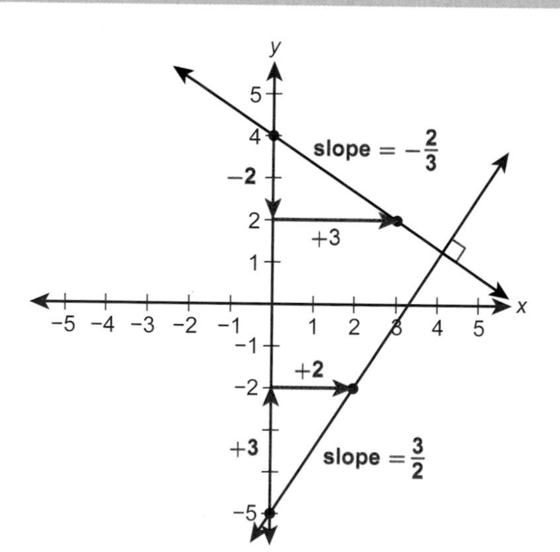

Two nonvertical lines are perpendicular if and only if they have opposite reciprocal slopes.

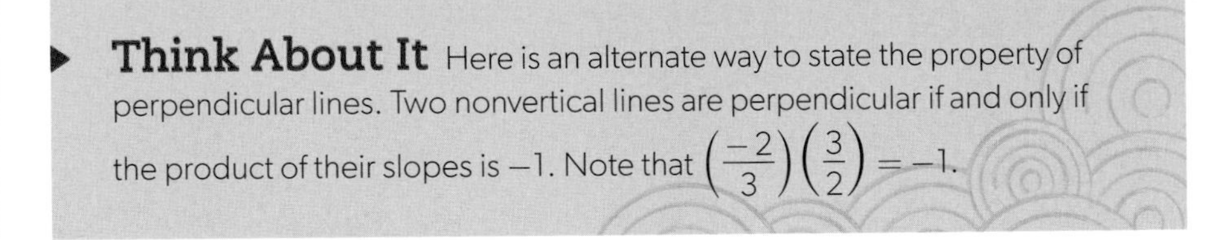

▶ **Think About It** Here is an alternate way to state the property of perpendicular lines. Two nonvertical lines are perpendicular if and only if the product of their slopes is −1. Note that $\left(\frac{-2}{3}\right)\left(\frac{3}{2}\right) = -1$.

EXAMPLE 4

Determine whether each pair of lines is parallel, perpendicular, or neither.

A $x + y = 3$
$y = 3x - 4$

SOLUTION
Write the equation $x + y = 3$ in slope-intercept form, $y = -x + 3$. The slope is -1. The slope of $y = 3x - 4$ is 3. The slopes are not equal and are not opposite reciprocals. The lines are neither parallel nor perpendicular.

B $y = -3x + 5$
$2y = 6 - 6x$

SOLUTION
Write the equation $2y = 6 - 6x$ in slope-intercept form, $y = -3x + 3$. The slopes of the lines are equal. The lines are parallel.

C $4x + 3y = 7$
$3x - 4y = 5$

SOLUTION
Write each equation in slope-intercept form.

$$y = -\frac{4}{3}x + \frac{7}{3}$$

$$y = \frac{3}{4}x - \frac{5}{4}$$

The slopes are opposite reciprocals. The lines are perpendicular. ■

Using Properties of Parallel or Perpendicular Lines to Find a Linear Equation

EXAMPLE 5

A Find an equation of the line that is parallel to $y = 5x - 6$ and passes through the point $(2, -3)$. Write the equation in slope-intercept form.

SOLUTION

The slope of the line $y = 5x - 6$ is 5. Because parallel lines have equal slopes, the desired line also has a slope of 5.

Substitute the slope and the coordinates of the known point into the slope-intercept form, and solve to find the desired y-intercept.

$$\begin{aligned} y &= mx + b \\ \mathbf{-3} &= \mathbf{5} \cdot \mathbf{2} + b \\ -3 &= 10 + b \\ -13 &= b \end{aligned}$$

Use m and b to write the equation: $y = 5x - 13$.

B Find an equation of the line that is perpendicular to $3x + y = 10$ and passes through the point $(-6, 2)$. Write the equation in slope-intercept form.

SOLUTION

Write the given equation in slope-intercept form: $y = -3x + 10$. The slope is -3. Perpendicular lines have opposite reciprocal slopes, so the desired line has a slope of $\frac{1}{3}$. Substitute the coordinates of the slope and the known point into the point-slope form, and then convert it to slope-intercept form.

$$\begin{aligned} y - y_1 &= m(x - x_1) \\ y - \mathbf{2} &= \mathbf{\tfrac{1}{3}}[x - (\mathbf{-6})] \\ y - 2 &= \frac{1}{3}x + 2 \\ y &= \frac{1}{3}x + 4 \end{aligned}$$

The equation is $y = \frac{1}{3}x + 4$. ■

Applications: Linear Equations

Many real-world situations involve slope and linear equations.

Using a Linear Model to Estimate

EXAMPLE 1

Dan and Ben begin a road trip. They set the trip meter to 0. Dan drives first, and then Ben begins driving at noon. Ben drives at a fairly constant speed. At 2 p.m., the trip meter reading is 180 mi. At 3:30 p.m., the reading is 267 mi.

A Write a linear equation in slope-intercept form that approximates the relationship between the trip meter reading and the amount of time Ben drives. Graph the equation.

SOLUTION

Slope-intercept form is $y = mx + b$. Let x represent the number of hours Ben drives, and let y represent the trip meter reading in miles. At 2 p.m., Ben has been driving for 2 h, and at 3:30 p.m., he has been driving for 3.5 h, so you know the following two data points: $(x_1, y_1) = (2, 180)$ and $(x_2, y_2) = (3.5, 267)$. Plot these two points. Find the slope:

$$\text{slope} = m = \frac{y_2 - y_1}{x_2 - y_1} = \frac{267\text{ mi} - 180\text{ mi}}{3.5\text{ h} - 2\text{ h}} = \frac{87\text{ mi}}{1.5\text{ h}} = \frac{58\text{ mi}}{1\text{ h}} = 58\text{ mph}$$

To solve for the y-intercept b, substitute 58 for m and $(2, 180)$ for (x, y) in the slope-intercept form.

$$\begin{aligned} y &= mx + b \\ \mathbf{180} &= \mathbf{58} \cdot \mathbf{2} + b \\ 180 &= 116 + b \\ 64 &= b \end{aligned}$$

The equation is $y = 58x + 64$. The graph of the equation is the line through the points $(2, 180)$ and $(3.5, 267)$.

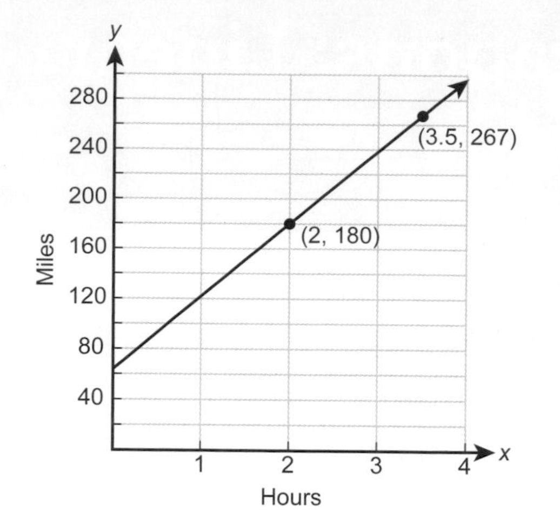

Think About It If Ben drives at a constant speed, then the equation developed in Example 1A is an exact model of the situation. But because Ben drives at a fairly constant speed, the equation is only an approximate model. The only exact data values that are known are those stated in the problem.

B Describe what the slope represents.

SOLUTION

Use units to figure this out. Since the numerator is miles and the denominator is hours, the ratio is miles per hour. In this situation, it is Ben's average speed, 58 mi/h.

C Estimate the number of miles Dan drove.

SOLUTION

When Ben begins driving, $x = 0$. If $x = 0$ in the equation $y = 58x + 64$, then $y = 64$. So based on the facts presented in the problem, 64 mi is the best estimate of the number of miles Dan drove. Verify that 64 is reasonable for the y-intercept of the graph. ■

Using a Linear Model to Solve a Problem

EXAMPLE 2

Leslie earns a base pay of \$12.50 per hour. She also earns time and a half for overtime (anything more than 40 h per week).

A Write and graph a linear equation that models Leslie's earnings for a week in which she works at least 40 h.

SOLUTION

Let t represent the number of hours of overtime Leslie works in a week. Let e represent her earnings for that week, in dollars.

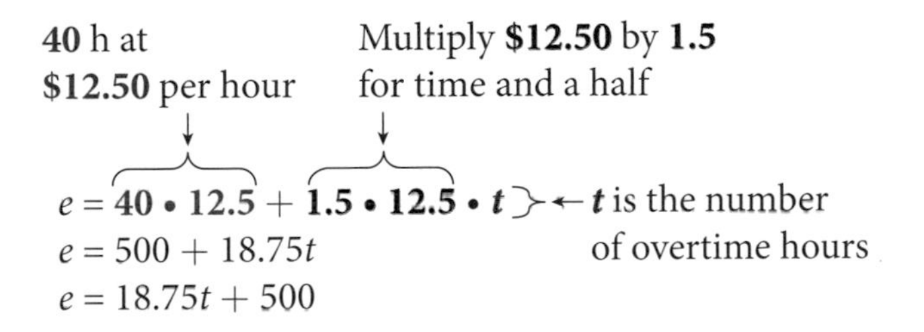

$$e = \mathbf{40 \cdot 12.5} + \mathbf{1.5 \cdot 12.5 \cdot} \boldsymbol{t}$$
$$e = 500 + 18.75t$$
$$e = 18.75t + 500$$

The equation $e = 18.75t + 500$ models Leslie's earnings for a week in which she works at least 40 h. To graph the equation, start with some ordered pairs and then draw a line through the points.

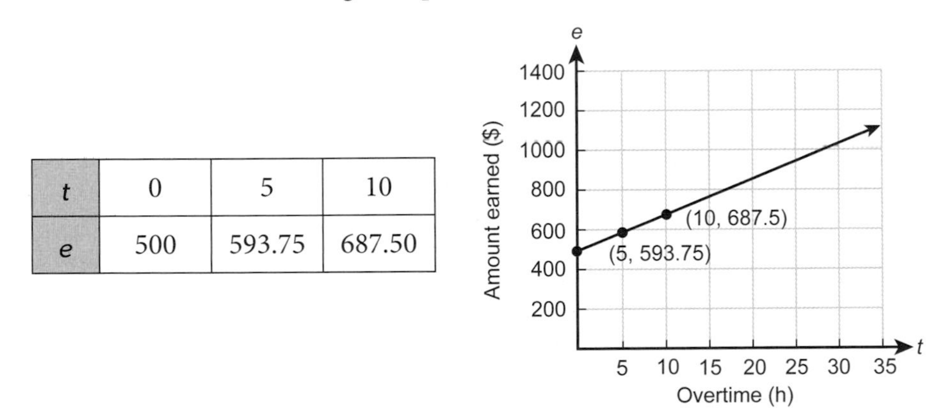

t	0	5	10
e	500	593.75	687.50

Leslie works at least 40 h, so only points with values $t \geq 0$ apply in this case.

B What does the slope of the equation represent?

SOLUTION

The slope, which is 18.75, represents the number of dollars per hour that Leslie earns at the overtime rate.

C Leslie reports her hours in quarter-hour increments. How many hours does Leslie need to work to earn $750 in 1 wk?

SOLUTION

To find the number of hours Leslie needs to work to earn $750 in 1 wk, substitute 750 for e and solve for t.

$$\begin{aligned} e &= 18.75t + 500 \\ \mathbf{750} &= 18.75t + 500 \\ 250 &= 18.75t \\ 13.33 &= t \end{aligned}$$

If Leslie needs to work 13.33 overtime hours, she needs to work a total of $40 + 13.33 = 53.33$ h.

Leslie reports her hours in quarter-hour increments, and $53.\overline{3}$ is between 53.25 and 53.5. So Leslie needs to work 53.5 h to earn $750 in 1 wk. ■

Using a Linear Model to Interpret Solutions

EXAMPLE 3

Ed is a lumber dealer. He sells two types of decking, earning 20% profit on synthetic decking and 16% profit on wood decking. Ed has a goal of earning a $2000 profit during the next month.

A Write an equation that represents the sales, in dollars, of each type of decking Ed can sell to earn a $2000 profit.

SOLUTION

Let s represent sales, in dollars, of synthetic decking. Let w represent sales, in dollars, of wood decking. Write an equation:

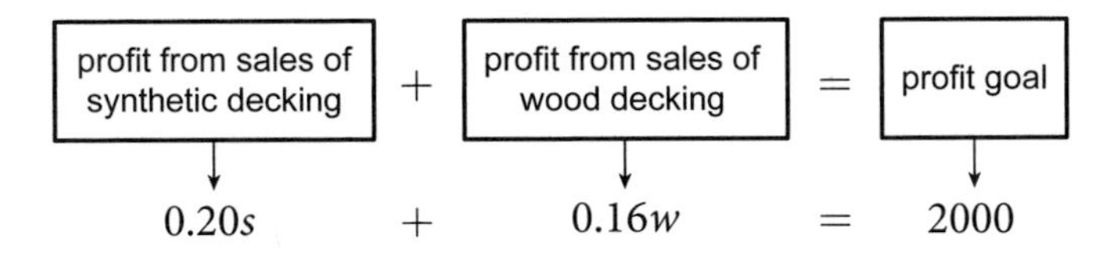

$$0.20s + 0.16w = 2000$$

B Graph the equation.

SOLUTION

Find the intercepts and use them to graph the equation. Label the horizontal axis s and the vertical axis w; points on the graph will have the form (s, w).

Find the s-intercept.

$$\begin{aligned} 0.20s + 0.16w &= 2000 \\ 0.20s + 0.16 \bullet \mathbf{0} &= 2000 \\ 0.20s &= 2000 \\ s &= 10{,}000 \end{aligned}$$

Plot the point $(10{,}000, 0)$.

Find the w-intercept.

$$\begin{aligned} 0.20s + 0.16w &= 2000 \\ 0.20 \bullet \mathbf{0} + 0.16w &= 2000 \\ 0.16w &= 2000 \\ w &= 12{,}500 \end{aligned}$$

Plot the point $(0, 12{,}500)$.

Connect the points with a line segment. The graph of the equation is a line, but in this application, only use Quadrant I.

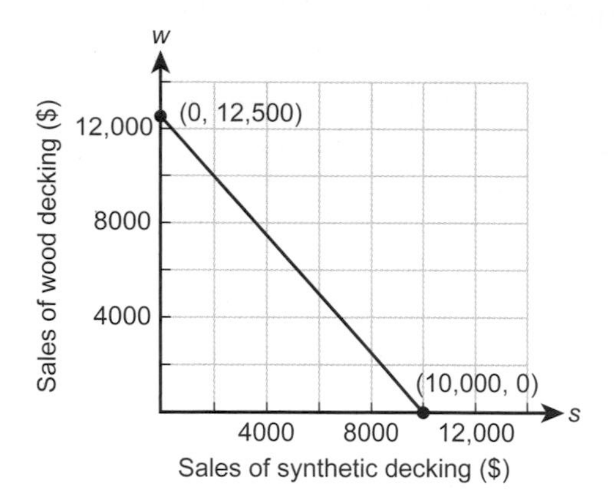

▸ **Think About It** In this situation, either variable can be the independent variable. You could label the horizontal axis *w* and the vertical axis *s*, obtaining a different graph.

C Identify three solutions to the equation and interpret their meaning.

SOLUTION

Example 1B shows two solutions to the equation: $(10{,}000, 0)$ and $(0, 12{,}500)$. To find another solution, substitute a convenient value for one variable in the equation and solve for the other variable. Substitute 6000 for s and solve to find that $w = 5000$. So a third solution is $(6000, 5000)$. Each solution is a combination of sales that result in a total profit of \$2000.

$$
\begin{aligned}
0.20s + 0.16w &= 2000 \\
0.20 \cdot \mathbf{6000} + 0.16w &= 2000 \\
1200 + 0.16w &= 2000 \\
0.16w &= 800 \\
w &= 5000
\end{aligned}
$$

Solution	What it represents
(10,000, 0)	\$10,000 sales of synthetic decking, \$0 sales of wood decking
(0, 12,500)	\$0 sales of synthetic decking, \$12,500 sales of wood decking
(6000, 5000)	\$6000 sales of synthetic decking, \$5000 sales of wood decking

Using a Linear Model to Make a Prediction

EXAMPLE 4

The table gives the median weekly earnings of full-time workers in the United States for 1980 through 2004. Find a model for the data. Then use your model to predict the median weekly earnings in 2010.

Year	Median weekly earnings (\$)
1980	262
1982	302
1984	326
1986	359
1988	385
1990	412
1992	440
1994	467
1996	490
1998	523
2000	576
2002	608
2004	638

U.S. Bureau of Labor Statistics 2015

SOLUTION

Let x represent the year and let y represent the median weekly earnings in dollars. Graph the ordered pairs. (The graph is called a scatter plot.) The data points form a linear pattern, so a linear function is a good model for the data. Draw a line that approximates the pattern.

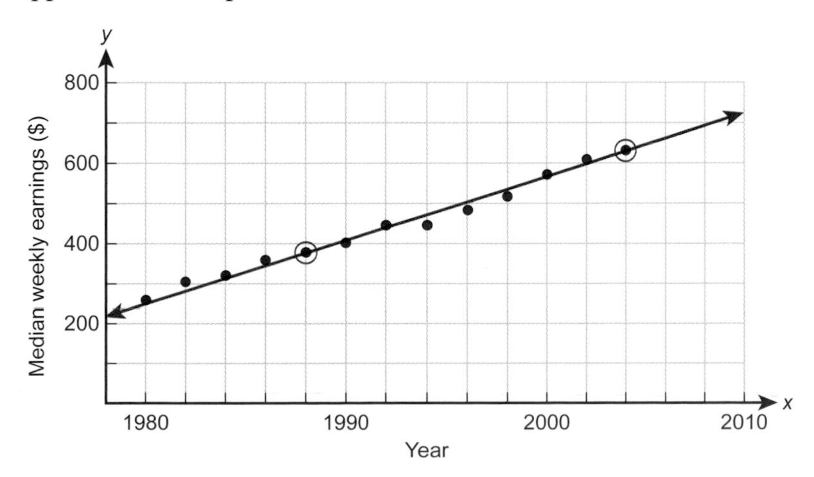

Finding the line of best fit is a strategy that makes it easy to find an equation to model the data. This line of fit passes through $(1988, 385)$ and $(2004, 638)$. Find an equation of the line. Use the point-slope form of a linear equation.

$$\begin{aligned} \text{slope} &= \frac{638 - 385}{2004 - 1988} \approx 15.8 \\ y - y_1 &= m(x - x_1) \\ y - \mathbf{385} &= \mathbf{15.8}(x - \mathbf{1988}) \\ y - 385 &= 15.8x - 31{,}410.4 \\ y &= 15.8x - 31{,}025.4 \end{aligned}$$

So a good linear model for the data is $f(x) = 15.8x - 31{,}025.4$.

To predict the median weekly earnings in 2010, substitute 2010 for x.

$$\begin{aligned} y &= 15.8x - 31{,}025.4 \\ y &= 15.8 \bullet \mathbf{2010} - 31{,}025.4 \\ y &= 732.6 \end{aligned}$$

According to this linear model, the predicted 2010 median weekly earnings for a full-time worker is about $733. ■

Graphing Linear Inequalities

You know how to graph linear equations. It is also possible to graph linear inequalities.

Solutions to Linear Inequalities in Two Variables

An ordered pair (x, y) is a solution to an inequality in two variables if substituting the values of x and y into the inequality yields a true statement.

EXAMPLE 1

Determine whether each ordered pair is a solution to the inequality $y < 4x - 8$.

A $(0, 0)$

SOLUTION

Test the ordered pair. Substitute the values of x and y into the inequality $y < 4x - 8$. Then simplify. If the resulting statement is true, the ordered pair is a solution.

$$(\mathbf{0}, \mathbf{0})$$

$$\begin{aligned} y &< 4x - 8 \\ \mathbf{0} &< 4 \cdot \mathbf{0} - 8 \\ 0 &< 0 - 8 \\ 0 &\not< -8 \end{aligned}$$

The ordered pair $(0, 0)$ is not a solution to the inequality $y < 4x - 8$.

B $(2, -10)$

SOLUTION

Test the ordered pair. Substitute the values of x and y into the inequality $y < 4x - 8$. Then simplify. If the resulting statement is true, the ordered pair is a solution.

$$(\mathbf{2}, \mathbf{-10})$$

$$\begin{aligned} y &< 4x - 8 \\ \mathbf{-10} &< 4 \bullet \mathbf{2} - 8 \\ -10 &< 8 - 8 \\ -10 &< 0 \checkmark \end{aligned}$$

The ordered pair $(2, -10)$ is a solution to the inequality $y < 4x - 8$. ■

Graphing a Linear Inequality in Two Variables

The graph of a linear inequality is a region of the coordinate plane called a half-plane.

▶ **Remember** The graph of a linear equation is a line in the coordinate plane. Each point that is a solution to the equation lies on the line.

A **boundary line** divides the coordinate plane into two half-planes. One of the half-planes contains all the points that are solutions to the inequality. The boundary line is dashed if the boundary is not part of the solution, so the inequality uses the operator $<$ or $>$. The boundary is a solid line if it is part of the solution, so the inequality uses the operator $\leq$ or $\geq$.

To graph a linear inequality in two variables, first graph the boundary line. Then determine which half-plane contains the solutions to the inequality and shade that half-plane. The shaded region represents all the solutions to the inequality.

How to Graph a Linear Inequality

Step 1 Graph the boundary line. If the boundary is included in the solution, use a solid line. If the boundary is not included in the solution, use a dashed line.

Step 2 Test a point that does not lie on the boundary line to determine whether the ordered pair is a solution to the inequality.

Step 3 If the ordered pair is a solution, shade the half-plane that contains the point. Otherwise shade the other half-plane.

Think About It If the boundary line does not pass through the origin, use the origin to test the solution of an inequality. If substituting the point $(0, 0)$ results in a true statement, shade toward the origin. If not, shade away from the origin.

EXAMPLE 2

Graph the inequality.

A $y > 2x - 1$

SOLUTION

Step 1 Graph the boundary line $y = 2x - 1$. Since the inequality contains the operator $>$, the boundary line is a dashed line.

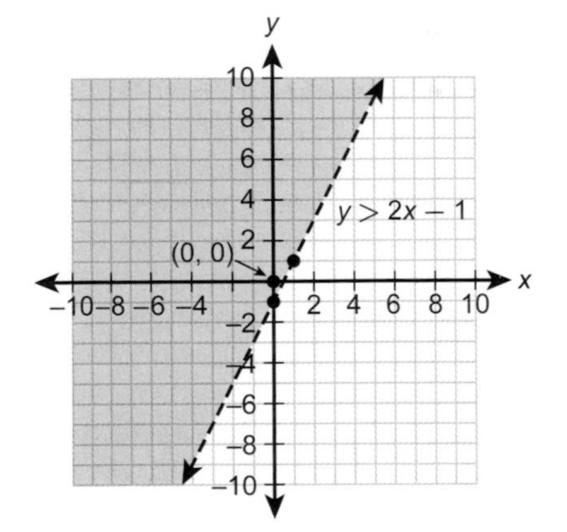

Step 2 Test a point that does not lie on the boundary line to determine if the ordered pair is a solution to the inequality. Test the point $(0, 0)$.

$$y > 2x - 1$$
$$\mathbf{0} \overset{?}{>} 2 \cdot \mathbf{0} - 1$$
$$0 > -1 \checkmark$$

The statement $0 > -1$ is true.

Step 3 Since $(0, 0)$ is a solution, shade the half-plane that contains the point $(0, 0)$.

B $3x - 4y \geq 8$

SOLUTION

Step 1 To graph the boundary line, first write the inequality in slope-intercept form.

$3x - 4y \geq 8$

$-4y \geq -3x + 8$	Subtract $3x$ from each side of the inequality.
$\frac{-4y}{-4} \leq \frac{-3x}{-4} + \frac{8}{-4}$	Divide each side of the inequality by −4. Since you are dividing an inequality by a negative number, switch the direction of the inequality.
$y \leq \frac{3}{4}x - 2$	Simplify.

Now graph the boundary line $y = \frac{3}{4}x - 2$. Since the inequality contains the operator $\leq$, the boundary line is a solid line.

Step 2 Test a point that does not lie on the boundary line to determine whether the ordered pair is a solution to the inequality. Test the point $(\mathbf{0}, \mathbf{0})$.

$$y \leq \frac{3}{4}x - 2$$

$$\mathbf{0} \stackrel{?}{\leq} \frac{3}{4} \cdot \mathbf{0} - 2$$

$$0 \nleq -2$$

The statement $0 \leq -2$ is false.

Step 3 Since $(0, 0)$ is not a solution, shade the half-plane that does not contain the point $(0, 0)$.

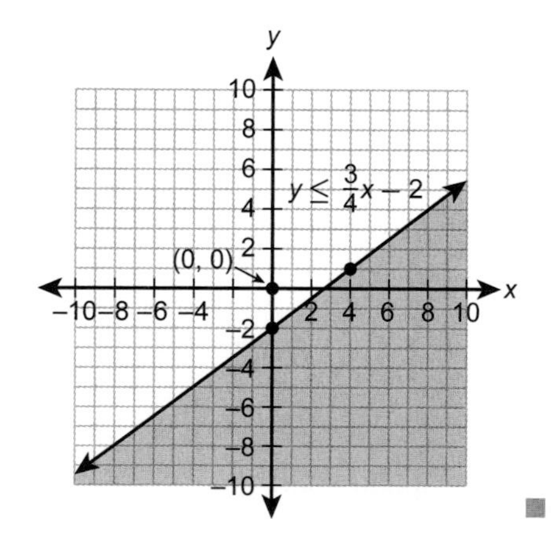

Application: Mixture

EXAMPLE 3

Audrina wants to create a blend of birdseed containing millet seed and sunflower seed. Millet seed costs \$3.50 per pound and sunflower seed costs \$2 per pound. She has \$28 to spend on the birdseed.

A Write an inequality to model the problem.

SOLUTION

Write an inequality that can be used to model the problem.

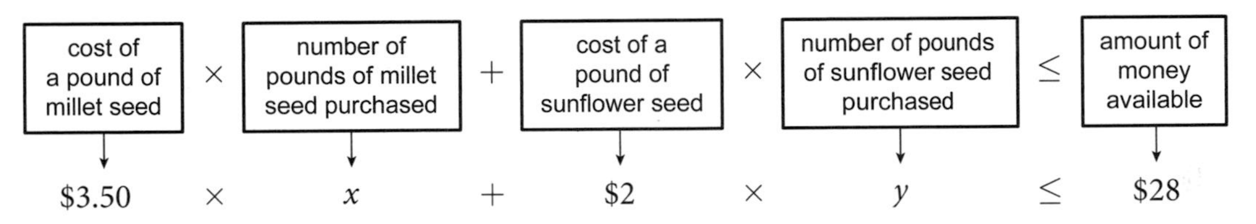

The problem is modeled by the inequality $3.5x + 2y \leq 28$.

B Graph the inequality.

SOLUTION

Graph the boundary line $3.5x + 2y = 28$. Since the inequality contains the operator $\leq$, the boundary line is a solid line. The points $(8, 0)$ and $(0, 14)$ are the x- and y-intercepts of the boundary line.

Test the point $(2, 2)$ to determine which side of the boundary line to shade.

$$\begin{aligned} 3.5x + 2y &\leq 28 \\ 3.5 \cdot \mathbf{2} + 2 \cdot \mathbf{2} &\overset{?}{\leq} 28 \\ 7 + 4 &\overset{?}{\leq} 28 \\ 11 &\leq 28 \checkmark \end{aligned}$$

Since $11 \leq 28$ is a true statement, shade the half-plane containing the point (2, 2). The number of pounds of millet and sunflower seed purchased must always be greater than or equal to zero, so the graph is restricted to Quadrant I.

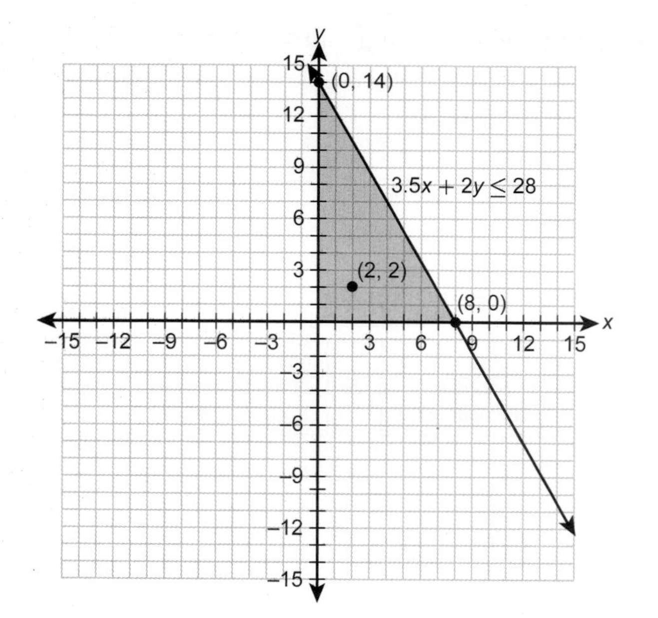

C What does the shaded area of the graph represent?

SOLUTION

The shaded area of the graph represents all the possible ordered pairs that are solutions to the inequality $3.5x + 2y \leq 28$. ■

Systems of Linear Inequalities

A system of linear inequalities is two or more linear inequalities in the same variables.

Geometrically, the solution to a system of linear inequalities is the graph of all the points that are solutions of the system. Every point in the solution region must make all the inequalities true.

Graphing a System of Linear Inequalities

How to Graph a System of Linear Inequalities

Step 1 Graph each inequality in the system.

Step 2 Shade the intersection of the half-planes that are the solutions to each inequality. The intersection is the solution to the system.

Step 3 Test a point in the intersection of the half-planes to determine whether the ordered pair is a solution to the system.

Graph the solution of the system of inequalities.

$$y \geq x - 2$$
$$y < 2x + 1$$

SOLUTION

Step 1 Graph each inequality in the system.

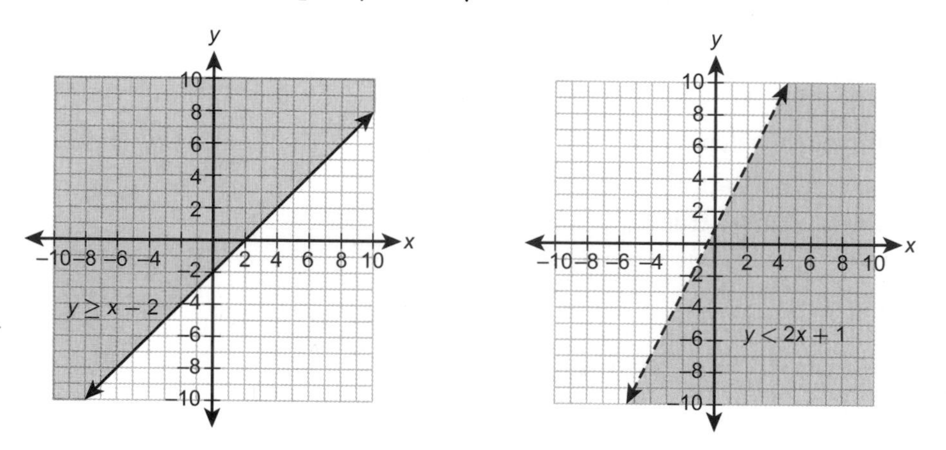

Step 2 Shade the intersection of the half-planes. Here, the green triangular region is the intersection of the half-planes. This triangular region is the solution to the system of inequalities.

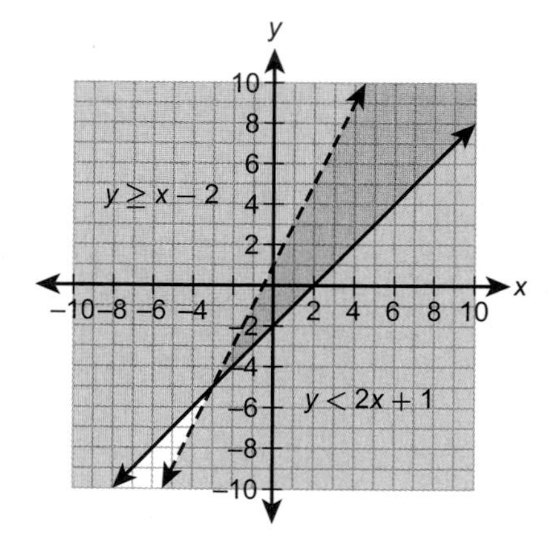

Step 3 Test a point in the intersection of the half-planes to determine if the ordered pair is a solution to the system. Test the point $(2, 3)$.

Substitute 2 for x and 3 for y in each inequality in the system.

$$y \geq x - 2 \qquad y < 2x + 1$$
$$3 \overset{?}{\geq} \mathbf{2} - 2 \qquad 3 \overset{?}{<} 2 \bullet \mathbf{2} + 1$$
$$3 \geq 0 \checkmark \qquad 3 \overset{?}{<} 4 + 1$$
$$3 < 5 \checkmark \blacksquare$$

EXAMPLE 2

Graph the solution of the system of inequalities.

$$y > \frac{1}{2}$$
$$y > 5x + \frac{1}{4}$$

SOLUTION

Step 1 Graph each inequality in the system.

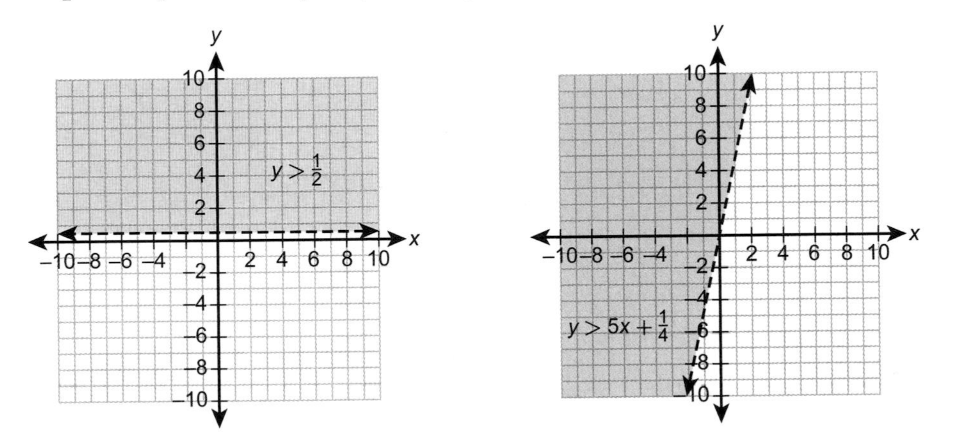

Step 2 Shade the intersection of the half-planes. In the graph, the green region is the intersection of the half-planes. This green region is the solution to the system of inequalities.

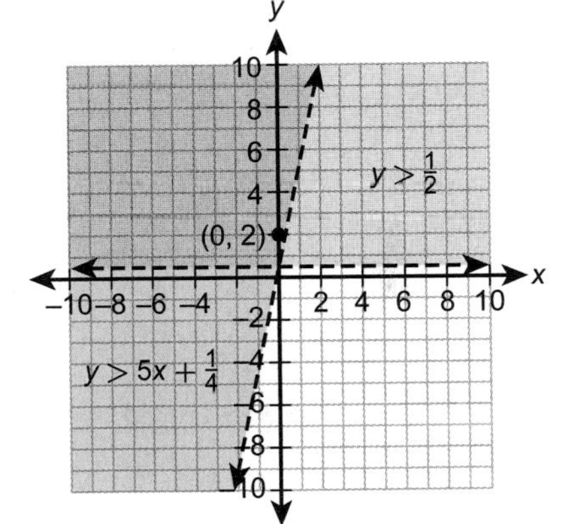

Step 3 Test a point in the intersection of the half-planes to determine if the ordered pair is a solution to the system. Test the point $(\mathbf{0}, \mathbf{2})$.

Substitute 0 for x and 2 for y in each inequality in the system.

$$y > \frac{1}{2} \qquad y > 5x + \frac{1}{4}$$
$$\mathbf{2} > \frac{1}{2} \checkmark \qquad \mathbf{2} \overset{?}{>} 5 \cdot \mathbf{0} + \frac{1}{4}$$
$$2 \overset{?}{>} 0 + \frac{1}{4}$$
$$2 > \frac{1}{4} \checkmark \ \blacksquare$$

EXAMPLE 3

Graph the solution of the system of inequalities.

$$y > 2x + 4$$
$$y < 2x + 1$$

SOLUTION

Step 1 Graph each inequality in the system.

Step 2 The boundary lines have the same slope, 2, so they are parallel. The half-planes do not intersect, so this system of inequalities has no solution.

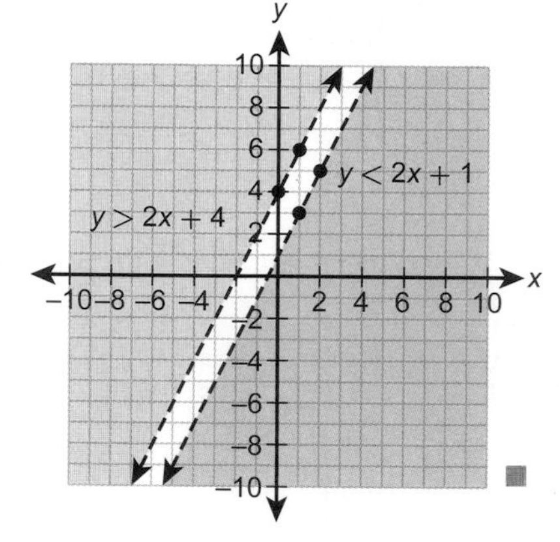

Writing a System of Linear Inequalities from a Graph

EXAMPLE 4

Write a system of inequalities that corresponds to the green shaded region of the graph.

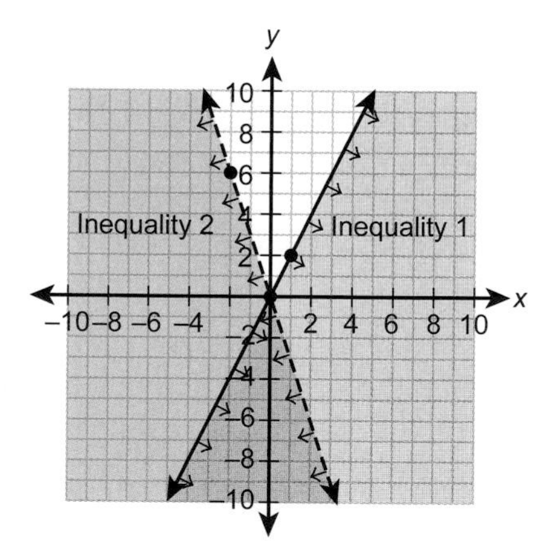

SOLUTION

Inequality 1 The points $(0, 0)$ and $(1, 2)$ lie on the boundary line of Inequality 1. Find the slope of the boundary line and, since you know the y-intercept is zero, use slope-intercept form to write its equation.

slope:

$$m = \frac{2 - 0}{1 - 0} = 2$$

equation:

$$y = mx + b$$
$$y = 2x + 0$$
$$y = 2x$$

Since the region below the line is shaded and the boundary line is solid, the first inequality in the system is $y \leq 2x$.

▶ **Think About It** You can use the small arrows when graphing inequalities to show which half-plane should be shaded.

Inequality 2 The points $(0, 0)$ and $(-2, 6)$ lie on the boundary line of Inequality 2. Find the slope of the boundary line and, since you know the y-intercept, use slope-intercept form to write its equation.

slope:

$$m = \frac{6 - 0}{-2 - 0} = -3$$

equation:

$$y = mx + b$$
$$y = -3x + 0$$
$$y = -3x$$

Since the region below the line is shaded and the boundary line is dashed, the second inequality in the system is $y < -3x$.

The system of inequalities is $\begin{matrix} y \le 2x \\ y < -3x \end{matrix}$. ■

Constraints

Many real-world problems have multiple combinations of answers.

Definitions

A **constraint** is a necessary condition in a problem. We often write a constraint in the form of an inequality. A set of constraints forms a system of inequalities.

The graph of the solutions of the system of inequalities is the **feasible region**. The feasible region contains every possible solution to the problem.

Application: Snack Mix

EXAMPLE 1

You are making a snack mix consisting of granola and peanuts. Granola has 3 g of fiber per ounce and peanuts have 2 g of fiber per ounce. You want the snack mix to have at least 16 g of fiber and weigh no more than 8 oz.

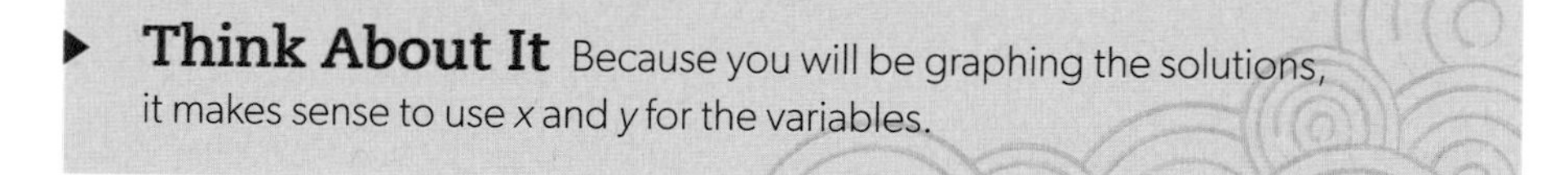

▶ **Think About It** Because you will be graphing the solutions, it makes sense to use x and y for the variables.

A Write the constraints that model the problem.

SOLUTION

First define your variables. Let x represent the number of ounces of granola. Let y represent the number of ounces of peanuts. Use the information in the problem to write a system of inequalities.

The snack mix consists of both granola and peanuts. You will have some number of ounces of each.	$x > 0$ $y > 0$
Granola has 3 g of fiber per ounce. Peanuts have 2 g of fiber per ounce. You want at least 16 g of fiber.	$3x + 2y \geq 16$
You want the snack mix to weigh no more than 8 oz.	$x + y \leq 8$

B Graph the feasible region

SOLUTION

Graph the system.

Two of the boundary lines are on the axes. The boundary lines of the other equations, in slope-intercept form, are $y = -\frac{3}{2}x + 8$ and $y = -x + 8$.

The feasible region is the intersection of all the half-planes.

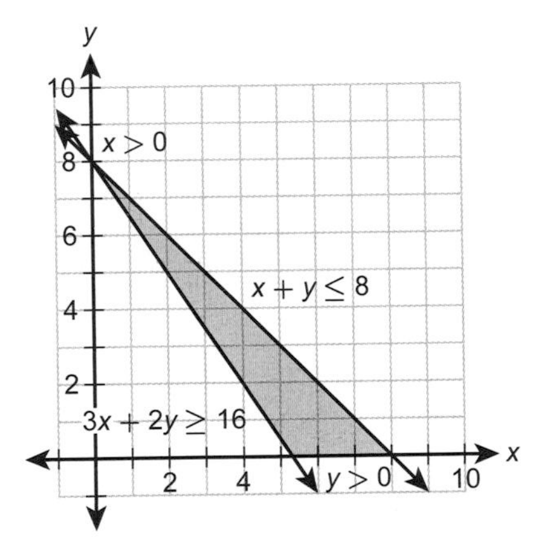

C What are two possible combinations of granola and peanuts that can be used to make the mix?

SOLUTION

Choose two points in the feasible region. Two possible choices are the ordered pairs $(4, 3)$ and $(5, 2)$. So two possible combinations for the snack mix are 4 oz of granola and 3 oz of peanuts, and 5 oz of granola and 2 oz of peanuts.

CHECK

The combination of 4 oz of granola and 3 oz of peanuts contains 18 g of fiber and weighs 7 oz. The combination of 5 oz of granola and 2 oz of peanuts contains 19 g of fiber and weighs 7 oz. Both combinations meet the given conditions. ■

Application: Small Business

EXAMPLE 2

The owners of a small knitting business have enough yarn to knit no more than 30 hats and 15 sweaters next month. They want to knit at least 10 hats and 5 sweaters. It costs them \$20 to knit a hat and \$40 to knit a sweater. They do not want their knitting costs to exceed \$1000.

A Write the constraints that model the problem.

SOLUTION

First define your variables. Let x represent the number of hats they knit. Let y represent the number of sweaters they knit. Use the information in the problem to write a system of inequalities.

They can knit no more than 30 hats and 15 sweaters.	$x \leq 30$ $y \leq 15$
They want to knit at least 10 hats and 5 sweaters.	$x \geq 10$ $y \geq 5$
It costs them \$20 to knit a hat and \$40 to knit a sweater. They do not want their knitting costs to exceed \$1000.	$20x + 40y \leq 1000$

B Graph the feasible region

SOLUTION

Graph the system.

Two of the boundary lines are horizontal and two of the boundary lines are vertical. The other boundary line is the graph of $20x + 40y \leq 1000$. The x-intercept is 50 and the y-intercept is 25.

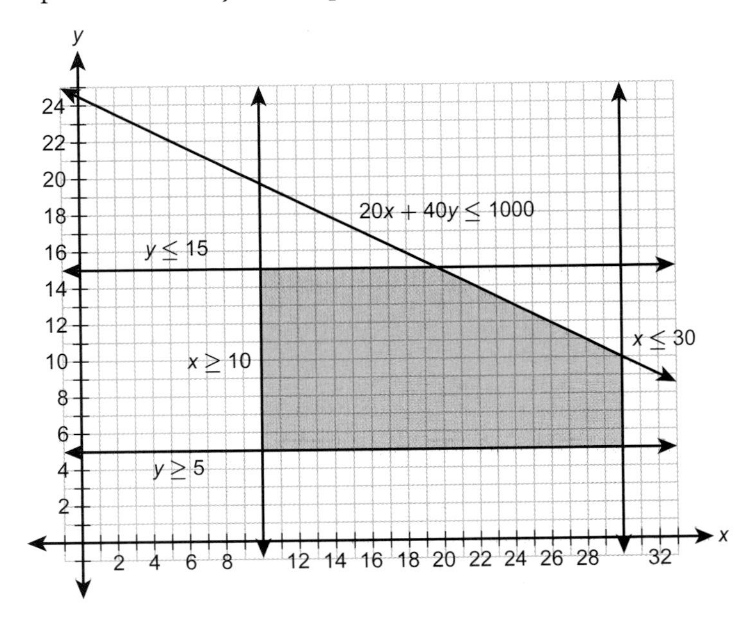

▶ **Think About It** It does the business no good to knit half a sweater or one-third of a hat. So, although every point in the shaded region is a solution of the system, only those points with whole-number coordinates are solutions to the problem.

C Does knitting 28 hats and 12 sweaters meet the given conditions?

SOLUTION

No, the point $(28, 12)$ falls outside the feasible region.

D Suppose the business owners knit 26 hats. How many sweaters can they knit in that month?

SOLUTION

Find 26 on the x-axis and look up. The y-values in the feasible region are greater than or equal to 5 and less than or equal to 12. So they can knit at least 5 sweaters but no more than 12 sweaters. ■

Working with Functions

Topic List

- Relations
- Functions
- Function Equations
- Linear Functions
- Function Parameters
- Thinking About Domain and Range
- Absolute Value Functions
- Piecewise Functions
- Step Functions

A solar cell is a little machine that takes in solar energy and puts out electricity. A mathematical function is a machine that takes in a number as an input and produces another number as an output.

Relations

In math, a mapping between two sets is called a relation.

Representing Relations in Different Ways

Definition

A **relation** is a mapping from a set of inputs to a set of outputs.

You can use a set of ordered pairs to represent a relation. The x-coordinates of the ordered pairs are the inputs and the y-coordinates are the outputs.

You can also display a relation using an arrow diagram, table, and graph.

EXAMPLE 1

In the relation $\{(8, 3), (8, 4), (10, 5), (12, 8), (13, 9)\}$, each x-coordinate represents a student's age and each y-coordinate represents the student's grade level in school. Display the relation in an arrow diagram, table, and graph.

SOLUTION

Arrow Diagram

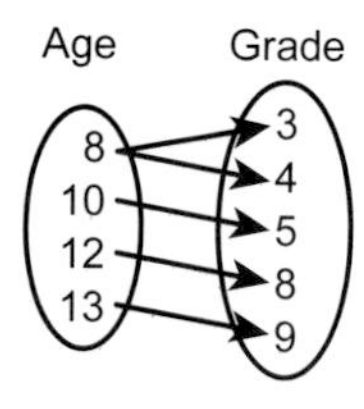

Table

Age	Grade
8	3
8	4
10	5
12	8
13	9

Graph

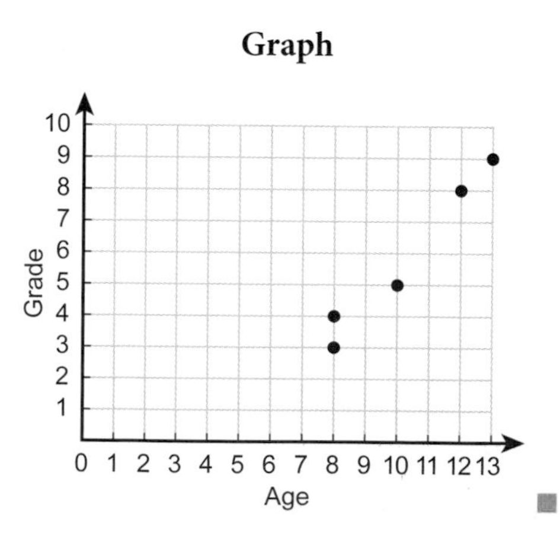

Finding the Domain and Range of a Relation

The **domain** of a relation is the set of allowable inputs and the **range** is the set of possible outputs.

▶ **Think About It** When writing the domain and range, list each number in each set only once.

EXAMPLE 2

Find the domain and range of the relation.

A $\{(-2, -4), (0, 3), (2, -4), (4, 1)\}$.

SOLUTION

The domain is the set of x-coordinates: $\{-2, 0, 2, 4\}$. The range is the set of y-coordinates: $\{-4, 1, 3\}$.

B

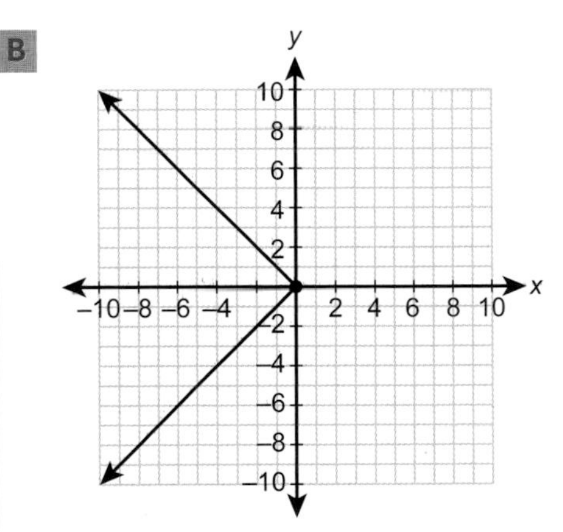

▶ **Think About It** On a graph, the horizontal axis represents the values of the domain, which are the values of the independent (input) variable. The vertical axis represents the values of the range, which are the values of the dependent (output) variable.

SOLUTION

The graph extends horizontally from 0 toward the negative numbers without end, and it extends vertically without beginning or end. The domain is all numbers less than or equal to zero, $\{x \mid x \leq 0\}$ and the range is all real numbers, $\{y \mid y \in \mathbb{R}\}$. ■

▶ **Think About It** Inequalities are often used to represent the domain and range of some relations.

Application: Fuel Consumption

EXAMPLE 3

The relation between four vehicles and their fuel consumption in miles per gallon is shown in the table. Write the relation as a set of ordered pairs. Then write the domain and range of the relation.

Vehicle (2008 model)	Average fuel consumption (mpg)
Ford Fusion	27
Lincoln Navigator	16
Toyota Camry	26
Honda Element	21

▶ **Think About It** The inputs and outputs in a relation do not have to be numeric.

SOLUTION

The relation can be written as $\{$(Ford Fusion, 27), (Lincoln Navigator, 16), (Toyota Camry, 26), (Honda Element, 21)$\}$.

The domain is $\{$Ford Fusion, Lincoln Navigator, Toyota Camry, Honda Element$\}$. The range is $\{16, 21, 26, 27\}$. ■

Functions

A function is a relation in which each input can have only one output.

Definition

A **function** is a relation in which every element of the domain is assigned to exactly one element of the range.

The relation between people and their height is a function because no person can have more than one height. For example, George cannot be 58 in. and 60 in. tall at the same time. However, George and Maria can both have the same height.

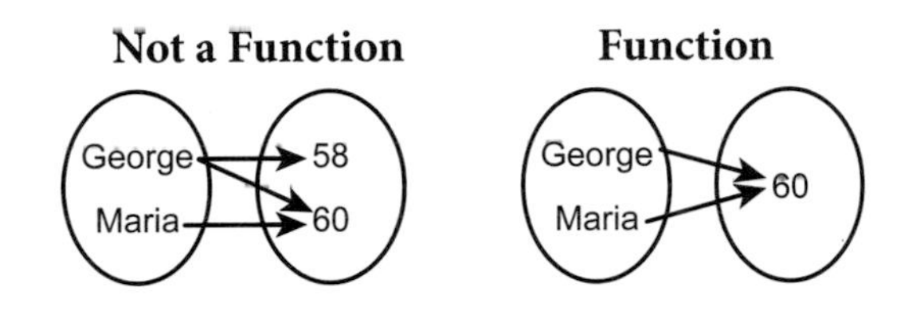

Determining Whether a Relation Is a Function

EXAMPLE 1

Determine whether the relation is a function.

A $\{(-5, 4), (-4, 0), (-2, 4), (-1, 0)\}$

SOLUTION

No element from the domain is paired with more than one element from the range. The relation is a function.

▶ **Think About It** In a table or a set of ordered pairs, if no x-values are repeated, the relation is a function.

B

x	2	2	2	4	5
y	−9	−7	−3	1	8

SOLUTION

The domain value of 2 is assigned to −9, −7, and −3.
The relation is not a function. ■

Applying the Vertical Line Test

When a function is graphed in the coordinate plane, each x-value is assigned to no more than one y-value. This makes it impossible for any vertical line to intersect the graph at more than one point.

Vertical Line Test

For any relation, if a vertical line intersects the graph more than once, the relation is not a function.

Also, if you cannot draw a vertical line that intersects a relation more than once, the relation is a function.

EXAMPLE 2

Determine whether the relation is a function.

▸ **Think About It** Place an uncooked piece of spaghetti over the graph of a relation vertically. Slide it over the graph from left to right. If the spaghetti intersects the graph more than once at any *x*-value, then the relation is not a function.

A

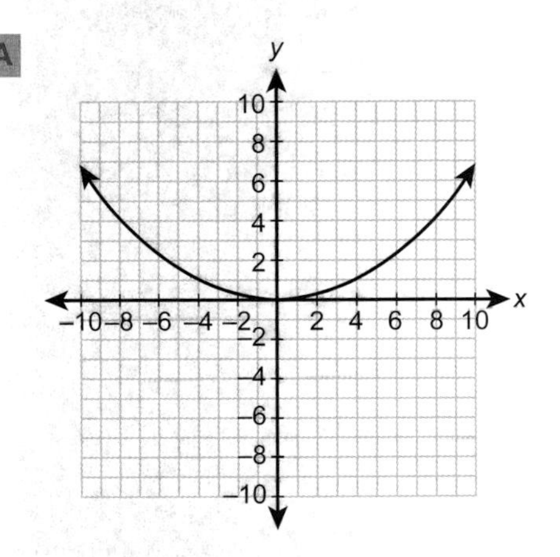

SOLUTION

No vertical line intersects the graph at more than one point.
The relation is a function.

B

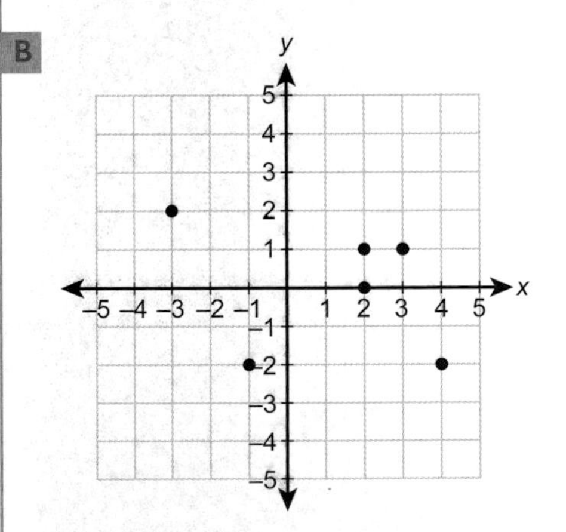

SOLUTION

There is a single vertical line that intersects both $(2, 1)$ and $(2, 0)$.
The relation is not a function. ■

Evaluating a Function

To evaluate a function, find the y-value that corresponds to a given x-value.

EXAMPLE 3

Evaluate the function at the given point.

A $x = 3$

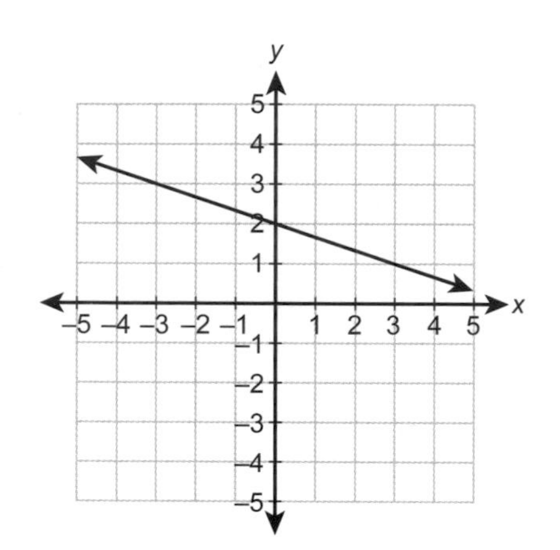

SOLUTION

Place your finger at 3 on the x-axis and slide it vertically until your finger reaches the graph. Then move your finger horizontally to find the corresponding y-value on the y-axis. When $x = 3$, the value of the function is $y = 1$.

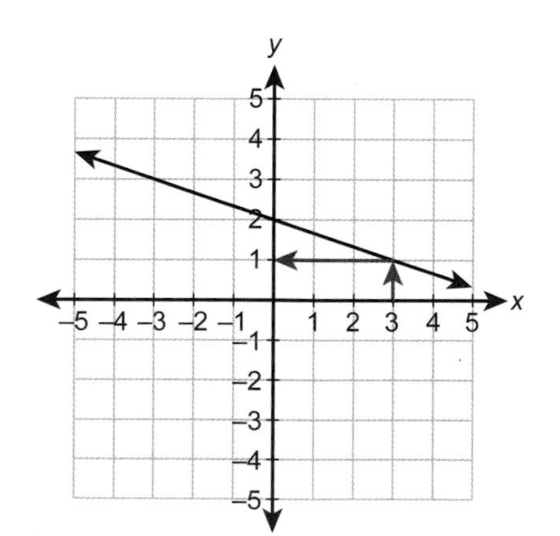

B $x = -1$

x	-3	-2	-1	0	1	2
y	-5	-4	-3	-2	-1	0

SOLUTION

Locate $x = -1$ in the top row of the table and then find the corresponding y-value. The value of the function at $x = -1$ is $y = -3$. ■

Applications: Donations, Distance, and Population

When choosing a graph to represent a real-life situation, consider whether a connected graph (called a continuous graph) or a graph of individual points (called a discrete graph) is appropriate.

EXAMPLE 4

A People registered for a charity event will tell three other people about the charity and ask for donations. Choose the graph that better represents the situation. Explain.

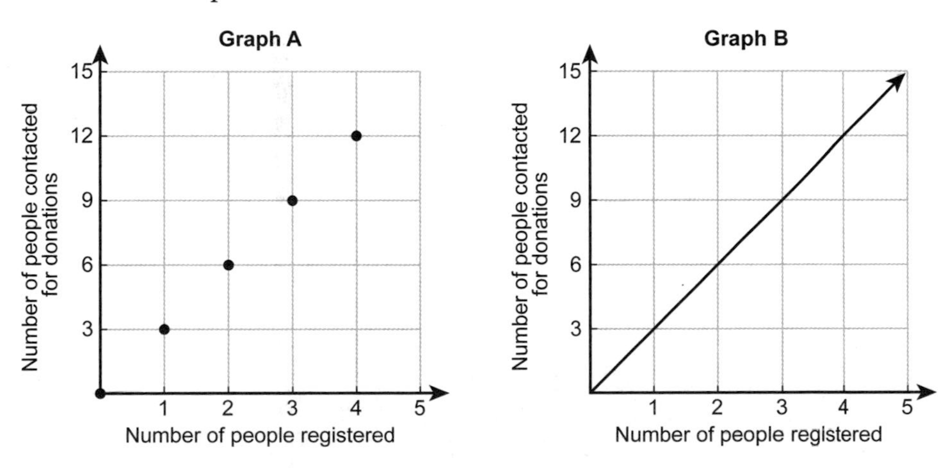

SOLUTION

There cannot be a fraction of a person, so Graph A is the better choice.

B Which graph better represents the function between the time Leroy leaves home on a bicycle and the distance he travels? Explain.

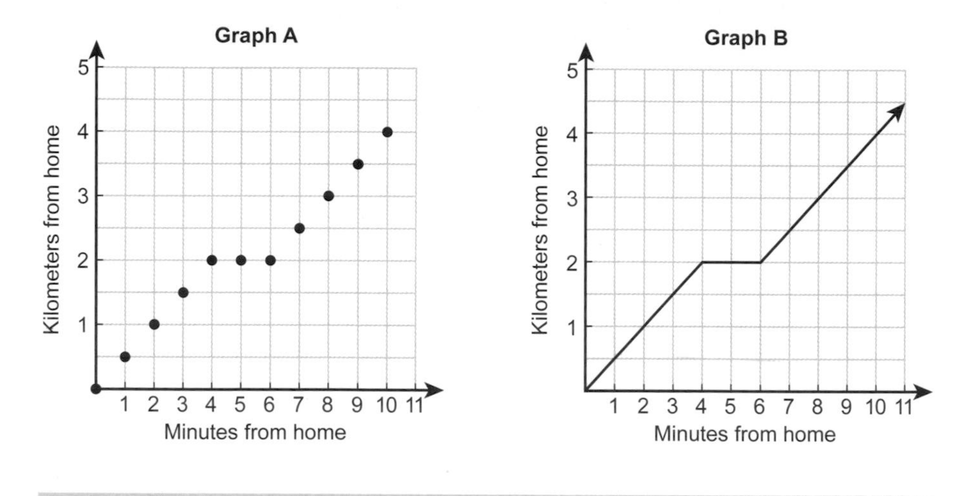

▸ **Think About It** The flat segment of Leroy's graph indicates no change in distance. Time continues to pass, yet distance does not increase—for instance, when Leroy stops at a traffic light.

SOLUTION

Time and distance are continuous, so Graph B is the better choice. ■

EXAMPLE 5

The graph shows the population of North Carolina every decade from 1940 to 2000. Use the graph to estimate the population in 1995.

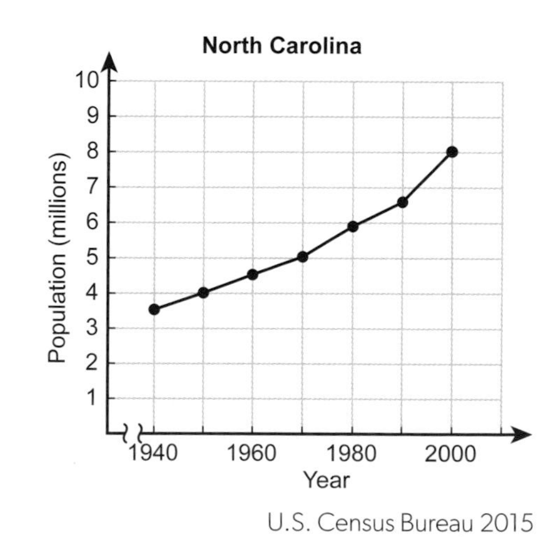

U.S. Census Bureau 2015

SOLUTION

Locate 1995 on the x-axis by putting your finger halfway between 1990 and 2000. Move your finger vertically until it reaches the graph. Move horizontally to the y-axis to estimate the value: about 7.4 million. ■

Function Equations

You can use equations to represent many functions.

Suppose every y-value of a function is one greater than three times the corresponding x-value. This function can be expressed as the equation $y = 3x + 1$. In this equation, x is the **independent variable** (the input variable), and y is the **dependent variable** (the output variable).

You can use **function notation** to rewrite a function equation by replacing the dependent variable with $f(x)$. For example, you can write the equation $y = 3x + 1$ as $f(x) = 3x + 1$ or $f: x \rightarrow 3x + 1$.

▸ Think About It

NOTATION The notation $f(x)$ is read as "f of x" or "f is a function of x."

Writing a Function Equation

EXAMPLE 1

Use function notation to write the equation of the line.

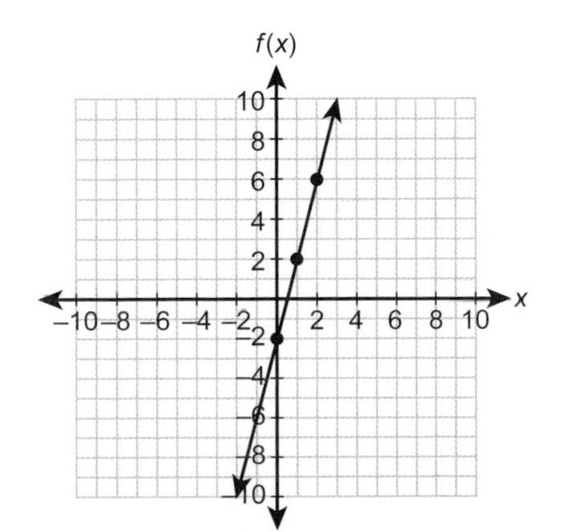

SOLUTION

The line has a slope of 4 and a y-intercept of -2, so write the equation in slope-intercept form: $y = 4x - 2$.

Now write the equation using function notation.

$$y = 4x - 2$$

$f(x) = 4x - 2$ Substitute $f(x)$ for y. ■

Evaluating Functions

To evaluate a function, substitute the given value of x into the function and then simplify the expression.

EXAMPLE 2

Evaluate $f(x) = -5x + 4$ for the given value of x.

A $f(-2)$

SOLUTION

Substitute -2 for x and simplify.

$f(\mathbf{-2}) = -5 \cdot (\mathbf{-2}) + 4$ Substitute -2 for x.

$= 10 + 4$ Multiply.

$= 14$ Add.

So $f(-2) = 14$, or when $x = -2, f(x) = 14$.

B $f(3)$

SOLUTION

Substitute 3 for x and simplify.

$f(\mathbf{3}) = -5 \cdot \mathbf{3} + 4$ Substitute 3 for x.

$= -15 + 4$ Multiply.

$= -11$ Add.

So $f(3) = -11$, or when $x = 3, f(x) = -11$. ■

EXAMPLE 3

Evaluate $g(x) = 5$ for the given value of x.

A $g(2)$

SOLUTION

For every value of x, $g(x)$ will equal 5, so $g(2) = 5$.

B $g(0)$

SOLUTION

For every value of x, $g(x)$ will equal 5, so $g(0) = 5$.

C $g(-3)$

SOLUTION

For every value of x, $g(x)$ will equal 5, so $g(-3) = 5$. ■

EXAMPLE 4

If $h(x) = 3x^2 - x$, find $h\left(\frac{1}{3}\right)$.

SOLUTION

Substitute $\frac{1}{3}$ for x, then simplify.

$h\left(\frac{1}{3}\right) = 3 \cdot \left(\frac{1}{3}\right)^2 - \frac{1}{3}$	Substitute $\frac{1}{3}$ for x.
$= 3 \cdot \frac{1}{9} - \frac{1}{3}$	Evaluate the power.
$= \frac{1}{3} - \frac{1}{3}$	Multiply.
$= 0$	Subtract.

So $h\left(\frac{1}{3}\right) = 0$. ■

▶ **Remember** Evaluate powers before multiplying.

Application: Graph of a Real-World Function

EXAMPLE 5

Ronnie went for a 20 min jog. The graph below shows her jogging distance as a function of time.

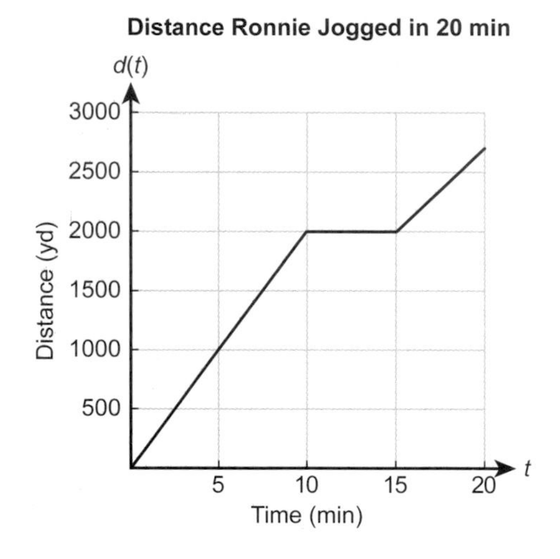

▶ **Think About It** Many real-world events can be modeled as functions.

A About how many yards did she jog after 5 min? 12 min?

SOLUTION

After 5 min, she jogged $d(5)$ yards. The function $d(5) = 1000$. After 12 min, she jogged $d(12)$ yards. The function $d(12) = 2000$. So after 5 min, she jogged 1000 yd, and after 12 min she jogged 2000 yd.

B How would you describe Ronnie's motion in the first 10 min, between 10 and 15 min, and in the last 5 min?

SOLUTION

In the first 10 min, the graph goes up at a constant rate, so Ronnie was moving at a constant speed.

The graph is constant from $t = 10$ min to $t = 15$ min, which means that Ronnie covered no distance and was not moving during this time.

In the last 5 min, she went back to jogging at the same speed she moved at during the first 10 min. ■

Linear Functions

The key features of a linear function include its slope and its intercepts.

Interpreting a Function Table

EXAMPLE 1

The number of times a company's commercial will air each week, $N(w)$, is a function of the number of weeks, w, into the contract, as shown in the table. The function is a linear function.

w	1	4	7	15	20
$N(w)$	38	32	26	10	0

A Identify the slope and explain what it means in the context of the situation.

SOLUTION

Choose any two ordered pairs to determine the slope. Using $(1, 38)$ and $(4, 32)$: $m = \frac{32 - 38}{4 - 1} = \frac{-6}{3} = -2$. Every week, the number of commercials that will air will decrease by 2.

B Identify the intercept shown in the table. Explain whether it is an x-intercept or a y-intercept and tell what it means in the context of the situation.

▶ **Remember** An x-intercept is the x-coordinate of a point where a graph intersects the x-axis, or where $y = 0$. A y-intercept is the y-coordinate of a point where a graph intersects the y-axis, or where $x = 0$.

SOLUTION

The intercept is 20, because it is a coordinate of the ordered pair $(20, 0)$. Because the output is 0, it is an x-intercept. It means that no commercials will air during Week 20. You can use the previous point and the slope to see that this week is the first that no commercials will air. ■

Graphing a Linear Function

You can graph a linear function using the same methods used for graphing a linear equation. Write the function in slope-intercept form, and use the slope and y-intercept to draw the line.

▶ **Think About It** The slope-intercept form of a linear equation is $y = mx + b$. Since $f(x)$ and y are equivalent, the slope-intercept form of a linear function is $f(x) = mx + b$.

EXAMPLE 2

Graph $f(x) = 5 - 4x$.

SOLUTION

Write the function in slope-intercept form.

$f(x) = 5 - 4x$	Original function.
$f(x) = -4x + 5$	Write in the form $f(x) = mx + b$.

Identify the slope: $m = -4 = \frac{-4}{1}$

Identify the y-intercept: $b = 5$

Plot the y-intercept at $(0, 5)$, and use the slope to plot additional points. Then draw a line through the points.

▶ **Remember** The slope of a line is the ratio of the line's vertical change to its horizontal change.

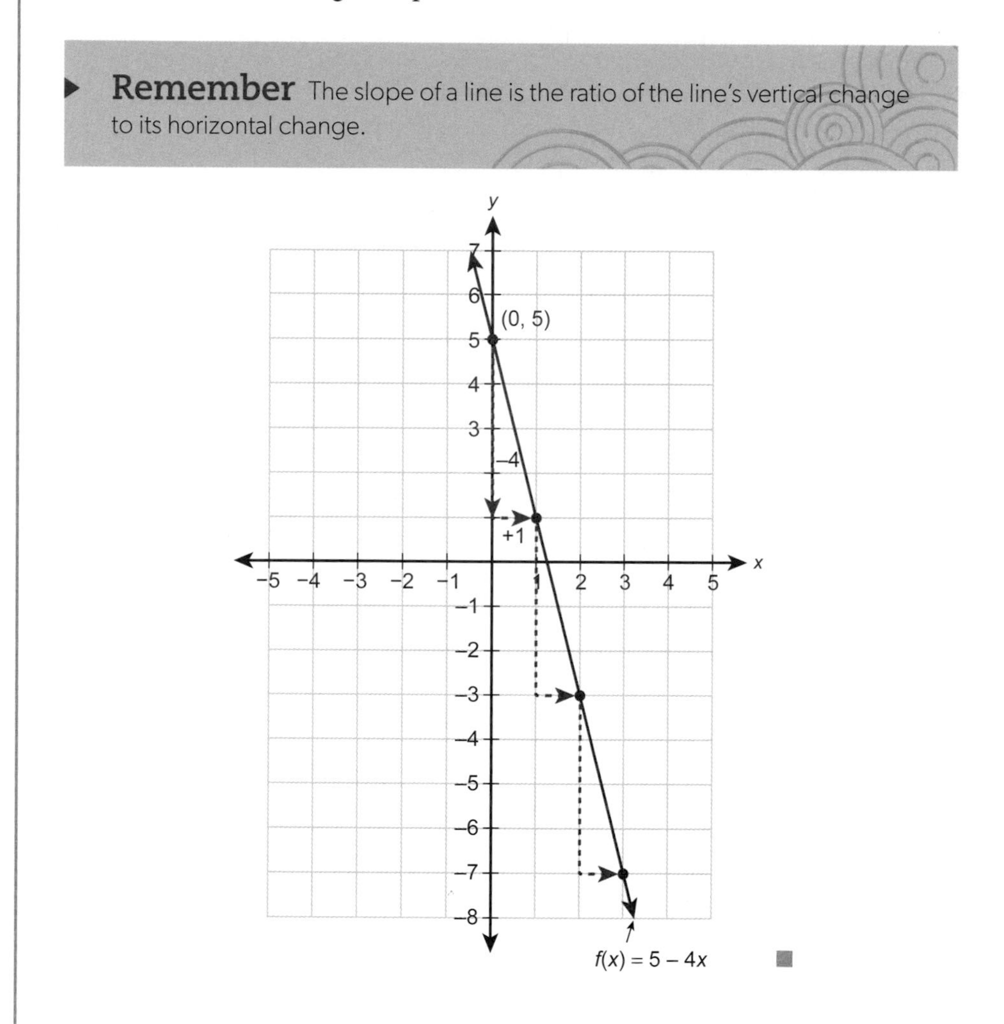

Sketching from a Verbal Description

EXAMPLE 3

Jenna has \$60 to spend on salad and steak for a party. The salad costs \$2 per pound. The steak costs 3 times as much as the salad. Sketch a graph that represents the situation. Label the intercepts.

SOLUTION

Step 1 Determine the equation that represents the situation. Begin by defining variables.

$$x = \text{pounds of salad}$$
$$y = \text{pounds of steak}$$

The salad costs \$2 per pound, so the steak must cost \$6 per pound. Therefore, the equation is $2x + 6y = 60$.

Step 2 Use the equation to determine the intercepts.

Substitute 0 for y and solve for x.

$$2x + 6 \bullet \mathbf{0} = 60$$
$$2x + 0 = 60$$
$$2x = 60$$
$$x = 30$$

Substitute 0 for x and solve for y.

$$2 \bullet \mathbf{0} + 6y = 60$$
$$0 + 6y = 60$$
$$6y = 60$$
$$y = 10$$

Plot and label the points that contain the intercepts $(30, 0)$ and $(0, 10)$. Connect the points with a line segment.

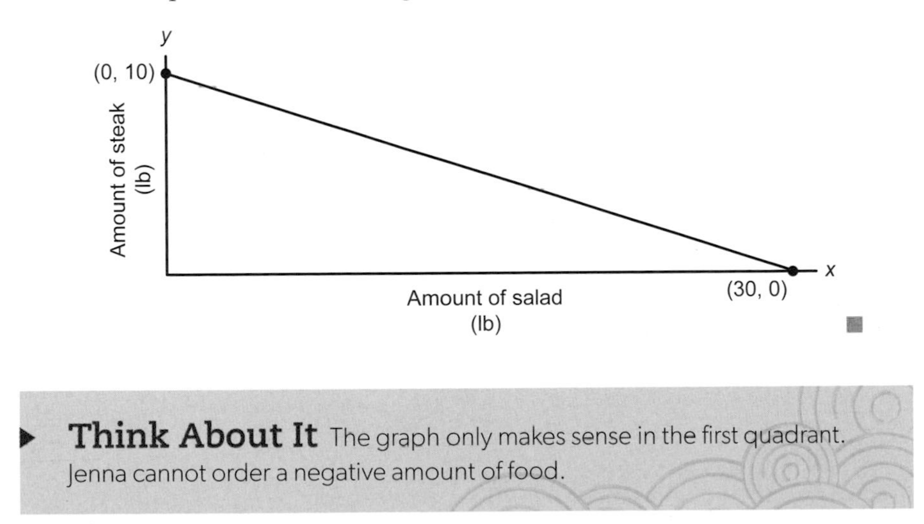

▶ **Think About It** The graph only makes sense in the first quadrant. Jenna cannot order a negative amount of food.

Sketching a Multipart Graph

EXAMPLE 4

For the first 30 min of his treadmill workout, Daniel jogged steadily at his normal pace. For the next 10 min, Daniel jogged at half his normal pace because his foot hurt. Sketch a graph of the situation.

▶ **Think About It** You know that each part of the graph is a line segment because you were told that Daniel ran steadily.

SOLUTION

Start the graph at the origin, which indicates both a time and a distance of 0. Draw a segment with a positive slope to represent the first 30 min. Draw a second segment, also with a positive slope (but less steep), to show a slower pace for the next 10 min. This segment should be half as steep as you drew the first segment. It should also be shorter, because the time spent jogging at this pace was one-third the time spent jogging at the original pace.

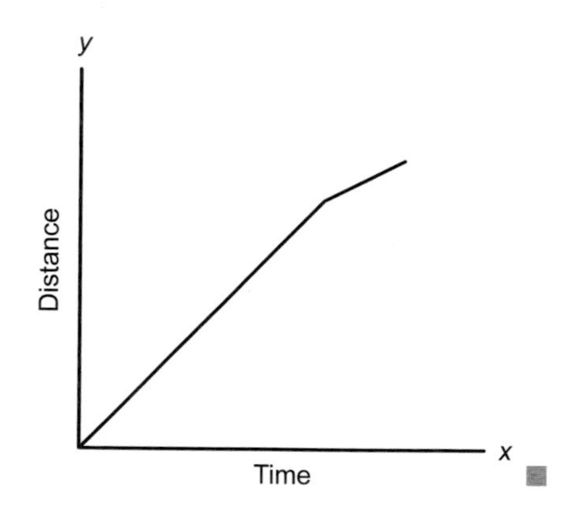

Features of Linear Graphs

EXAMPLE 5

Alexandra bought a tomato plant at the beginning of the summer and planted it in her backyard. She measured the height of the plant each week and recorded the values on the graph.

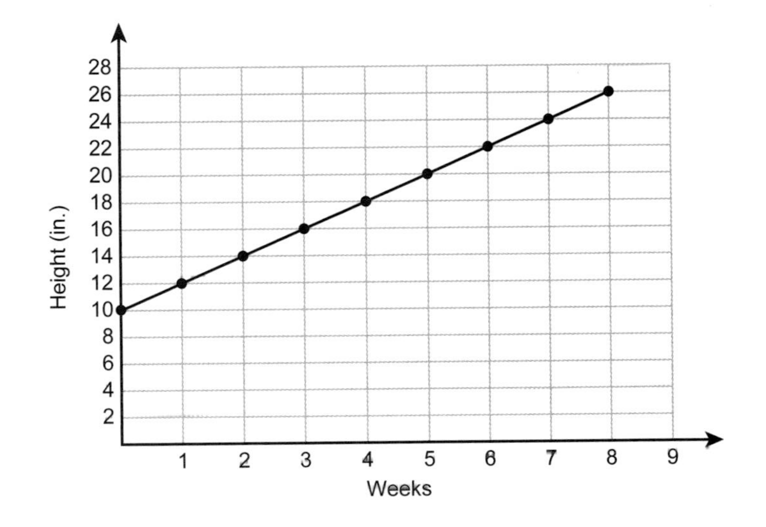

A Identify the slope and explain what it means in the context of the situation.

SOLUTION

Choose any two points on the graph to determine the slope. Using $(0, 10)$ and $(5, 20)$, $m = \frac{20 - 10}{5 - 0} = \frac{10}{5} = 2$. Every week, the tomato plant grew 2 in.

B Identify the y-intercept shown on the graph and explain what it means in the context of the situation.

SOLUTION

The y-intercept is 10. This means that when Alexandra bought the tomato plant, it was 10 in. tall. ■

Function Parameters

Changing the parameters of a function affects the shape and position of the graph.

You can change the shape or position of the graph of a function by changing the parameters of the function. The letter k is used to represent this parameter. There are four ways the parameter k can affect the function.

▶ **Remember** In function notation, x is the input variable and $f(x)$ is the output variable.

If k is added to the input, $f(x + k)$, the result is a horizontal translation of $f(x)$ by k units. When k has a positive value, $f(x)$ is translated to the left, and when k has a negative value, $f(x)$ is translated to the right.

If k is added to the output, $f(x) + k$, the result is a vertical translation of $f(x)$ by k units. When k has a positive value, $f(x)$ is translated up, and when k has a negative value, $f(x)$ is translated down.

If k is multiplied by the input, $f(k \cdot x)$, the result is a horizontal stretch or compression of $f(x)$ by a factor of k. For a linear function, the y-intercept does not change. When k is greater than 1, the graph is compressed horizontally closer to the y-axis. When k is less than 1, the graph is stretched horizontally away from the y-axis.

If k is multiplied by the output, $f(x) \cdot k$, the result is a vertical stretch or compression of $f(x)$ by a factor of k. For a linear function, the x-intercept does not change. When k is greater than 1, the graph is stretched vertically away from the x-axis. When k is less than 1, the graph is compressed vertically closer to the x-axis.

Think About It If k is multiplied by the input of a linear function, the slope changes but the y-intercept stays the same. If k is multiplied by the output of a linear function, both the slope and the y-intercept change.

Function Parameters and Graphs

EXAMPLE 1

A Suppose $f(x) = -5x - 4$. How does the graph of $g(x) = f(x + 6)$ compare to the graph of $f(x)$?

SOLUTION

Step 1 Identify the general form that matches $g(x)$ and determine the value of k.

$f(x + k)$ General form

$g(x) = f(x + 6)$

$k = 6$

Step 2 Identify the type of transformation. In the function $g(x)$, 6 is added directly to the input, x. So $g(x)$ is the function $f(x)$ translated horizontally 6 units to the left.

Remember A horizontal translation of positive k units means translating k units to the left, not to the right.

CHECK

Graph both equations on the same coordinate plane.

$f(x) = -5x - 4$; $m = -5$ and $b = -4$

$g(x) = f(x + 6)$

$g(x) = -5(x + 6) - 4$

$g(x) = -5x - 30 - 4$

$g(x) = -5x - 34$; $m = -5$ and $b = -34$

Use the y-intercepts and slopes to graph each line. This confirms $g(x)$ is the function $f(x)$ translated horizontally 6 units to the left.

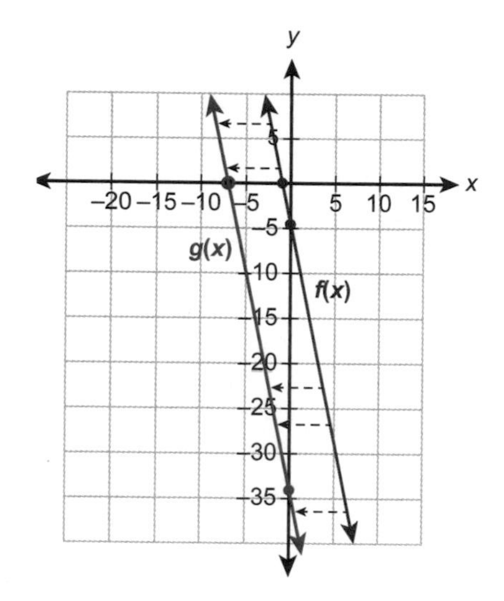

B Suppose $f(x) = \frac{1}{2}(x + 10)$. How does the graph of $g(x) = f(2x)$ compare to the graph of $f(x)$?

SOLUTION

The general form that matches $g(x)$ is $f(k \bullet x)$, so $k = 2$. Multiplying k by the input indicates a horizontal compression closer to the y-axis by a factor of 2.

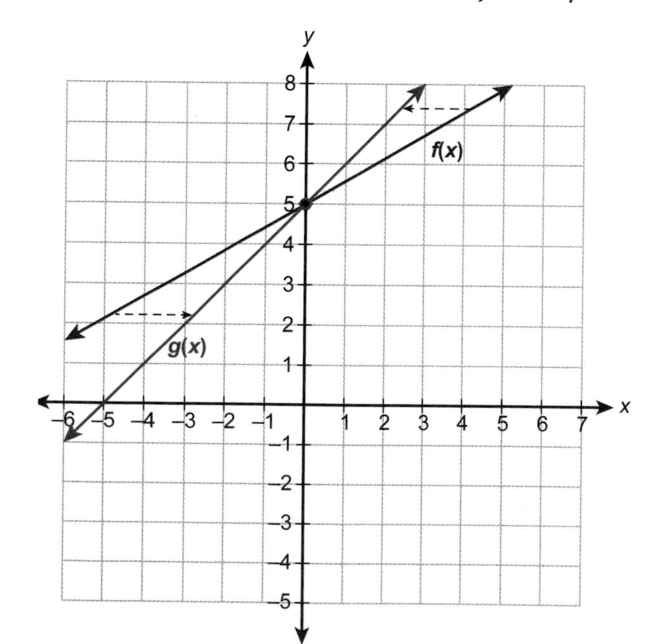

Function Parameters and Function Equations

EXAMPLE 2

Suppose $f(x) = 3x + 4$, and the graph of $g(x)$ is a vertical translation of $f(x)$ down 7 units. What is the equation of $g(x)$?

SOLUTION

Step 1 Identify which general form indicates a vertical translation. The general form $f(x) + k$, or k added to the output, indicates a vertical translation.

Step 2 Write a new function using the general form and the given value for k. To translate the function down 7 units, use $k = -7$.

$$f(x) = 3x + 4$$
$$g(x) = f(x) - 7$$
$$g(x) = (3x + 4) - 7$$
$$g(x) = 3x + 4 - 7$$
$$g(x) = 3x - 3$$

The slopes of the two functions are the same and the y-intercepts differ by 7 units, confirming the difference between the two functions is a vertical translation of 7 units down. ■

EXAMPLE 3

Describe the transformation that takes the graph of $f(x) = \frac{2}{3}x + 6$ to the graph of $g(x) = 2x + 6$.

SOLUTION

Step 1 Compare the two functions. The only difference between $f(x)$ and $g(x)$ is to the input variable, x.

$$f(x) = \frac{2}{3}x + 6 \qquad g(x) = 2x + 6.$$

Multiplying the input of $f(x)$ by a factor of 3 results in the input shown in $g(x)$.

$$3 \bullet \frac{2}{3}x = 2x$$

Step 2 Identify the general form that indicates a factor multiplied by the input.

The general form $f(k \bullet x)$ indicates a factor of k multiplied by the input. Write an equation to check that $g(x) = f(3x)$.

$$f(x) = \frac{2}{3}x + 6$$
$$g(x) = f(3x)$$
$$g(x) = \frac{2}{3}(3x) + 6$$
$$g(x) = 2x + 6$$

The transformation that takes the graph of $f(x)$ to the graph of $g(x)$ is multiplying the input by a factor of 3, or $g(x) = f(3x)$. ■

Thinking About Domain and Range

Sometimes, only some of the domain and range values of a function make sense for a given situation.

Two Types of Domains and Ranges

Definitions

The **theoretical domain and range** of a function are the sets of all allowable inputs and outputs. The **practical domain and range** of a function are the sets of all realistic inputs and outputs for a particular situation.

EXAMPLE 1

A vendor has 20 umbrellas to sell. He sells them for \$15 each. The function $m(u) = 15u$ models the total amount of money the vendor makes from selling u umbrellas.

A What is the theoretical domain of the function?

SOLUTION
You can substitute any real number into the function rule, $15u$.
The theoretical domain is the set of all real numbers.

B What is the practical domain of the function?

SOLUTION
The fewest number of umbrellas the vendor can sell is 0. The greatest number of umbrellas the vendor can sell is 20. It does not make sense for the vendor to sell part of an umbrella, so the practical domain is the set of all integers from 0 to 20, inclusive.

C What is the theoretical range of the function?

SOLUTION

Any real number could be the result of multiplying another real number by 15. The theoretical range is the set of all real numbers.

D What is the practical range of the function?

SOLUTION

The total amount of money the vendor makes is \$15 times the number of umbrellas he sells. He can sell as few as 0 and as many as 20 umbrellas, so he can make as little as \$0 and as much as \$300. The practical range is the set of all multiples of 15 between 0 and 300, inclusive. ■

> **Think About It**
>
> NOTATION You can write the practical range as $\{m(u) \mid m(u) = 15k, k \in \mathbb{Z}, k \geq 0, k \leq 20\}$.

EXAMPLE 2

Graph $m(u)$ from Example 1 over its theoretical domain and over its practical domain.

A What is the theoretical domain of the function?

SOLUTION

theoretical domain: $\{u \mid u \in \mathbb{R}\}$

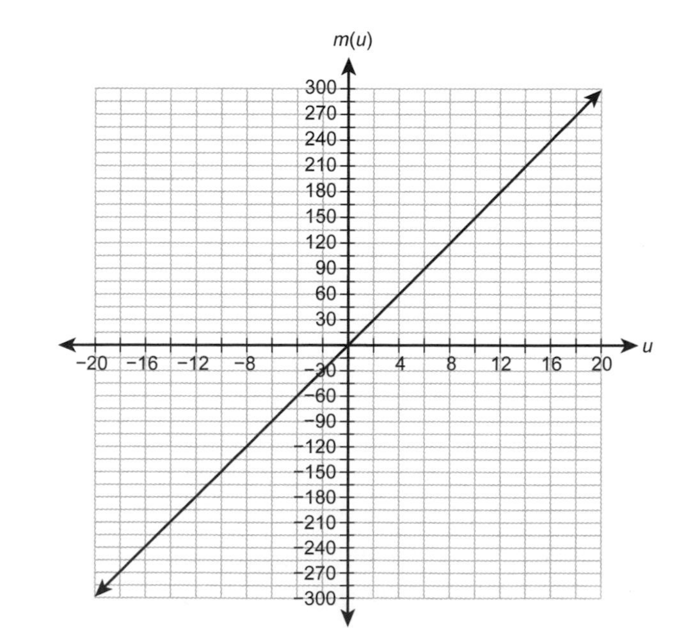

B What is the practical domain of the function?

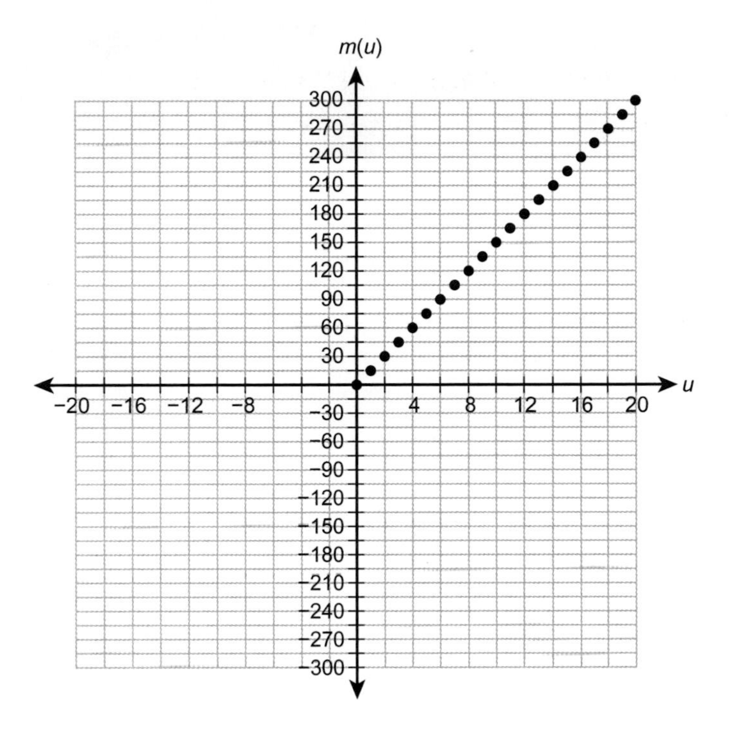

SOLUTION

practical domain: $\{u \mid u \in \mathbb{Z}, u \geq 0, u \leq 20\}$ ■

Absolute Value Functions

A **family of functions** is a group of functions with the same fundamental characteristics.

Definition

An **absolute value function** is a function whose rule contains an absolute value expression.

Remember The absolute value of a number is its distance from zero on the number line.

The basic function in a family of functions is called the **parent function.** The parent function of the absolute value family of functions is $f(x) = |x|$. A table of ordered pairs and the graph of the function are shown.

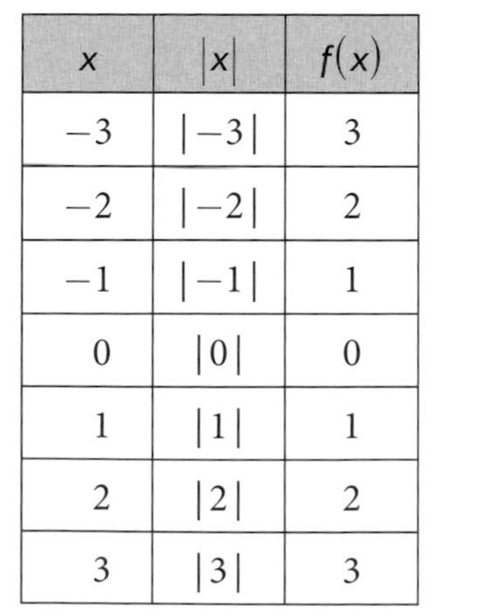

x	$\lvert x \rvert$	$f(x)$
-3	$\lvert -3 \rvert$	3
-2	$\lvert -2 \rvert$	2
-1	$\lvert -1 \rvert$	1
0	$\lvert 0 \rvert$	0
1	$\lvert 1 \rvert$	1
2	$\lvert 2 \rvert$	2
3	$\lvert 3 \rvert$	3

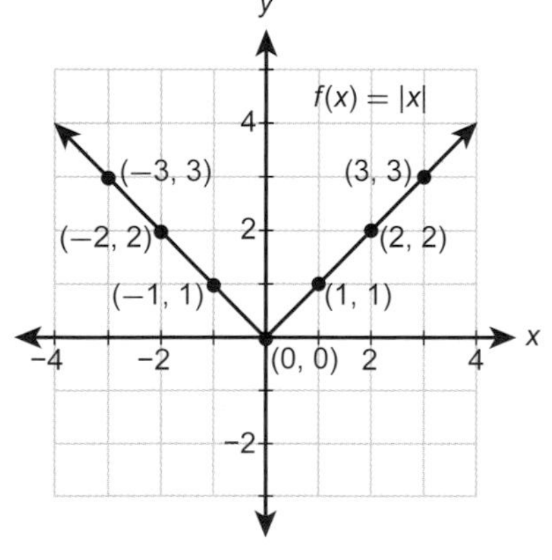

The graph is made up of two pieces—two rays that extend from a common vertex, forming a V-shape. All absolute value functions are V-shaped. Their vertex position, orientation, and width, however, can vary.

Graphing Absolute Value Functions by Plotting Points

EXAMPLE 1

Graph $f(x) = |x - 4| - 3$.

▸ **Think About It** Choose x-values that allow you to determine the position of the vertex as well as both rays.

SOLUTION

Make a table of values and plot the ordered pairs.

x	$\|x - 4\| - 3$	$f(x)$
1	$\|\mathbf{1} - 4\| - 3$	0
2	$\|\mathbf{2} - 4\| - 3$	−1
3	$\|\mathbf{3} - 4\| - 3$	−2
4	$\|\mathbf{4} - 4\| - 3$	−3
5	$\|\mathbf{5} - 4\| - 3$	−2
6	$\|\mathbf{6} - 4\| - 3$	−1
7	$\|\mathbf{7} - 4\| - 3$	0

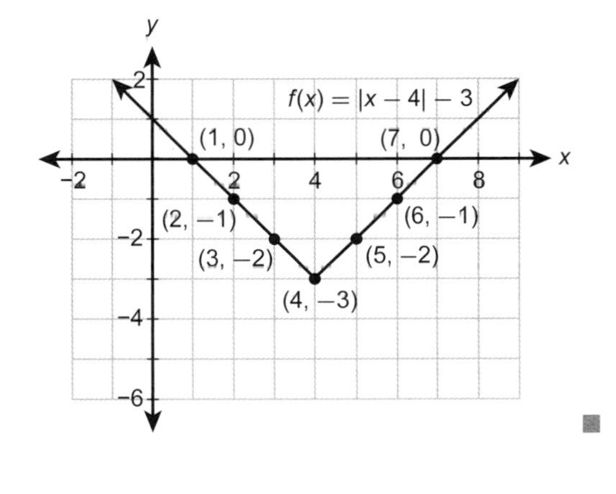

Translating Absolute Value Functions

Graphing an absolute value function by plotting points can take some guess-and-check work to determine which values in the domain you should use. In a family of functions, however, once you know the graph of the parent function, you can use transformations to graph related functions. A transformation is a one-to-one mapping between two sets of points. One type of transformation is a translation, or slide. You can translate a function horizontally, vertically, or both.

Graphs of Absolute Value Functions

Absolute Value Function Graph Family: $f(x) = |x - h| + k$

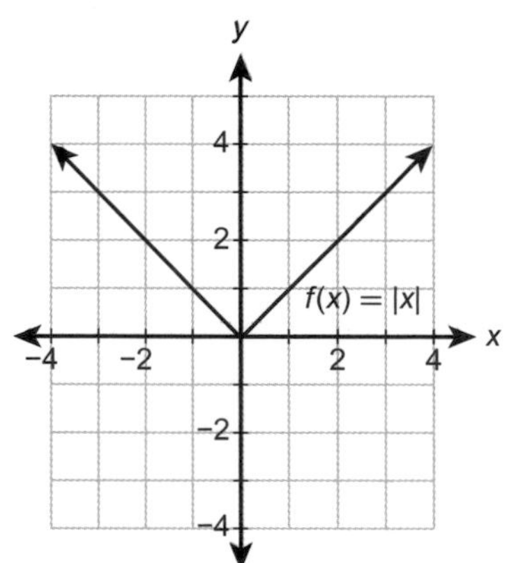

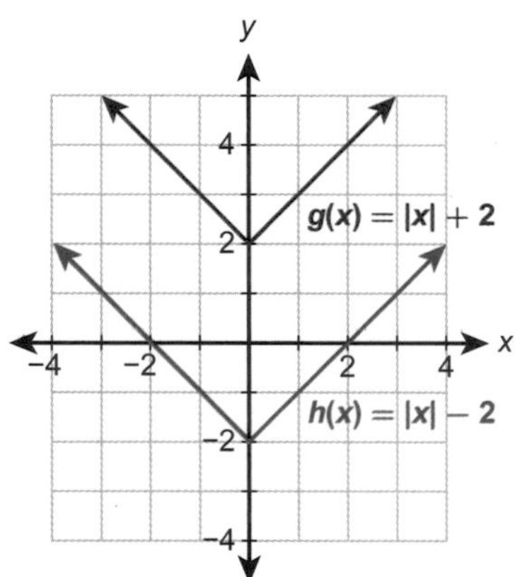

When $f(x) = |x|$ is translated k units vertically and h units horizontally, the function becomes $g(x) = |x - h| + k$. The vertex shifts from $(0, 0)$ to (h, k).

If k is positive, then the vertex is shifted up. If k is negative, then the vertex is shifted down.

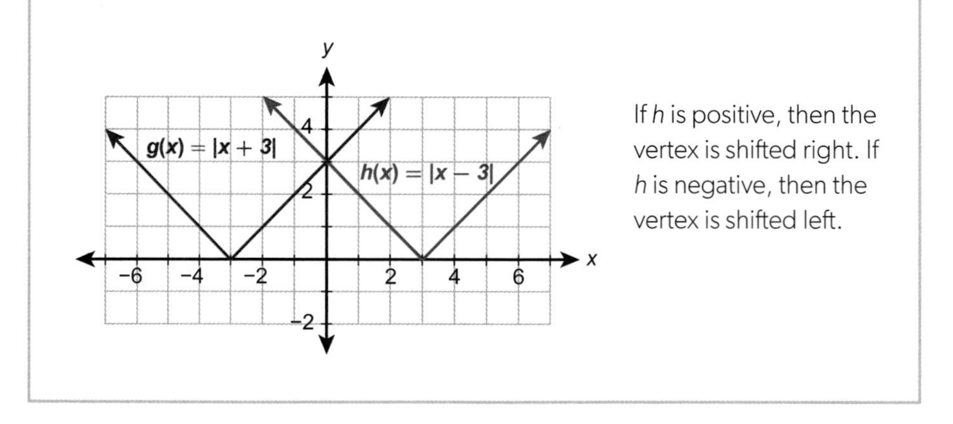

If h is positive, then the vertex is shifted right. If h is negative, then the vertex is shifted left.

It may seem odd that a negative sign before h indicates a translation to the right and a positive sign indicates a translation to the left. The key is the minus sign in $g(x) = |x - h| + k$. For a translation 3 units to the left, $h = -3$ and $k = 0$ in the general form $g(x) = |x - h| + k$. In that case, the function is written $g(x) = |x - (-3)| = |x + 3|$.

EXAMPLE 2

Graph the function.

A $g(x) = |x - 2|$

SOLUTION

The graph is a horizontal translation of the parent function, 2 units to the right. You can write the function as $g(x) = |x - 2| + 0$; the vertex (h, k) is located at $(2, 0)$.

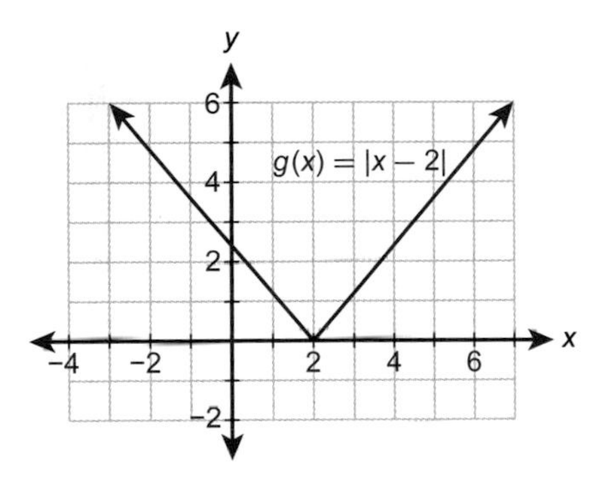

B $h(x) = |x + 1| - 2$

SOLUTION

The graph is a vertical and horizontal translation of the parent function. It is translated 1 unit left and 2 units down. You can write the function as $h(x) = |x - (-1)| + (-2)$; the vertex is located at $(-1, -2)$.

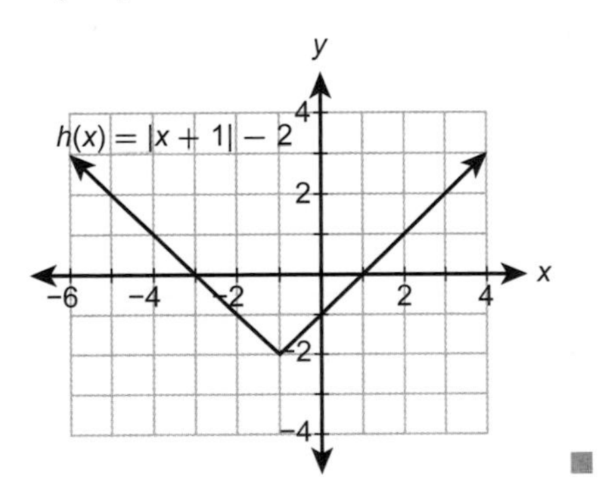

■

Describing Graphs of Absolute Value Functions

When the absolute value expression in the parent function $f(x) = |x|$ is multiplied by -1, the graph is reflected across the x-axis, making an upside-down V-shape. You can write this function as $g(x) = -1|x|$ or $g(x) = -|x|$.

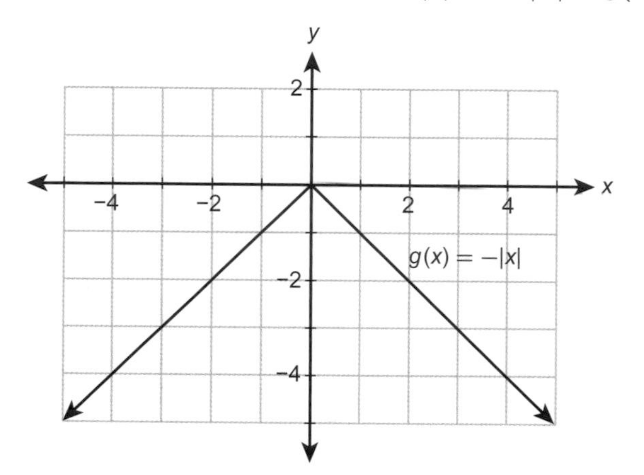

If the absolute value expression is multiplied by any factor other than 1 or -1, the graph becomes narrower or wider. For $g(x) = a|x|$, the graph becomes wider (or vertically compressed) if $0 < |a| < 1$ and narrower (or vertically stretched) if $|a| > 1$.

Compare the graphs of $g(x) = \frac{1}{4}|x|$ and $h(x) = 4|x|$ to $f(x) = |x|$.

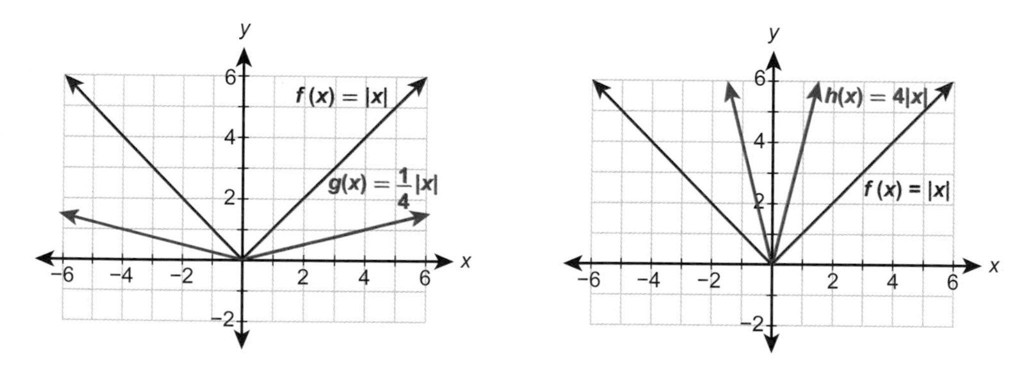

EXAMPLE 3

Describe how the graph of the function differs from the graph of $f(x) = |x|$. Then determine the domain and range.

A $g(x) = 0.8|x|$

SOLUTION

Because $|a|$ is between 0 and 1, the graph will be wider than the graph of the parent function. The vertex remains at $(0, 0)$.

domain: $\{x \mid x \in \mathbb{R}\}$, range: $\{y \mid y \geq 0\}$

B $g(x) = 3|x - 8|$

SOLUTION

The graph is translated 8 units to the right. Because $|a| > 1$, the graph will be narrower than the graph of the parent function.

domain: $\{x \mid x \in \mathbb{R}\}$, range: $\{y \mid y \geq 0\}$

C $g(x) = -2|x| + 5$

SOLUTION

The graph is translated 5 units up. Because $|a| > 1$, the graph will be narrower than the graph of the parent function. Because a is negative, the shape of the graph is an upside-down V.

domain: $\{x \mid x \in \mathbb{R}\}$, range: $\{y \mid y \leq 5\}$ ■

Finding the Equation of an Absolute Value Function

EXAMPLE 4

Write the equation of $g(x)$, which is graphed.

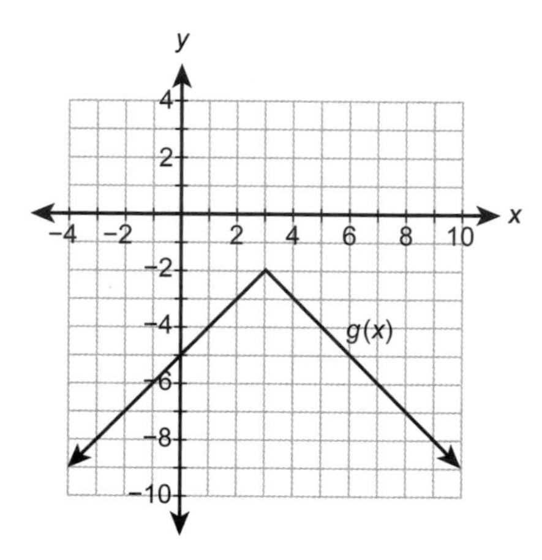

SOLUTION

The vertex is located at $(3, -2)$. Using the parent function $f(x) = |x|$ as a reference, the horizontal and vertical translations indicate that $h = 3$ and $k = -2$.

The graph, which moves up or down 1 unit for every horizontal move of 1 unit, is neither narrower nor wider than that of the parent function, so $|a| = 1$. Because the graph is upside-down, $a = -1$, making the equation $g(x) = -|x - 3| - 2$. ■

Piecewise Functions

Some functions, such as absolute value functions, can be defined in pieces.

The functions in the following examples are piecewise functions.

Definition

A **piecewise function** is a function defined using different rules for different intervals of the domain.

Graphing a Special Piecewise Function

EXAMPLE 1

Graph the piecewise function $f(x) = \begin{cases} -x & \text{if } x \leq 0 \\ x & \text{if } x > 0. \end{cases}$

SOLUTION

Create a table of ordered pairs for the first piece in the function.

x	-3	-2	-1	0
$f(x)$	3	2	1	0

The domain of the first piece includes 0 because it is defined for $x \leq 0$.

Create a table of ordered pairs for the second piece in the function.

x	1	2	3	4
$f(x)$	1	2	3	4

The domain of the second piece includes all numbers greater than 0.

Plot the points from both tables. Since both pieces of the function are linear, connect the points of each piece with a ray, starting at $(0, 0)$.

Together, the pieces of the graph form the graph of the absolute value function, $f(x) = |x|$.

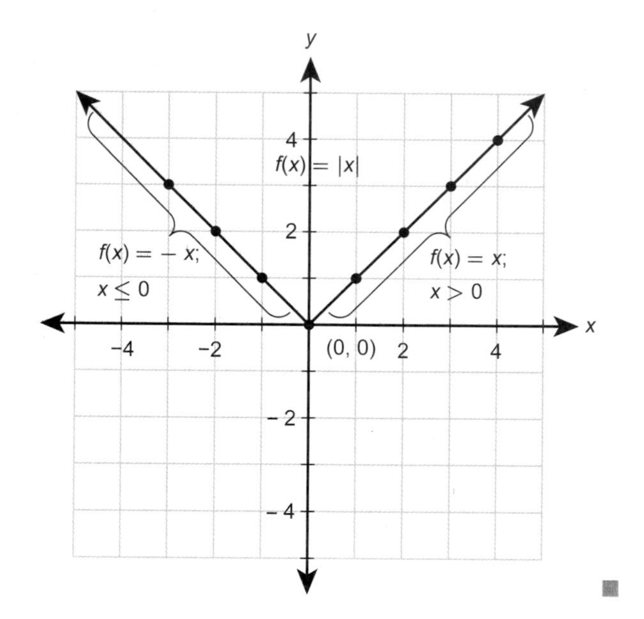

Writing an Absolute Value Function as a Piecewise Function

EXAMPLE 2

Write the absolute value function $f(x) = |x + 4|$ as a piecewise function.

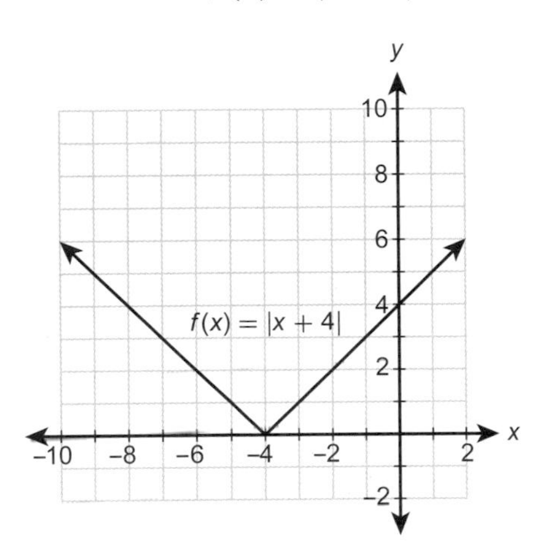

SOLUTION

There are two pieces.

The piece on the left is a ray with a boundary point at $(-4, 0)$. Study the table of ordered pairs for points of that piece and determine a rule.

x	-7	-6	-5	-4
$f(x)$	3	2	1	0

Each range value is 4 subtracted from the opposite of the domain value: $f(x) = -x - 4$.

The piece on the right is also a ray with a boundary point at $(-4, 0)$. Study the table of ordered pairs for points of that piece and determine a rule.

x	−4	−3	−2	−1
f(x)	0	1	2	3

Each range value is 4 added to the domain value: $f(x) = x + 4$.

Put both rules together. Include the boundary point in only one of the pieces.

$$f(x) = \begin{cases} -x - 4 & \text{if } x \leq -4 \\ x + 4 & \text{if } x > -4 \end{cases} \blacksquare$$

Graphing a Piecewise Function

EXAMPLE 3

Graph the function $g(x) = \begin{cases} 2x & \text{if } x < 1 \\ 1 & \text{if } x = 1 \\ x + 3 & \text{if } x > 1. \end{cases}$

SOLUTION

The domain is divided into three intervals.

For the interval $x < 1$, make a table of values. Although 1 is not included in this interval, use 1 as a value in the table. The point that has 1 as its x-coordinate will be a boundary for this section of the graph. Use an open circle when graphing the boundary point.

x	−2	−1	0	1
$g(x) = 2x$	$2(-2) = -4$	$2(-1) = -2$	$2(0) = 0$	$2(1) = 2$

For the value $x = 1$, $g(x) = 1$, so graph the point $(1, 1)$.

For the interval $x > 1$, make a table of values. Again, 1 is not included in this interval, but use 1 as a value in the table and use an open circle when graphing the boundary point.

x	1	2	3	4
$g(x) = x + 3$	$1 + 3 = 4$	$2 + 3 = 5$	$3 + 3 = 6$	$4 + 3 = 7$

Graph the function.

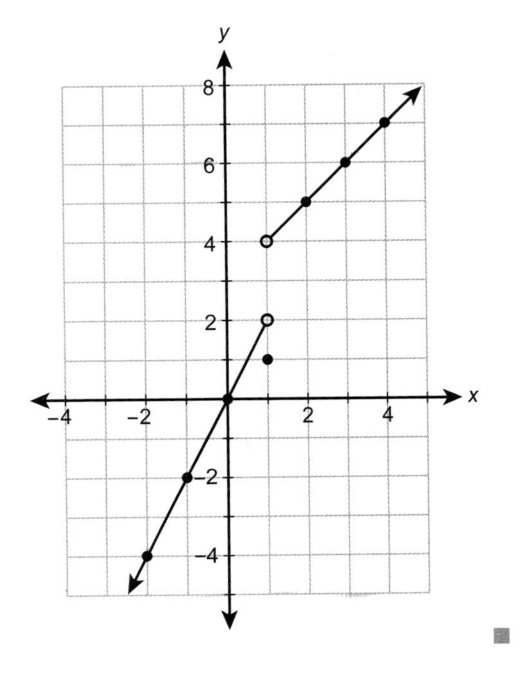

Writing a Rule for a Piecewise Function

EXAMPLE 4

A Write a rule for the graphed piecewise function.

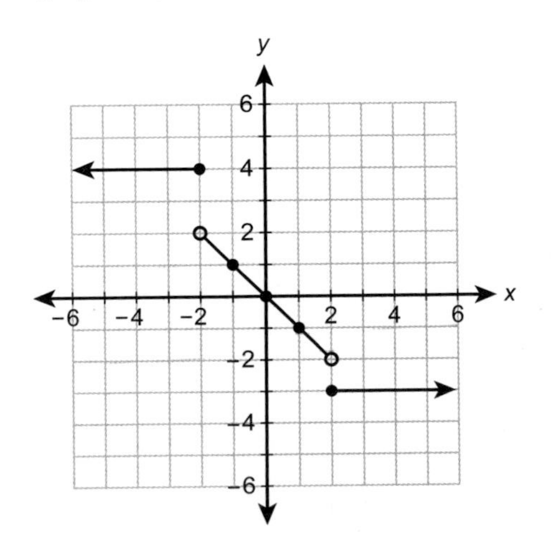

▶ **Remember** Use open circles for < and >. Use closed circles for $\leq$ and $\geq$.

SOLUTION

The left piece is a horizontal ray that extends to the left without end from the point $(-2, 4)$. So it has a constant function value of 4, and the interval of domain values is given by the inequality $x \leq -2$. The rule for this piece is $f(x) = 4$.

The center piece is a line segment that slants down from the point $(-2, 2)$ to the point $(2, -2)$. However, the open circles at $(-2, 2)$ and $(2, -2)$ indicate that these two points are not included in this piece of the graph. Therefore, the interval of domain values is given by the compound inequality $-2 < x < 2$. To find a rule for this piece, create a chart and look for a pattern.

x	-1	0	1
y	1	0	-1

Because y is the opposite of x, the rule is $y = -x$, or $f(x) = -x$.

The right piece is a horizontal ray that extends to the right without end from the point $(2, -3)$. So it has a constant function value of -3, and the interval of domain values is given by the inequality $x \geq 2$. The rule for this piece is $f(x) = -3$.

Altogether, the rule for the function is $f(x) = \begin{cases} 4 & \text{if } x \leq -2 \\ -x & \text{if } -2 < x < 2 \\ -3 & \text{if } x \geq 2 \end{cases}$.

B Write a rule for the graphed piecewise function.

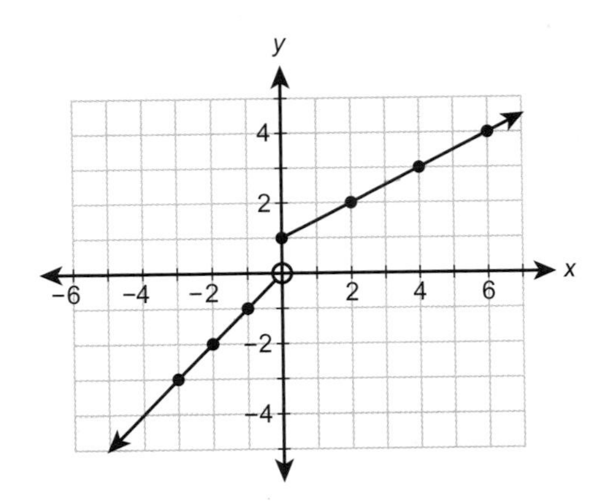

SOLUTION

The left piece is a ray that slants down to the left without end from the point $(0, 0)$, but it does not include $(0, 0)$. To find a rule for this piece, create a chart and look for a pattern.

x	−1	−2	−3
y	−1	−2	−3

The rule is $y = x$, or $f(x) = x$.

The right piece is a ray that slants up to the right without end from the point $(0, 1)$ and includes $(0, 1)$. Find a rule for this piece.

x	0	2	4	6
y	1	2	3	4

The rule is $y = \frac{1}{2}x + 1$, or $f(x) = \frac{1}{2}x + 1$.

The rule for the function is $f(x) = \begin{cases} x & \text{if } x < 0 \\ \frac{1}{2}x + 1 & \text{if } x \geq 0. \end{cases}$ ■

Finding Function Values of a Piecewise Function

EXAMPLE 5

Find $g(-5), g(-3), g(1)$, and $g(4)$ for the function g.

$$g(x) = \begin{cases} x - 1 & \text{if } x < -3 \\ x^2 - 1 & \text{if } -3 \leq x \leq 3 \\ 2x + 1 & \text{if } x > 3 \end{cases}$$

SOLUTION

Because -5 is in the interval $x < -3$, $g(-5) = \mathbf{-5} - 1 = -6$; -3 is in the interval $-3 \leq x \leq 3$, so $g(-3) = (\mathbf{-3})^2 - 1 = 9 - 1 = 8$; 1 is in the interval $-3 \leq x \leq 3$, so $g(1) = \mathbf{1}^2 - 1 = 1 - 1 = 0$. Since 4 is in the interval $x > 3$, $g(4) = 2 \bullet \mathbf{4} + 1 = 8 + 1 = 9$. ■

Step Functions

One type of piecewise function is a step function.

Definition

A **step function** is a function defined using a rule that produces a constant value for each designated interval of the domain.

As the name implies, the graph of a step function looks like a set of stairs. Each step is just a line segment with an open or closed circle on each end. Where the segments are placed and how long they are, as well as whether each endpoint is open or closed, depends on the particular function.

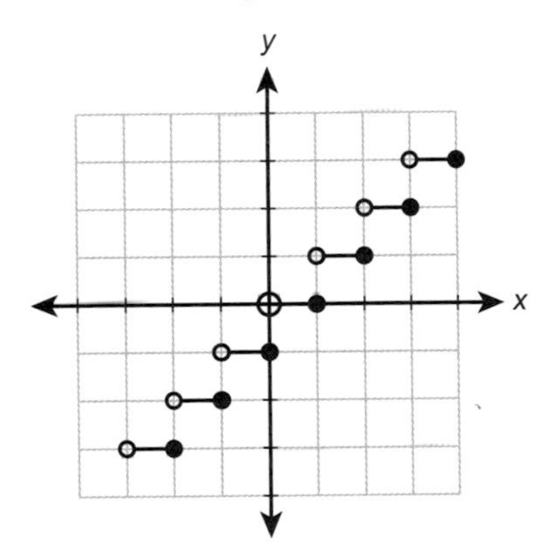

The Greatest Integer Function

The **greatest integer function**, denoted by $f(x) = \lfloor x \rfloor$, assigns the greatest integer less than or equal to each real number in an interval.

▶ Think About It

NOTATION The greatest integer function may also be given by $f(x) = \lfloor x \rfloor$ or $f(x) = \text{int}(x)$. It is sometimes called the floor function.

EXAMPLE 1

Graph the function $f(x) = \lfloor x \rfloor$ over the interval $-3 \leq x \leq 3$.

SOLUTION

Make a table of values to examine how the function behaves. The function will behave the same way in each unit interval.

x	-2.6	-2	-1.3	0	0.7	1	1.2	1.5	1.9	2
$f(x) = \lfloor x \rfloor$	-3	-2	-2	0	0	1	1	1	1	2

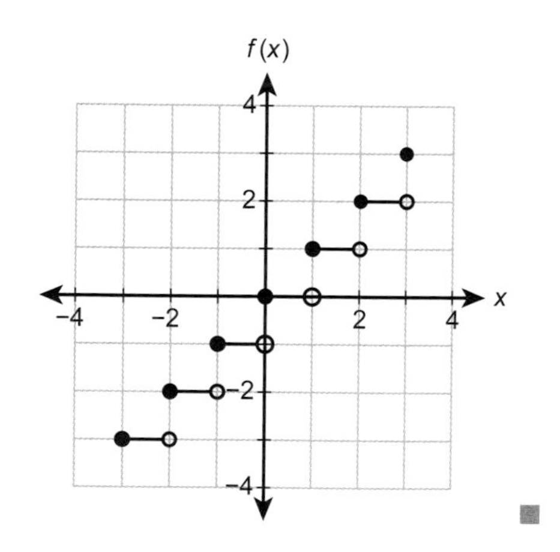

■

Graphs of Greatest Integer Functions

Greatest Integer Function Graph Family: $f(x) = a\lfloor x \rfloor + k$

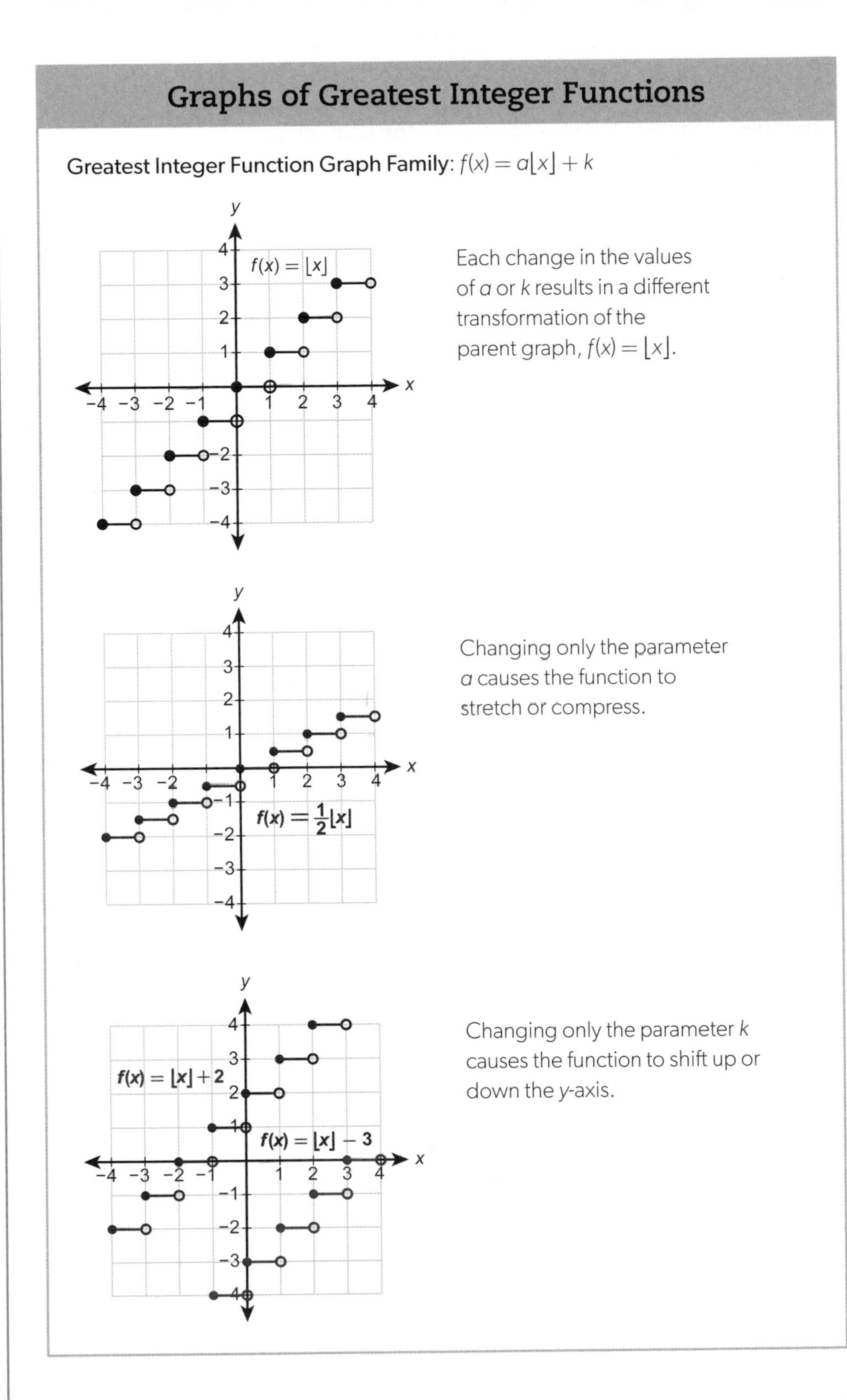

Each change in the values of a or k results in a different transformation of the parent graph, $f(x) = \lfloor x \rfloor$.

Changing only the parameter a causes the function to stretch or compress.

Changing only the parameter k causes the function to shift up or down the y-axis.

The Least Integer Function

The **least integer function**, denoted by $f(x) = \lceil x \rceil$, assigns the least integer greater than or equal to each real number in an interval.

▶ **Think About It** The least integer function is sometimes called the ceiling function.

EXAMPLE 2

Write a rule for $f(x) = \lceil x \rceil$ over the interval $-2 \leq x \leq 2$.

SOLUTION

There are four segments. The left endpoint of each segment is graphed with an open circle; the right endpoint is graphed with a solid circle.

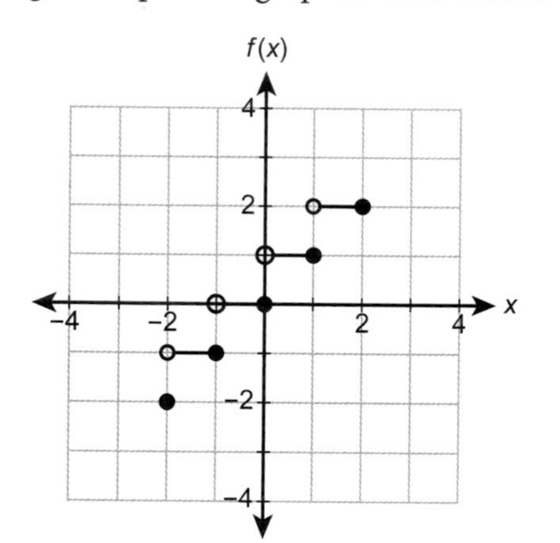

To every real number in the interval $(-2, -1]$, the function assigns the value -1. The rule for this piece is $f(x) = -1$. That is to say, -1 is the least integer greater than or equal to every number in the interval $(-2, -1]$.

x	-2	-1.8	-1	-0.3	0	0.5	1	1.6	2	2
$f(x) = \lceil x \rceil$	-2	-1	-1	0	0	1	1	2	2	2

The rule for the function is

$$f(x) = \begin{cases} -2 & \text{if } x = -2 \\ -1 & \text{if } -2 < x \leq -1 \\ 0 & \text{if } -1 < x \leq 0 \\ 1 & \text{if } 0 < x \leq 1 \\ 2 & \text{if } 1 < x \leq 2 \end{cases} . \blacksquare$$

Graphs of Least Integer Functions

Least Integer Function Graph Family: $f(x) = a\lceil x \rceil + k$

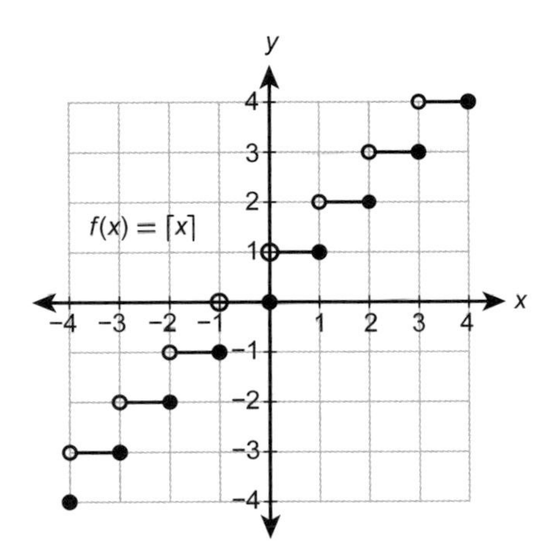

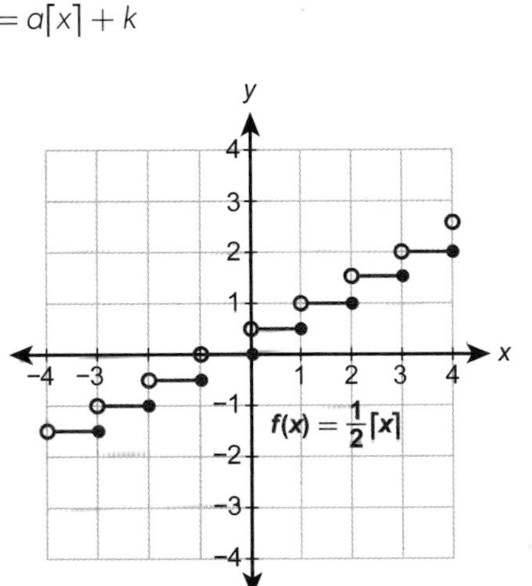

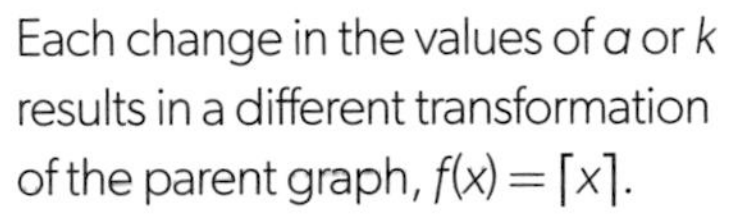
Each change in the values of a or k results in a different transformation of the parent graph, $f(x) = \lceil x \rceil$.

Changing only the parameter a causes the function to stretch or compress.

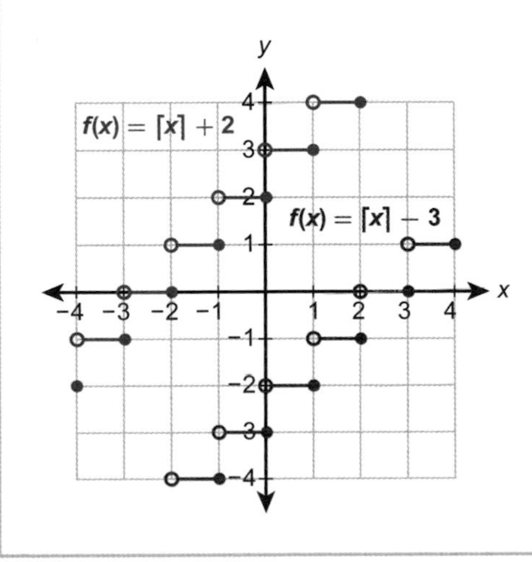

Changing only the parameter k causes the function to shift up or down on the x-axis.

Analyzing the Graph of the Nearest Integer Function

The **nearest integer function**, denoted by $\text{nint}(x)$, assigns the nearest integer to each real number in an interval. To avoid confusion for numbers such as -1.5 and 3.5, the function assigns the nearest even integer to each input value. So $\text{nint}(-1.5) = -2$, while $\text{nint}(3.5) = 4$. The nearest integer for numbers in the interval $[-0.5, 0.5]$ is zero.

▶ **Think About It** The nearest integer function is sometimes called the round function.

EXAMPLE 3

Graph the function $f(x) = \text{nint}(x)$ over the interval $-2.5 \leq x \leq 2.5$. Explain the pattern of horizontal segments on the graph.

SOLUTION

Study a table of values of the function for x in the interval $-2.5 \leq x \leq -1.5$. The value of the function for every real number in this interval, including the endpoints, is -2. The horizontal segment on the graph for this interval will include the endpoints -2.5 and -1.5.

x	−2.5	−2.3	−2.0	−1.8	−1.5
$f(x) = \text{nint}(x)$	−2	−2	−2	−2	−2

Next, study a table of values of the function for x in the interval $-1.5 \leq x \leq -0.5$. The values assigned to the endpoints of this interval are not the same as the value assigned to the other numbers in the interval. Therefore, the horizontal segment on the graph for this interval will not include the endpoints -1.5 and -0.5.

x	−1.5	−1.3	−1.0	−0.8	−0.5
$f(x) = \text{nint}(x)$	−2	−1	−1	−1	0

On the graph of the nearest integer function, the segments alternate between those including endpoints (solid circles) and those excluding the endpoints (open circles). This alternating pattern is a result of the rule to round each number to the nearest even integer.

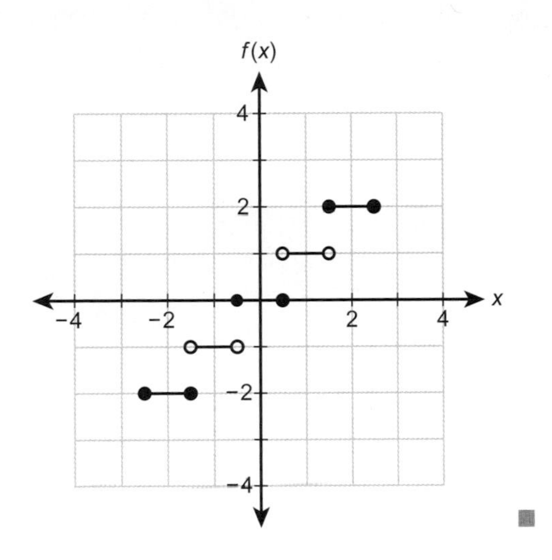

Radicals and Exponents

Topic List

- Irrational Numbers
- Simplifying Radical Expressions
- Properties of Rational and Irrational Numbers
- Properties of Exponents
- Exponential Expressions and Equations
- Applications: Growth and Decay

Lyme Regis in England has fossils that date from the Early Jurassic epoch (almost 200 million years ago). How do we know how old the fossils are? Paleontologists use exponential models of radioactive decay to determine these ages.

Irrational Numbers

Real numbers that are not rational numbers are irrational numbers.

Unlike a rational number, an **irrational number** is a real number that cannot be written in the form $\frac{a}{b}$ for any integers a and b. The set of rational numbers $\mathbb{Q}$ and the set of irrational numbers $\mathbb{I}$ make up the set of real numbers $\mathbb{R}$.

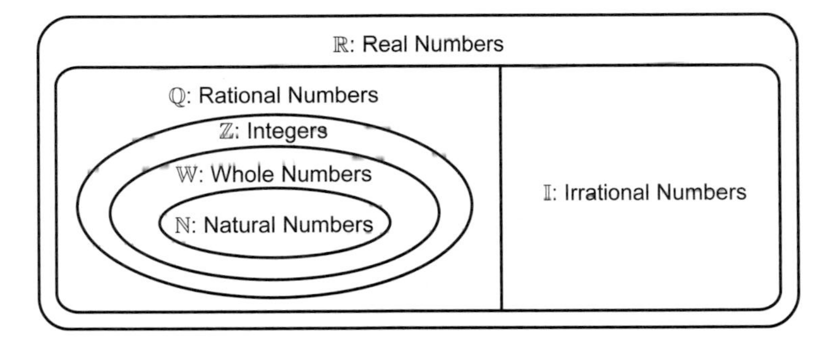

▶ **Think About It**

NOTATION The letter $\mathbb{I}$ denotes the set of irrational numbers.

Determining Whether a Number Is Rational or Irrational

Every real number can be written as a decimal. Any decimal that is nonterminating and nonrepeating is an irrational number. The number π is an example of an irrational number. There is no way to convert the decimal into a fraction of integers because there is no repeating block of digits.

Remember $\pi = 3.14159...$

A **perfect square** is a rational number whose square root is also rational. Examples of perfect squares are 9, 25, and $\frac{4}{9}$. The square root of any number that is not a perfect square is an irrational number, such as $\sqrt{2}$ and $\sqrt{14}$.

Rational numbers	Irrational numbers
$\sqrt{9} = 3$, $\sqrt{25} = 5$, $\sqrt{36} = 6$	$\sqrt{2} = 1.414213562...$ $\sqrt{14} = 3.741657387...$

Think About It A decimal with a finite number of digits cannot accurately represent an irrational number, but a decimal can approximate its value. $\sqrt{2}$ is an exact value; 1.414 approximates $\sqrt{2}$.

EXAMPLE 1

Determine whether the number is rational or irrational.

A $\sqrt{90}$

SOLUTION

Because 90 is not a perfect square, $\sqrt{90}$ is irrational.

B $\sqrt{256}$

SOLUTION

Because $16 \cdot 16 = 256$, 256 is a perfect square. So $\sqrt{256}$ is rational.

C $-\sqrt{121}$

SOLUTION

The square root of 121 is 11. The opposite of 11 is -11, which is rational, so $-\sqrt{121}$ is rational.

D $\sqrt{\frac{1}{5}}$

SOLUTION

Because no number times itself equals 5, there is no number that can be multiplied by itself to equal $\frac{1}{5}$. Therefore, $\sqrt{\frac{1}{5}}$ is irrational.

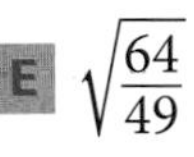

$\sqrt{\frac{64}{49}}$

SOLUTION

Both 64 and 49 are perfect squares. Since $\sqrt{\frac{64}{49}} = \frac{8}{7} = 1.\overline{142857}$, $\sqrt{\frac{64}{49}}$ is rational. ■

Simplifying Radicals

To simplify radicals, use $\sqrt{ab} = \sqrt{a} \bullet \sqrt{b}$. When a radical expression contains no radicands with factors that are perfect squares other than 1, the expression is in **simplified radical form**.

EXAMPLE 2

Simplify.

A $\sqrt{40}$

SOLUTION

Choose two factors of 40 so that one factor is a perfect square.

$$\begin{aligned}\sqrt{40} &= \sqrt{4 \bullet 10} \\ &= \sqrt{4} \bullet \sqrt{10} \\ &= \mathbf{2\sqrt{10}}\end{aligned}$$

Ten is not a perfect square and there are no factors of 10 that are perfect squares other than 1, so $\sqrt{40}$ simplifies to $2\sqrt{10}$.

B $\sqrt{108}$

SOLUTION

Choose two factors of 108 so that one factor is a perfect square.

$$\begin{aligned}\sqrt{108} &= \sqrt{36 \cdot 3} \\ &= \sqrt{36} \cdot \sqrt{3} \\ &= \mathbf{6}\sqrt{3}\end{aligned}$$

So $\sqrt{108}$ simplifies to $6\sqrt{3}$. ■

> **Think About It** Make a list of the first 15 perfect squares to refer to while simplifying radicals.

It is possible to choose a perfect square factor that is not the greatest perfect square factor. Suppose you chose 4 and 27.

$$\begin{aligned}\sqrt{108} &= \sqrt{4 \cdot 27} \\ &= \sqrt{4} \cdot \sqrt{27} \\ &= \mathbf{2} \cdot \sqrt{27} \\ &= 2 \cdot \sqrt{9} \cdot \sqrt{3} \\ &= 2 \cdot \mathbf{3} \cdot \sqrt{3} = 6\sqrt{3}\end{aligned}$$

Application: Proving That a Square Root Is Irrational

The square of an even number is always an even number and the square of an odd number is always an odd number. Use these facts in the following example.

EXAMPLE 3

Prove that $\sqrt{2}$ is irrational.

SOLUTION

Assume that $\sqrt{2}$ is rational. Then it would be possible to represent the value as a simplified fraction $\frac{a}{b}$, where a and b are integers and b is not zero. Because the fraction is simplified, a and b have no common factors other than 1.

> **Think About It** If $\frac{a}{b}$ is not a simplified fraction, then common factors can be divided out until it is, resulting in an equivalent fraction.

$\sqrt{2} = \frac{a}{b}$	
$\left(\sqrt{2}\right)^2 = \left(\frac{a}{b}\right)^2$	Square both sides of the equation.
$2 = \frac{a^2}{b^2}$	$\sqrt{2} \bullet \sqrt{2} = \sqrt{4} = 2$ and $\frac{a}{b} \bullet \frac{a}{b} = \frac{a^2}{b^2}$
$2b^2 = a^2$	Means-Extremes Product Property

Since a number with a factor of 2 is an even number, $2b^2$ is an even number. That means a^2 is an even number, and since only an even number squared can result in an even number, a must also be even.

Since a is an even number, it can be written as a product with a factor of 2. Let $a = 2c$, where c is an integer.

$2b^2 = a^2$	Last line from above
$2b^2 = (2c)^2$	Substitution Property of Equality
$2b^2 = 4c^2$	$2c \bullet 2c = 4c^2$
$b^2 = 2c^2$	Divide each side by 2.

Now b^2 is shown to be an even number because it is equal to a product with a factor of 2. Since b^2 is even, b is even.

Both a and b have been shown to be even, which means they both have a common factor of 2. However, it was stated in the beginning of the proof that a and b have no common factors other than 1, which is a contradiction. Therefore, the assumption that $\sqrt{2}$ is rational must be incorrect. A number is either rational or irrational, so $\sqrt{2}$ is irrational. ■

▶ **Think About It** When an assumption leads to a contradiction (two statements with opposite ideas), the assumption is false.

Simplifying Radical Expressions

A square root expression is in simplified radical form if the radicand is not a fraction, there are no radicals in the denominator, and none of the factors is a perfect square other than 1.

Simplified Radical Form

You can use properties of radicals to simplify expressions.

Product Property of Radicals

For real numbers $a \geq 0$ and $b \geq 0$,

$$\sqrt{ab} = \sqrt{a} \cdot \sqrt{b}.$$

Quotient Property of Radicals

For real numbers $a \geq 0$ and $b > 0$,

$$\sqrt{\frac{a}{b}} = \frac{\sqrt{a}}{\sqrt{b}}.$$

EXAMPLE 1

Write the expression in simplified radical form.

A $\sqrt{80}$

SOLUTION

$\sqrt{80} = \sqrt{16 \bullet 5}$	Use a perfect square to factor the radicand.
$= \sqrt{16} \bullet \sqrt{5}$	Product Property of Radicals
$= 4\sqrt{5}$	Simplify.

B $\sqrt{\frac{2}{9}}$

SOLUTION

$\sqrt{\frac{2}{9}} = \frac{\sqrt{2}}{\sqrt{9}}$	Quotient Property of Radicals
$= \frac{\sqrt{2}}{3}$	Simplify.

C $\sqrt{15}$

SOLUTION

$\sqrt{15}$ is in simplified radical form because the radicand is not a fraction, there are no radicals in the denominator, and none of the factors $(1, 3, 5, \text{or } 15)$ is a perfect square other than 1. ■

Rationalizing a Denominator

When a radical is in the denominator of a fraction, you can simplify it by multiplying both the numerator and denominator by the radical. This process is called rationalizing the denominator.

EXAMPLE 2

Write $\frac{3}{\sqrt{5}}$ in simplified radical form.

SOLUTION

$\frac{3}{\sqrt{5}} = \frac{3}{\sqrt{5}} \bullet \frac{\sqrt{5}}{\sqrt{5}}$ Multiply the numerator and denominator by $\sqrt{5}$.

$= \frac{3\sqrt{5}}{\sqrt{5 \bullet 5}}$ Product Property of Radicals

$= \frac{3\sqrt{5}}{\sqrt{25}}$ Simplify.

$= \frac{3\sqrt{5}}{5}$ Simplify. ■

Simplifying Algebraic Expressions

Here are examples of how you can use the product property of radicals to simplify the square root of a power of a variable.

Let $x \geq 0$.

$$\sqrt{x^2} = x$$

$$\sqrt{x^3} = \sqrt{x^2 \bullet x} = \sqrt{x^2} \bullet \sqrt{x} = x\sqrt{x}$$

$$\sqrt{x^4} = \sqrt{\left(x^2\right)^2} = x^2$$

$$\sqrt{x^5} = \sqrt{x^4 \bullet x} = \sqrt{x^4} \bullet \sqrt{x} = x^2\sqrt{x}$$

EXAMPLE 3

Write the expression in simplified radical form. Assume all variables are positive.

A $\sqrt{27x^2y^3}$

SOLUTION

$\sqrt{27x^2y^3} = \sqrt{9 \bullet 3 \bullet x^2 \bullet y^2 \bullet y}$ Factor the radicand.

$= \sqrt{9} \bullet \sqrt{3} \bullet \sqrt{x^2} \bullet \sqrt{y^2} \bullet \sqrt{y}$ Product Property of Radicals

$= 3\sqrt{3} \bullet xy\sqrt{y}$ Simplify.

$= 3xy\sqrt{3y}$ Simplify.

B $\dfrac{a}{\sqrt{a^3}}$

SOLUTION

$\dfrac{a}{\sqrt{a^3}} = \dfrac{a}{\sqrt{a^2 \bullet a}}$ Factor the denominator.

$= \dfrac{a}{\sqrt{a^2} \bullet \sqrt{a}}$ Product Property of Radicals

$= \dfrac{a}{a\sqrt{a}}$ Simplify.

$= \dfrac{1}{\sqrt{a}} \bullet \dfrac{\sqrt{a}}{\sqrt{a}}$ Multiply the numerator and denominator by $\sqrt{a}$.

$= \dfrac{\sqrt{a}}{a}$ Simplify.

C $\sqrt{7hg}$

SOLUTION

$\sqrt{7hg}$ is in simplified radical form because the radicand is not a fraction, there are no radicals in the denominator, and none of the factors is a perfect square other than 1. ■

Multiplying Radical Expressions

To multiply radical expressions, use the product property of radicals.

EXAMPLE 4

Multiply. Assume all variables are positive.

A $\sqrt{8} \cdot \sqrt{32}$

SOLUTION

$$\begin{aligned} \sqrt{8} \cdot \sqrt{32} &= \sqrt{8 \cdot 32} && \text{Product Property of Radicals} \\ &= \sqrt{256} && \text{Multiply.} \\ &= \sqrt{16^2} && \text{Identify that } 256 = 16^2. \\ &= 16 && \text{Simplify.} \end{aligned}$$

B $\sqrt{2r^3s^9} \cdot 4\sqrt{8r^5s^2}$

SOLUTION

$$\begin{aligned} \sqrt{2r^3s^9} \cdot 4\sqrt{8r^5s^2} &= 4\sqrt{2r^3s^9 \cdot 8r^5s^2} && \text{Product Property of Radicals} \\ &= 4\sqrt{16r^8s^{11}} && \text{Product of Powers Property} \\ &= 4\sqrt{16r^8s^{10}s} && \text{Product of Powers Property} \\ &= 4\sqrt{4^2 \cdot \left(r^4\right)^2 \cdot \left(s^5\right)^2 \cdot s} && \\ &= 4 \cdot 4 \cdot r^4 \cdot s^5 \cdot \sqrt{s} && \text{Simplify.} \\ &= 16r^4s^5\sqrt{s} && \text{Simplify.} \ \blacksquare \end{aligned}$$

Adding and Subtracting Radical Expressions

Like radicals have the same index and radicand. You can use the distributive property to add or subtract like radicals.

EXAMPLE 5

Add or subtract. Assume all variables are positive.

A $8\sqrt{6} + \sqrt{5} + \sqrt{6}$

SOLUTION

$$\begin{aligned} 8\sqrt{6} + \sqrt{5} + \sqrt{6} &= 8\sqrt{6} + \sqrt{6} + \sqrt{5} \\ &= (8 + 1)\sqrt{6} + \sqrt{5} \\ &= 9\sqrt{6} + \sqrt{5} \end{aligned}$$

B $5\sqrt{12} - 3\sqrt{48}$

SOLUTION

$$\begin{aligned} 5\sqrt{12} - 3\sqrt{48} &= 5\sqrt{4 \cdot 3} - 3\sqrt{16 \cdot 3} \\ &= 5\sqrt{4} \cdot \sqrt{3} - 3\sqrt{16} \cdot \sqrt{3} \\ &= 10\sqrt{3} - 12\sqrt{3} \\ &= (10 - 12)\sqrt{3} \\ &= -2\sqrt{3} \end{aligned}$$

C Simplify $\sqrt{48t^5} - \sqrt{3t^5} - \sqrt{3t}$.

SOLUTION

$$\begin{aligned}\sqrt{48t^5} - \sqrt{3t^5} - \sqrt{3t} &= \sqrt{16t^4} \bullet \sqrt{3t} - \sqrt{t^4} \bullet \sqrt{3t} - \sqrt{3t} \\ &= 4t^2\sqrt{3t} - t^2\sqrt{3t} - \sqrt{3t} \\ &= \left(4t^2 - t^2\right)\sqrt{3t} - \sqrt{3t} \\ &= 3t^2\sqrt{3t} - \sqrt{3t} \text{ or } \left(3t^2 - 1\right)\sqrt{3t}\end{aligned}$$ ■

▶ **Think About It** $\left(3t^2 - 1\right)\sqrt{3t}$ is an alternate simplified form of $3t^2\sqrt{3t} - \sqrt{3t}$.

Properties of Rational and Irrational Numbers

When rational numbers and irrational numbers are multiplied, divided, added, and subtracted, certain key properties apply.

Sum of a Rational Number and an Irrational Number

The sum of a rational number and an irrational number always results in the same type of real number.

EXAMPLE 1

Add. Round each sum to 10 decimal places.

A $\frac{1}{2} + 2\sqrt{3}$

SOLUTION

Use a calculator to find the sum to 10 decimal places.

$$\frac{1}{2} + 2\sqrt{3} \approx 3.9641016151\ldots$$

B $-5\pi + \frac{49}{2}$

SOLUTION

Use a calculator to find the sum to 10 decimal places.

$$-5\pi + \frac{49}{2} \approx 8.7920367321\ldots$$

C $7\sqrt{7} + 0$

SOLUTION

Use a calculator to find the sum to 10 decimal places.

$$7\sqrt{7} + 0 \approx 18.5202591775\ldots \blacksquare$$

EXAMPLE 2

The courtyard at Monroe High School is shaped like a rectangle with the dimensions shown.

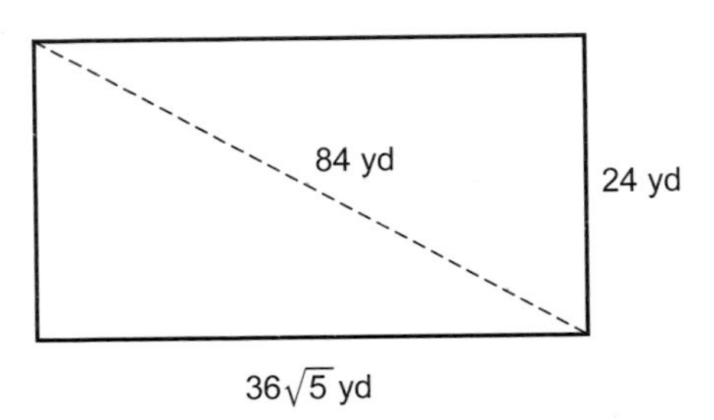

A Find the perimeter of the courtyard to 10 decimal places.

SOLUTION

Write an expression for the perimeter of the rectangle.

$$P = l + l + w + w$$

$$P = 36\sqrt{5} + 36\sqrt{5} + 24 + 24$$

$$P = 72\sqrt{5} + 48$$

Use a calculator to find the sum to 10 decimal places.

$$P = 72\sqrt{5} + 48 \approx 208.9968943790\ldots$$

The perimeter of the courtyard is approximately 208.9968943790 yd.

B Classify the perimeter of the courtyard as rational or irrational.

SOLUTION

The perimeter is a decimal that does not terminate or repeat. It is an irrational number. ■

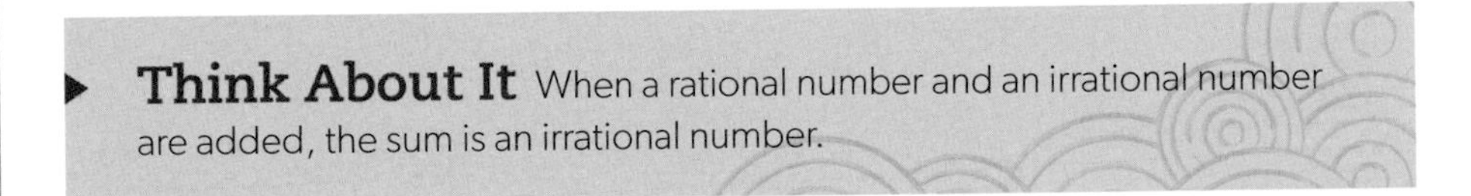

▶ **Think About It** When a rational number and an irrational number are added, the sum is an irrational number.

Product of a Rational Number and an Irrational Number

The product of a rational number and an irrational number always results in the same type of real number.

EXAMPLE 3

Multiply. Round each product to 10 decimal places.

A $-4 \times 7\sqrt{5}$

SOLUTION

Use a calculator to find the product to 10 decimal places.

$$-4 \times 7\sqrt{5} \approx -62.6099033700\ldots$$

B $\frac{2}{3} \times 3\pi$

SOLUTION

Use a calculator to find the product to 10 decimal places.

$$\frac{2}{3} \times 3\pi \approx 6.2831853072\ldots$$

C $-2\sqrt{17}\left(-4\frac{4}{5}\right)$

SOLUTION

Use a calculator to find the product to 10 decimal places.

$$-2\sqrt{17}\left(-4\frac{4}{5}\right) \approx 39.5818140059\ldots$$ ■

EXAMPLE 4

A circular ice-skating rink has a diameter of $98\frac{1}{2}$ ft.

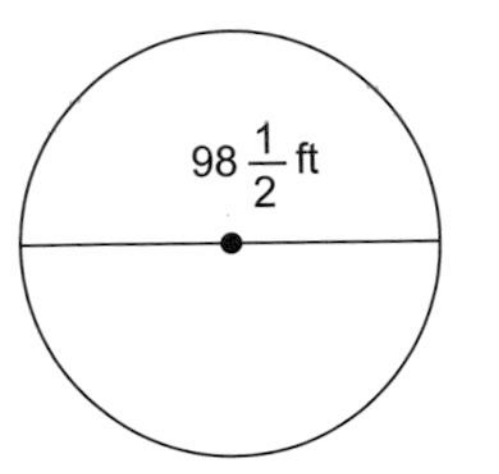

A Find the circumference of the skating rink to 10 decimal places.

SOLUTION

Write an expression for the circumference of the circle.

$$C = \pi d$$

$$C = \pi\left(98\frac{1}{2}\right)$$

Use a calculator to find the product to 10 decimal places.

$$C = \pi\left(98\frac{1}{2}\right) \approx 309.4468763786\ldots$$

The circumference of the skating rink is approximately 309.4468763786 ft.

B Classify the circumference of the skating rink as rational or irrational.

SOLUTION

The circumference is a decimal that does not terminate or repeat. It is an irrational number. ■

▶ **Think About It** When a rational number (not equal to 0) and an irrational number are multiplied, the product is an irrational number.

The Closure Property

If you multiply two integers, the result is always an integer. If you add two whole numbers, the result is always a whole number. Both are examples of the closure property.

Definition

A set is **closed** under an operation if, for any two numbers in the set, the result of the operation is also in the set.

A set can be closed under one operation and not closed under another operation. To show that a set is not closed under an operation, find a counterexample.

▸ **Remember** A counterexample is an example that is used to disprove a statement.

For example, the set of whole numbers is not closed under subtraction because you can find a counterexample.

$$4 - 7 = -3$$

The numbers 4 and 7 belong to the set of whole numbers but -3 does not belong to the set, so the set of whole numbers is not closed under subtraction.

EXAMPLE 5

Let $\frac{a}{b}$ and $\frac{c}{d}$ represent any two rational numbers, where a, b, c, and d are integers, $b \neq 0$, and $d \neq 0$. Show that the set of rational numbers is closed under the given operations.

A multiplication

SOLUTION

Find the product of the rational numbers.

$$\frac{a}{b} \times \frac{c}{d} = \frac{ac}{bd}$$

Integers are closed under multiplication, so ac is an integer and bd is a nonzero integer. Therefore, the product $\frac{ac}{bd}$ is a rational number by definition. The set of rational numbers is closed under multiplication.

B addition

SOLUTION

Find the sum of the rational numbers.

$$\frac{a}{b} + \frac{c}{d} = \frac{ad}{bd} + \frac{bc}{bd} = \frac{ad + bc}{bd}$$

Integers are closed under multiplication and addition, so $ad + bc$ is an integer and bd is a nonzero integer. Therefore, the sum $\frac{ad + bc}{bd}$ is a rational number by definition. The set of rational numbers is closed under addition. ■

You can also show that rational numbers are closed under subtraction and division (by a nonzero divisor). Irrational numbers are not closed under any operation.

Properties of Rational and Irrational Numbers

- The sum of a rational number and an irrational number is irrational.
- The product of a nonzero rational number and an irrational number is irrational.
- Rational numbers are closed under addition, subtraction, multiplication, and division (by a nonzero divisor).
- Irrational numbers are not closed under addition, subtraction, multiplication, or division.

Properties of Exponents

You can use definitions and properties to simplify expressions containing powers.

For the power a^n, the exponent n can be positive, negative, or zero.

Definition of Integer Exponents

For any $a \in \mathbb{R}$,

- If n is a positive integer, $a^n = \overbrace{a \cdot a \cdot a \cdot \ldots \cdot a}^{n \text{ factors}}$.
- If $n = 0$ and $a \neq 0$, $a^n = 1$.
- For any n and nonzero a, $a^{-n} = \frac{1}{a^n}$.

Think About It The definition of integer exponents also implies that $\frac{1}{a^{-n}} = a^n$.

EXAMPLE 1

Evaluate the power.

A 6^0

SOLUTION

Any nonzero number raised to the power 0 has a value of 1.

$$6^0 = 1$$

B 3^{-2}

SOLUTION

Any nonzero number raised to a negative integer power is equal to its reciprocal with the opposite exponent.

$$3^{-2} = \frac{1}{3^2} = \frac{1}{9} \blacksquare$$

Properties Involving Multiplication

Properties of Exponents Involving Products

Let $a \in \mathbb{R}$, $b \in \mathbb{R}$, $a \neq 0$, $b \neq 0$, $m \in \mathbb{R}$, and $n \in \mathbb{R}$.

Product of Powers $a^m \cdot a^n = a^{m+n}$

Power of a Product $(ab)^n = a^n b^n$

Power of a Power $(a^m)^n = a^{mn}$

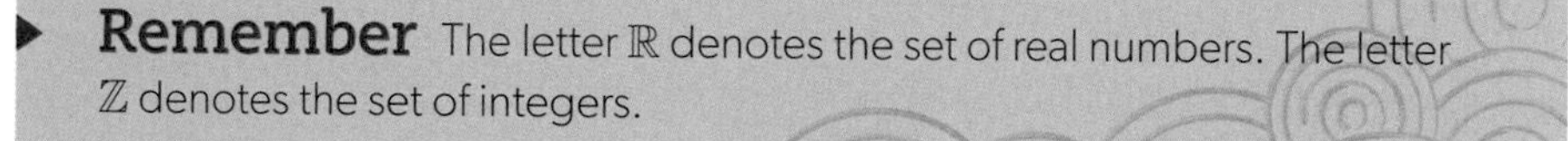

Remember The letter $\mathbb{R}$ denotes the set of real numbers. The letter $\mathbb{Z}$ denotes the set of integers.

EXAMPLE 2

Simplify.

A $g^4 \cdot g^2$

SOLUTION

By the product of powers property, to multiply powers with the same base, keep the base and add the exponents.

$$\begin{aligned} g^4 \cdot g^2 &= g^{4+2} \\ &= g^6 \end{aligned}$$

B $(5x)^3$

SOLUTION

By the power of a product property, to raise a product to a power, raise each factor to that power.

$$\begin{aligned}(5x)^3 &= 5^3 \bullet x^3 \\ &= 125x^3\end{aligned}$$

C $\left(t^3\right)^4$

SOLUTION

By the power of a power property, to raise a power to a power, keep the base and multiply the exponents.

$$\begin{aligned}\left(t^3\right)^4 &= t^{3 \bullet 4} \\ &= t^{12}\end{aligned}$$ ■

Properties Involving Division

Properties of Exponents Involving Quotients

Let $a \in \mathbb{R}$, $b \in \mathbb{R}$, $a \neq 0$, $b \neq 0$, $m \in \mathbb{R}$, and $n \in \mathbb{R}$.

Quotient of Powers $\frac{a^m}{a^n} = a^{m-n}$

Power of a Quotient $\left(\frac{a}{b}\right)^n = \frac{a^n}{b^n}$

EXAMPLE 3

Simplify.

A $\frac{w^9}{w^4}$

SOLUTION

By the quotient of powers property, to divide powers with the same base, keep the base and subtract the exponents.

$$\begin{aligned}\frac{w^9}{w^4} &= w^{9-4}\\ &= w^5\end{aligned}$$

B $\left(\frac{2}{x}\right)^5$

SOLUTION

By the power of a quotient property, to raise a quotient to a power, raise the numerator and denominator to that power.

$$\begin{aligned}\left(\frac{2}{x}\right)^5 &= \frac{2^5}{x^5}\\ &= \frac{32}{x^5}\end{aligned}$$ ■

Combining Properties

To simplify some expressions, you have to combine properties of exponents and the definition of integer exponents.

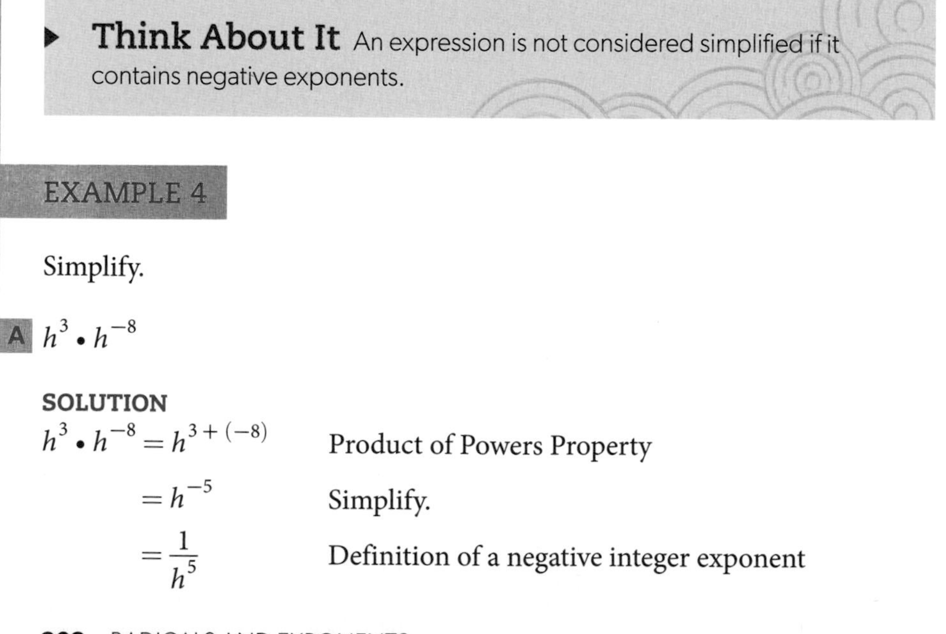

▶ **Think About It** An expression is not considered simplified if it contains negative exponents.

EXAMPLE 4

Simplify.

A $h^3 \bullet h^{-8}$

SOLUTION

$h^3 \bullet h^{-8} = h^{3+(-8)}$	Product of Powers Property
$= h^{-5}$	Simplify.
$= \frac{1}{h^5}$	Definition of a negative integer exponent

B $\left(\frac{c^{10}}{c^3}\right)^4$

SOLUTION

Method 1

$$\left(\frac{c^{10}}{c^3}\right)^4 = \left(c^{10-3}\right)^4 \quad \text{Quotient of Powers Property}$$

$$= \left(c^7\right)^4 \quad \text{Simplify.}$$

$$= c^{28} \quad \text{Power of a Power Property}$$

Method 2

$$\left(\frac{c^{10}}{c^3}\right)^4 = \frac{\left(c^{10}\right)^4}{\left(c^3\right)^4} \quad \text{Power of a Quotient Property}$$

$$= \frac{c^{40}}{c^{12}} \quad \text{Power of a Power Property}$$

$$= c^{40-12} \quad \text{Quotient of Powers Property}$$

$$= c^{28} \quad \text{Simplify.}$$

C $\frac{\left(xy^2\right)^3}{z^0}$

SOLUTION

$$\frac{\left(xy^2\right)^3}{z^0} = \frac{\left(xy^2\right)^3}{1} \quad \text{Definition of a zero exponent}$$

$$= \left(xy^2\right)^3 \quad \text{Simplify.}$$

$$= x^3 \cdot \left(y^2\right)^3 \quad \text{Power of a Product Property}$$

$$= x^3y^6 \quad \text{Power of a Power Property} \; \blacksquare$$

▶ **Remember** A variable without an exponent has an implied exponent of 1.

$$x = x^1$$

Exponential Expressions and Equations

Any root of a number can be written as a fractional power of the number.

Rational Exponents and Radical Form

Property of Rational Exponents

For any positive integers n and m, where $n \neq 0$, and any $b \in \mathbb{R}$,

$$b^{\frac{m}{n}} = \left(\sqrt[n]{b}\right)^m = \sqrt[n]{b^m},$$

except when $b < 0$ and n is even.

Remember A rational exponent is an exponent that can be written as a fraction.

EXAMPLE 1

Express in radical form.

A $10^{\frac{5}{4}}$

SOLUTION

$$\begin{aligned} 10^{\frac{5}{4}} &= \left(\sqrt[4]{10}\right)^5 \\ &= \sqrt[4]{10^5} \end{aligned}$$

B $(-3)^{\frac{2}{3}}$

SOLUTION

$$\begin{aligned} (-3)^{\frac{2}{3}} &= \sqrt[3]{(-3)^2} \\ &= \sqrt[3]{9} \end{aligned}$$

C $\left(2^{\frac{1}{6}}\right)^3$

SOLUTION

$$\begin{aligned} \left(2^{\frac{1}{6}}\right)^3 &= 2^{\frac{1}{6} \cdot 3} \\ &= 2^{\frac{1}{2}} \\ &= \sqrt{2} \ ■ \end{aligned}$$

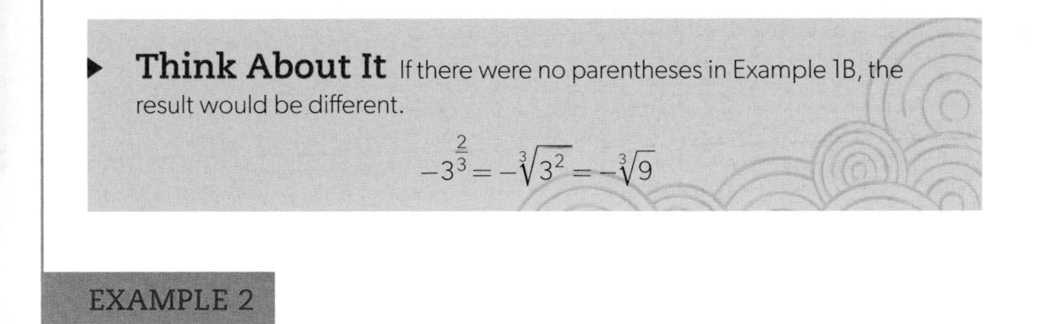

▶ **Think About It** If there were no parentheses in Example 1B, the result would be different.

$$-3^{\frac{2}{3}} = -\sqrt[3]{3^2} = -\sqrt[3]{9}$$

EXAMPLE 2

Express in rational exponent form.

A $\sqrt[4]{6^3}$

SOLUTION

$\sqrt[4]{6^3} = 6^{\frac{3}{4}}$

B $\sqrt[5]{(-2)^3}$

SOLUTION

$\sqrt[5]{(-2)^3} = (-2)^{\frac{3}{5}}$

C $\left(\sqrt[3]{7^4}\right)^{\frac{1}{2}}$

SOLUTION

$$\begin{aligned}\left(\sqrt[3]{7^4}\right)^{\frac{1}{2}} &= \left(7^{\frac{4}{3}}\right)^{\frac{1}{2}}\\ &= 7^{\frac{4}{3} \cdot \frac{1}{2}}\\ &= 7^{\frac{2}{3}} \blacksquare\end{aligned}$$

Using Properties of Exponents to Simplify Expressions

The properties of exponents can be used to simplify expressions containing rational exponents.

EXAMPLE 3

Simplify. Assume all variables are positive.

A $4^{\frac{1}{2}} \cdot 4^{\frac{3}{2}}$

SOLUTION

Here are two strategies you can use to simplify this expression.

Method 1

Combine exponents first.

$4^{\frac{1}{2}} \cdot 4^{\frac{3}{2}} = 4^{\left(\frac{1}{2}+\frac{3}{2}\right)}$

$= 4^{\frac{4}{2}} = 4^2 = 16$

Method 2

Simplify each factor first.

$4^{\frac{1}{2}} \cdot 4^{\frac{3}{2}} = \sqrt{4} \cdot \left(\sqrt{4}\right)^3$

$= 2 \cdot 2^3 = 2 \cdot 8 = 16$

▶ **Think About It** When you solve problems with fractional exponents, values are usually easier to work with if you find the root before raising to the power. For example, $4^{\frac{3}{2}} = \left(\sqrt{4}\right)^3 = 2^3 = 8$ has smaller values than $\sqrt{4^3} = \sqrt{64} = 8$ does.

B $\dfrac{8}{8^{\frac{1}{3}}}$

SOLUTION

$\dfrac{8}{8^{\frac{1}{3}}} = 8^{1-\frac{1}{3}}$	Quotient of Powers Property
$= 8^{\frac{2}{3}}$	Subtract: $\frac{3}{3} - \frac{1}{3} = \frac{2}{3}$.
$= \left(\sqrt[3]{8}\right)^2$	Property of Rational Exponents
$= 2^2 = 4$	Find the cube root of 8 and simplify.

C $\left(16^{\frac{1}{2}}a^2b^{-2}\right)^{\frac{1}{2}}$

SOLUTION

$\left(16^{\frac{1}{2}}a^2b^{-2}\right)^{\frac{1}{2}} = \left(4a^2b^{-2}\right)^{\frac{1}{2}}$	$16^{\frac{1}{2}} = \sqrt{16} = 4$
$= 4^{\frac{1}{2}}a^{2 \cdot \frac{1}{2}}b^{-2 \cdot \frac{1}{2}}$	Power of a Power Property
$= 4^{\frac{1}{2}}ab^{-1}$	Simplify.
$= \dfrac{\sqrt{4} \cdot a}{b}$	Property of Rational Exponents
$= \dfrac{2a}{b}$	Simplify.

D $\left(\dfrac{4x^{2r}y^{4r}z^{8r}}{25z^{2r}}\right)^{\frac{1}{2}}$

SOLUTION

$$\left(\frac{4x^{2r}y^{4r}z^{8r}}{25z^{2r}}\right)^{\frac{1}{2}} = \frac{\left(4x^{2r}y^{4r}z^{8r}\right)^{\frac{1}{2}}}{\left(25z^{2r}\right)^{\frac{1}{2}}} \qquad \text{Power of a Quotient Property}$$

$$= \frac{4^{\frac{1}{2}}x^{\frac{2r}{2}}y^{\frac{4r}{2}}z^{\frac{8r}{2}}}{25^{\frac{1}{2}}z^{\frac{2r}{2}}} \qquad \text{Power of a Product Property}$$

$$= \frac{\sqrt{4} \bullet x^{r}y^{2r}z^{4r}}{\sqrt{25} \bullet z^{r}} \qquad \text{Property of Rational Exponents}$$

$$= \frac{2x^{r}y^{2r}z^{4r-r}}{5} \qquad \text{Quotient of Powers Property}$$

$$= \frac{2x^{r}y^{2r}z^{3r}}{5} \qquad \text{Simplify. ■}$$

▶ **Think About It** If x, y, or z in Example 3D is less than zero and n is even, the property of rational exponents is not valid. If $x = -3$, for example, $\left(x^2\right)^{\frac{1}{2}} = \sqrt{(-3)^2} = 3 = x$. This is a contradiction.

Using Rational Exponents to Express Radical Expressions in Simplified Radical Form

EXAMPLE 4

Express in simplified radical form with the smallest index possible.

A $\sqrt[10]{50^5}$

SOLUTION

$\sqrt[10]{50^5} = 50^{\frac{5}{10}}$	Rewrite in rational exponent form.
$= 50^{\frac{1}{2}}$	Simplify.
$= (25 \bullet 2)^{\frac{1}{2}}$	Factor.
$= 25^{\frac{1}{2}} \bullet 2^{\frac{1}{2}}$	Power of a Product Property
$= \sqrt{25} \bullet \sqrt{2}$	Property of Rational Exponents
$= 5\sqrt{2}$	Simplify.

B $\sqrt[8]{a^2b^4}$

SOLUTION

$\sqrt[8]{a^2b^4} = a^{\frac{2}{8}}b^{\frac{4}{8}}$	Rewrite in rational exponent form.
$= a^{\frac{1}{4}}b^{\frac{2}{4}}$	Simplify.
$= \left(ab^2\right)^{\frac{1}{4}}$	Product Property of Exponents
$= \sqrt[4]{ab^2}$	Property of Rational Exponents

C $\left(\sqrt[12]{16x^8y^4}\right)$

SOLUTION

$\left(\sqrt[12]{16x^8y^4}\right) = \left(\sqrt[12]{2^4x^8y^4}\right)$	$16 = 2^4$
$= \left(2^4x^8y^4\right)^{\frac{1}{12}}$	Rewrite in rational exponent form.
$= \left(2^4\right)^{\frac{1}{12}}\left(x^8\right)^{\frac{1}{12}}\left(y^4\right)^{\frac{1}{12}}$	Product Property of Exponents
$= \left(2^{4\cdot\frac{1}{12}}\right)\left(x^{8\cdot\frac{1}{12}}\right)\left(y^{4\cdot\frac{1}{12}}\right)$	Power of a Power Property
$= \left(2^{\frac{1}{3}}\right)\left(x^{\frac{2}{3}}\right)\left(y^{\frac{1}{3}}\right)$	Simplify.
$= \left(2x^2y\right)^{\frac{1}{3}}$	Product Property of Exponents
$= \sqrt[3]{2x^2y}$	Property of Rational Exponents ■

Solving Exponential Equations

An **exponential equation** is an equation with variable expressions as exponents.

Property of Equality for Exponental Equations

If a is a positive number other than 1, then $a^x = a^y$ if and only if $x = y$.

The property of equality for exponential equations can be used to solve some types of exponential equations.

EXAMPLE 5

Solve and then check.

A $4^x = 8$

SOLUTION

$4^x = 8$

$(2^{2x}) = 2^3$ Rewrite each term so that the bases are the same.

$2^{2x} = 2^3$ Power of a Power Property

$2x = 3$ Property of Equality for Exponential Equations

$x = \frac{3}{2}$ Division Property of Equality

CHECK

$4^x \stackrel{?}{=} 8$

$4^{\frac{3}{2}} \stackrel{?}{=} 8$

$\sqrt{4^3} \stackrel{?}{=} 8$

$\sqrt{64} \stackrel{?}{=} 8$

$8 = 8$ ✓

The solution is correct.

B $5^y = 5^{2y+4}$

SOLUTION

$5^y = 5^{2y+4}$

$y = 2y + 4$ Property of Equality for Exponential Equations

$y = -4$ Solve for y.

CHECK

$5^y = 5^{2y+4}$

$5^{-4} \stackrel{?}{=} 5^{2(-4)+4}$

$5^{-4} \stackrel{?}{=} 5^{-8+4}$

$5^{-4} = 5^{-4}$ ✓

The solution is correct.

▶ **Think About It** Always check for extraneous solutions when you solve exponential equations.

C $8^{x^2} = 64$

SOLUTION

$8^{x^2} = 64$

$8^{\mathbf{x^2}} = 8^{\mathbf{2}}$ Rewrite each term so that the bases are the same.

$\mathbf{x^2 = 2}$ Property of Equality for Exponential Equations

$x = \pm\sqrt{2}$ Solve for x.

CHECK

Substitute $\sqrt{2}$ for x.

$$8^{x^2} \stackrel{?}{=} 64$$

$$8^{(\sqrt{2})^2} \stackrel{?}{=} 64$$

$$8^2 \stackrel{?}{=} 64$$

$$64 = 64 \checkmark$$

Substitute $-\sqrt{2}$ for x.

$$8^{x^2} \stackrel{?}{=} 64$$

$$8^{(-\sqrt{2})^2} \stackrel{?}{=} 64$$

$$8^2 \stackrel{?}{=} 64$$

$$64 = 64 \checkmark$$

The solution set is $\{\pm\sqrt{2}\}$. ■

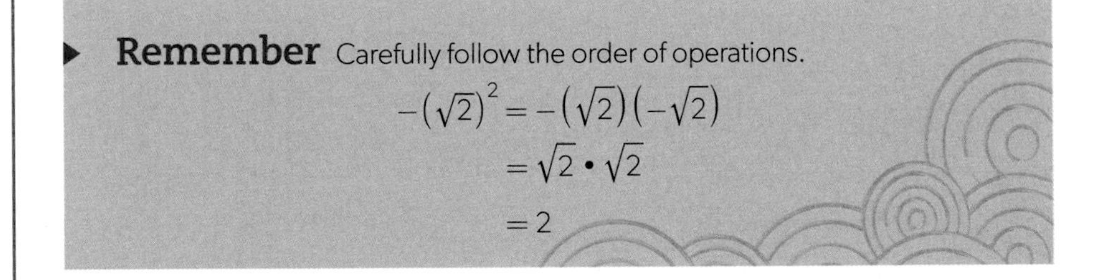

Interpreting and Transforming Exponential Expressions

You can use the properties of exponents to interpret and transform exponential expressions.

EXAMPLE 6

What is the base and exponent when the expression $81 \bullet 3^x$ is simplified?

SOLUTION

Simplify the expression and then determine the base and the exponent.

$81 \bullet 3^x = 3^4 \bullet 3^x$ $\quad$ $81 = 3^4$

$= 3^{4+x}$ $\quad$ Product of Powers Property

The base of the expression is 3 and the exponent is $4 + x$. ■

EXAMPLE 7

Rewrite the annual population growth equation $y = 1200(1.4)^{\frac{x}{3}}$ to reveal the annual rate of increase as a percent.

SOLUTION

Step 1 Rewrite the equation so that the exponent is x.

$y = 1200(1.4)^{\frac{x}{3}}$

$y = 1200\left(1.4^{\frac{1}{3}}\right)^x$ $\quad$ Power of a Power Property

$y = 1200\left(\sqrt[3]{1.4}\right)^x$ $\quad$ Property of Rational Exponents

$y = 1200(1.119)^x$ $\quad$ Simply.

Step 2 The formula for an exponential growth function is $y = b(1 + r)^x$, where b is the initial amount and r is the annual rate of increase. In this annual population growth equation, $(1 + r)$ is equal to 1.119. Solve for r.

$$1 + r = 1.119$$
$$r = 0.119$$

The annual rate of increase is 11.9%. ■

Applications: Growth and Decay

Exponential equations can be used to solve many real-world problems.

Money in a bank and populations of people or bacteria often grow, while radioactive substances gradually lose their radioactivity. Exponential formulas can help you solve many problems involving growth or decay.

Solving Growth Problems

Exponential Growth Formula

If a quantity is growing exponentially from initial amount b for time t and with growth rate r, then the total amount y is

$$y = b(1 + r)^t.$$

▶ **Think About It** The exponential models in this topic look a little different from the simple general form of an exponential function $f(x) = b^x + k$, but they behave pretty similarly.

EXAMPLE 1

Suki starts a bacterial culture in her biology class. She records her observations for the first several hours. How many bacteria should Suki expect to see after 5 h, 10 h, 15 h, and 24 h?

Hour	0	1	2
Bacteria (in thousands)	10	20	40

SOLUTION

The initial amount is 10,000 bacteria, so $b = 10$. The bacteria are expected to grow at a rate of 100% each hour, so $r = 1$. Use the exponential growth formula, $y = b(1 + r)^t$.

$$y = b(1 + r)^t$$
$$y = 10(1 + 1)^t$$
$$y = 10 \bullet 2^t$$

Hour	0	1	2	5	10	15	24
Bacteria (in thousands)	10	20	40	320	10,240	327,680	167,772,160

▶ **Think About It** At some point in time, the bacteria will stop growing because of the limited amount of food in a petri dish. This exponential model has its limits.

EXAMPLE 2

In 2000, the population of a country was 10,234,678. The population is expected to grow at a rate of 0.8% each year.

▶ **Think About It** Populations can also decrease at a constant rate. In such a case, you would use an exponential decay formula.

A Predict the population of the country in 2015.

SOLUTION

The initial population is 10,234,678, so $b = 10{,}234{,}678$. The growth rate is 0.8%, so $r = 0.008$. The time period is years, and the difference between 2015 and 2000 is 15 years, so $t = 15$. Use the exponential growth formula.

$$y = b(1 + r)^t$$
$$y = 10{,}234{,}678(1 + 0.008)^{15}$$
$$y = 10{,}234{,}678(1.008)^{15}$$
$$y \approx 10{,}234{,}678(1.26958651)$$
$$y \approx 11{,}534{,}059$$

If the growth rate of 0.8% remains constant, the population in 2015 will be approximately 11,534,059.

B In what year will the population first exceed 12 million?

SOLUTION

Since the population is predicted to be 11,534,059 in 2015, you can predict that it will exceed 12 million sometime after 2015. Plug in some values of t that are greater than 15 to test if the population becomes greater than 12 million. It seems reasonable to begin by testing $t = 20$.

$$y = 10{,}234{,}678(1 + 0.008)^{20}$$
$$y = 10{,}234{,}678(1.008)^{20}$$
$$y \approx 10{,}234{,}678(1.172764043)$$
$$y \approx 12{,}002{,}862$$

The population is a little more than 12 million in 2020. Testing $t = 19$, you can show that the population is 11,907,601, which is less than 12 million, in 2019. So the population first exceeds 12 million in 2020. ■

Solving Decay Problems

Exponential Decay Formula

If a quantity is decaying exponentially from initial amount b for time t and with decay rate r, then the amount y remaining is

$$y = b(1 - r)^t.$$

EXAMPLE 3

The sales of a popular doll decreased from 2000 to 2005, as shown in the table. If the decrease in sales continues at this rate, what would the sales be for 2010 and 2020?

Year	2000	2001	2002	2003	2004	2005
Sales ($)	1,496,330	1,421,515	1,350,440	1,283,001	1,218,769	1,158,037

SOLUTION

Step 1 Determine the decay rate. Divide the sales for each year by the sales for the previous year. The sales have declined at a constant rate of approximately 5% every year, so $r = 0.05$.

Step 2 Use the exponential decay formula to determine the equation. The initial population is 1,496,330, so $b = 1{,}496{,}330$. From Step 1, $r = 0.05$.

$$y = b(1 - r)^t$$
$$y = 1{,}496{,}330(1 - 0.05)^t$$
$$y = 1{,}496{,}330(0.95)^t$$

Step 3 Substitute 10 (for 2010) and 20 (for 2020) for t.

$$y = 1{,}496{,}330(0.95)^t \qquad y = 1{,}496{,}330(0.95)^t$$
$$y = 1{,}496{,}330(0.95)^{10} \qquad y = 1{,}496{,}330(0.95)^{20}$$
$$y \approx 895{,}908 \qquad y \approx 536{,}413$$

The sales for 2010 would fall to about $895,908, and the sales in 2020 would fall to about $536,413. ■

Radioactive Decay

Every substance that is radioactive loses particles or energy from the nucleus of its atoms. As a result, radioactive elements change from one kind of atom to another over time. This process of a radioactive substance changing from one kind of atom to another is called radioactive decay.

Definition

The **half-life** of a radioactive substance is the length of time it takes for one-half the substance to decay.

Half-Life Formula

The amount y of a radioactive substance after t time periods, where b is the initial amount and h is the half-life, is

$$y = b\left(\frac{1}{2}\right)^{\frac{t}{h}}.$$

EXAMPLE 4

Carbon-14 has a half-life of 5730 years. Archaeologists find bone material from what seems to be a human leg. One of the archaeologists thinks the leg is 10,000 years old. What percentage of normal carbon-14 levels should she expect to find in the leg?

SOLUTION

The half-life is 5730, so $h = 5730$. The time is 10,000 years, so $t = 10{,}000$. You don't know the original amount, so just use 1 for b. The answer for y will give a value you can treat as a percentage.

$$y = \left(\frac{1}{2}\right)^{\frac{t}{h}}$$

$$y = \left(\frac{1}{2}\right)^{\frac{10{,}000}{5730}}$$

$$y = \left(\frac{1}{2}\right)^{1.7452}$$

$$y = 0.2983$$

After 10,000 years, the archaeologist should expect about 29.83% of normal carbon-14 levels. ■

Compound Interest

Using compound interest is one good way to earn money. It is interest that is earned on both the principle and on any interest that has already been earned.

Compound Interest Formula

The total amount A of an investment with initial principal P, earning compound interest at an annual interest rate r and compounded n times per year for t years, is given by the formula

$$A = P\left(1 + \frac{r}{n}\right)^{nt}.$$

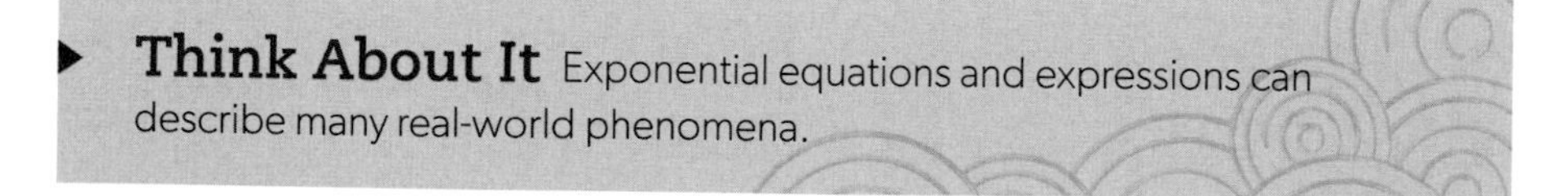

EXAMPLE 5

Find the total amount after 2 years of an investment of $1500 in an account paying 4% interest, compounded for each of the given time periods.

A annually

SOLUTION

The initial amount invested is $1500, so $P = 1500$. The interest rate is 4%, so $r = 0.04$. You are finding the balance after 2 years, so $t = 2$.

When the interest is compounded annually, $n = 1$.

$$A = P\left(1 + \frac{r}{n}\right)^{nt}$$

$$A = 1500\left(1 + \frac{0.04}{1}\right)^{1 \cdot 2}$$

$$A = 1500\,(1.04)^2$$

$$A = 1500 \cdot 1.0816$$

$$A = 1622.40$$

The total amount after 2 years is $1622.40.

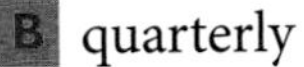
quarterly

SOLUTION

A quarterly event happens four times a year, so $n = 4$.

$$A = P\left(1 + \frac{r}{n}\right)^{nt}$$

$$A = 1500\left(1 + \frac{0.04}{4}\right)^{4 \cdot 2}$$

$$A = 1500\,(1.01)^8$$

$$A \approx 1500 \cdot 1.082856706$$

$$A \approx 1624.29$$

The total amount after 2 years is $1624.29. ■

Exponential Functions

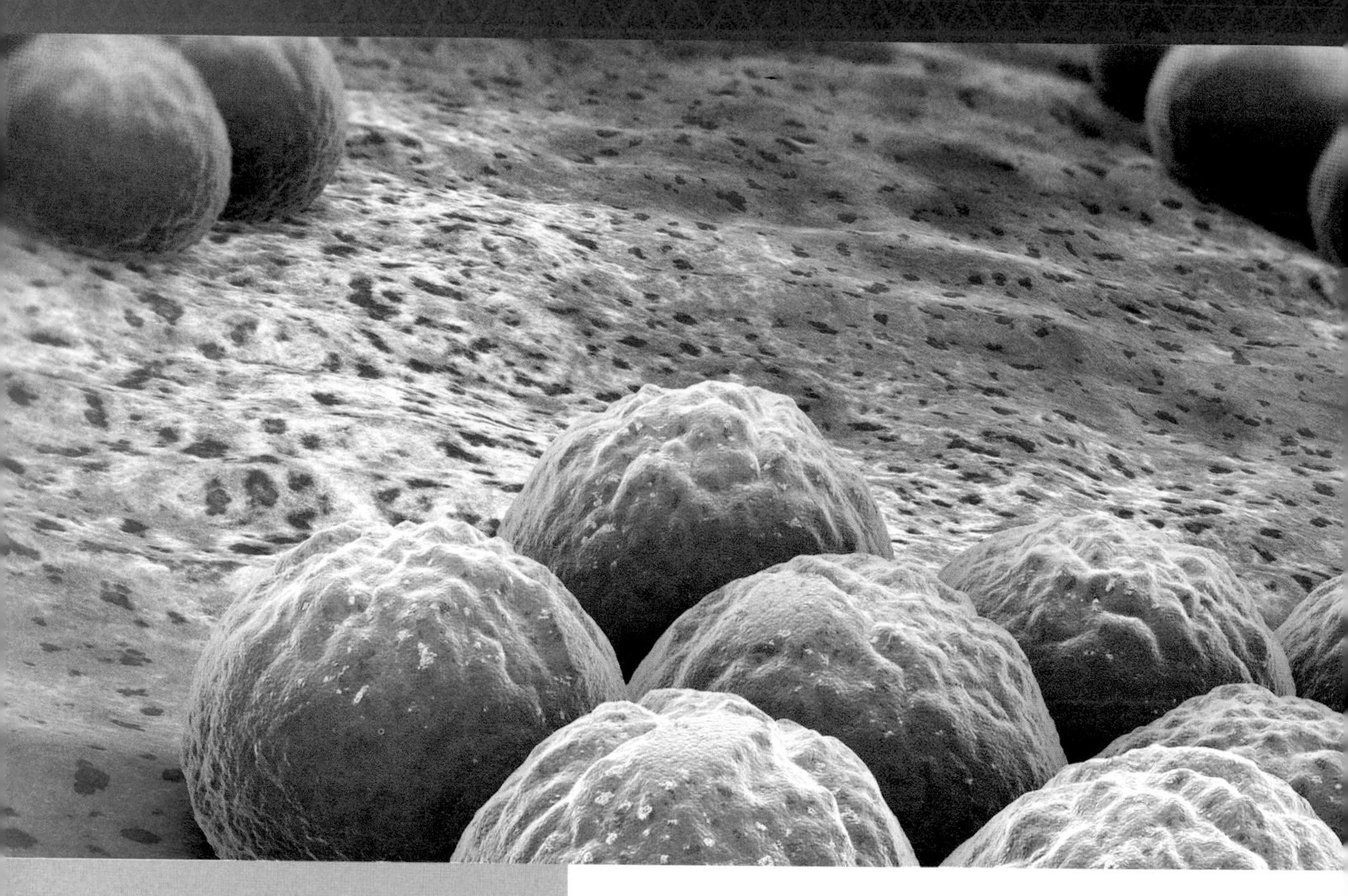

Topic List

- Graphing Exponential Functions
- Features of Exponential Functions
- Average Rate of Change
- Comparing Models
- Multiple Representations

In the right environment, the rate of growth of the number of bacteria in a petri dish may continuously increase. You can describe this kind of growth with an exponential function.

Graphing Exponential Functions

An **exponential function** has an equation of the form $f(x) = b^x + k$, where $b > 0$, and $b \neq 1$.

The function $f(x) = b^x$ is the parent function for the family of exponential functions.

Exponential Functions of the Form $f(x) = b^x$

When $b > 1$, the function $f(x) = b^x$ is called an exponential growth function.

general shape:

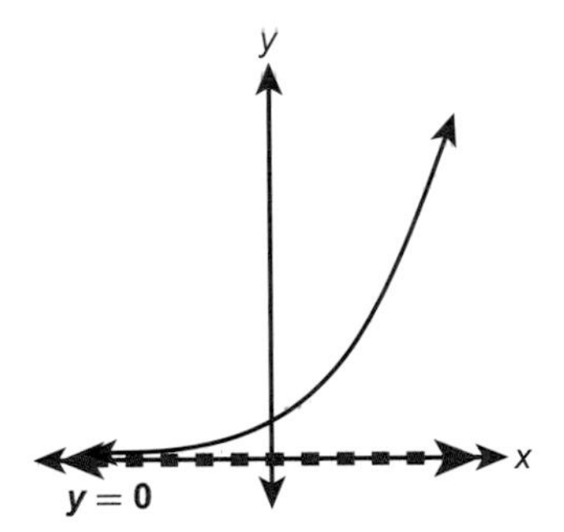

end behavior: The graph is a curve that grows at an increasing rate from left to right.

When $0 < b < 1$, the function $f(x) = b^x$ is called an exponential decay function.

general shape:

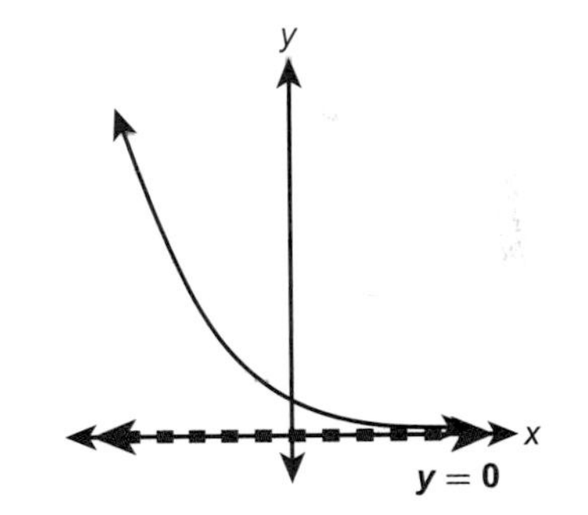

end behavior: The graph is a curve that decays at a decreasing rate from left to right.

The following properties are common to both types of exponential functions:

- asymptote: An **asymptote** is a line that a graph of a given function approaches without touching. Because the graph gets close to the axis but never meets or crosses it, the line $y = 0$ (the x-axis) is the asymptote of the graph.
- domain: the set of all real numbers
- range: all real numbers greater than 0
- y-intercept: 1

Using a Table of Values to Graph an Exponential Function

EXAMPLE 1

Use a table of values to graph.

A $f(x) = 2^x$

SOLUTION

In the function $f(x) = \mathbf{2}^x$, $b = \mathbf{2}$. Since $b > 1$, this function is an exponential growth function.

Step 1 Make a table of values. Use both positive and negative values of x. Since this is an exponential growth function of the form $f(x) = b^x$, you know that the y-intercept is 1 and that the point (1, 2) lies on the graph.

x	-3	-2	-1	0	1	2	3
$f(x)$	$\frac{1}{8}$	$\frac{1}{4}$	$\frac{1}{2}$	1	2	4	8

▶ **Think About It** Point $(1, b)$ will always lie on the graph of an exponential function of the form $f(x) = b^x$ since any number raised to the power 1 equals that number.

$$b^1 = b$$

Step 2 Plot the points from the table. Then connect the points in a smooth curve. Use the general shape of an exponential growth function as a guide. Since $2x$ is always a positive number, the range of the function is $f(x) > 0$. The graph of the function gets close to the x-axis but does not meet or cross it, so the line $y = 0$ is an asymptote of the function.

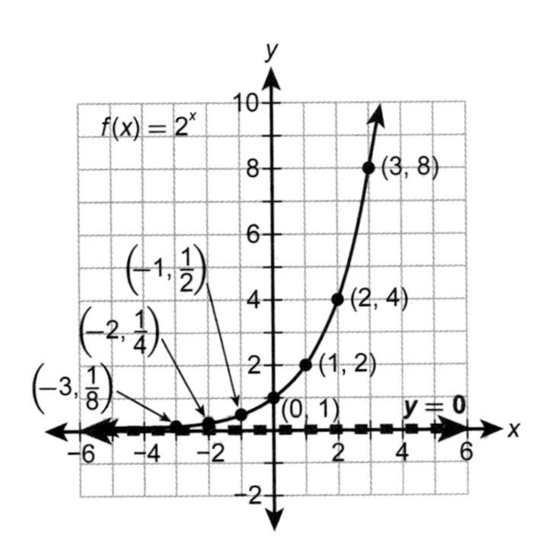

B $f(x) = (0.5)^x$

SOLUTION

In the function $f(x) = \mathbf{0.5}^x$, $b = \mathbf{0.5}$. Since $0 < b < 1$, this function is an exponential decay function.

Step 1 Make a table of values. Since this function is an exponential decay function of the form $f(x) = b^x$, you know that the y-intercept is 1 and that the point (1, 0.5) lies on the graph.

x	−3	−2	−1	0	1	2	3
f(x)	8	4	2	1	0.5	0.25	0.125

Step 2 Plot the points from the table. Then connect the points in a smooth curve. Use the general shape of an exponential decay function as a guide. Since 0.5^x is always a positive number, the range of the function is $f(x) > 0$. The x-axis is an asymptote of the function.

Notice that the graph of $f(x) = 0.5^x$ is a reflection across the y-axis of the graph of $f(x) = 2^x$.

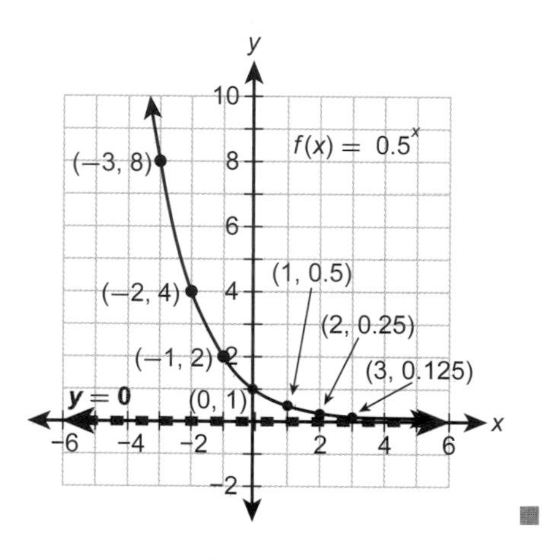

In a family of functions, once you know the graph of the parent function, you can use transformations to graph related functions. One type of transformation is a vertical translation.

When $f(x)$ is translated k units vertically, the function becomes $g(x) = b^x + k$. The graph moves up if $k > 0$. The graph moves down if $k < 0$.

The graph of $g(x) = b^x + k$ has asymptote $y = k$. The domain of the function is the set of all real numbers, and the range, for $b > 0$, is the set of all real numbers greater than k.

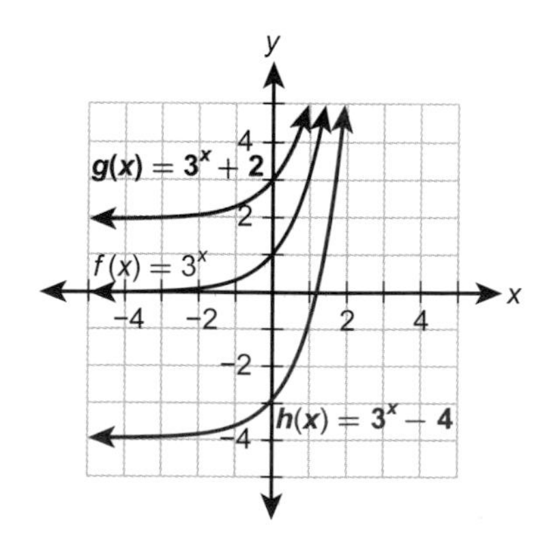

Using a Parent Function to Graph a Related Function

EXAMPLE 2

Graph $g(x) = 0.5^x - 2.5$, given the graph of the parent function, $f(x)$.

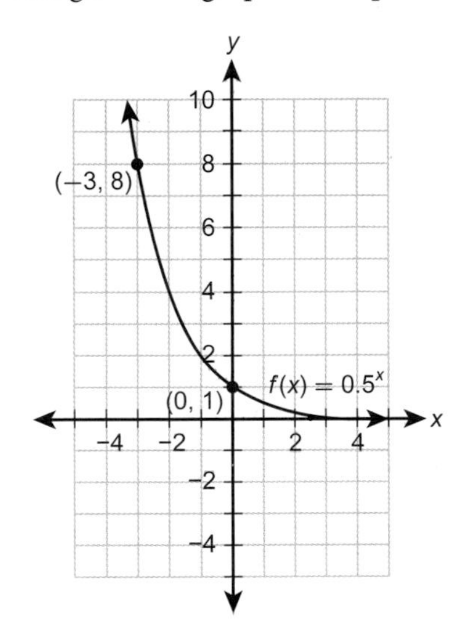

SOLUTION

Because $k = -2.5$, graph $g(x)$ by translating the graph of $f(x)$ 2.5 units down, which is the same as subtracting 2.5 from every y-coordinate.

For example, the point $(-3, 8)$ becomes $(-3, 5.5)$, and the point $(0, 1)$ becomes $(0, -1.5)$.

The asymptote shifts from $y = 0$ to $y = -2.5$. The graph approaches the line $y = -2.5$ but never touches it.

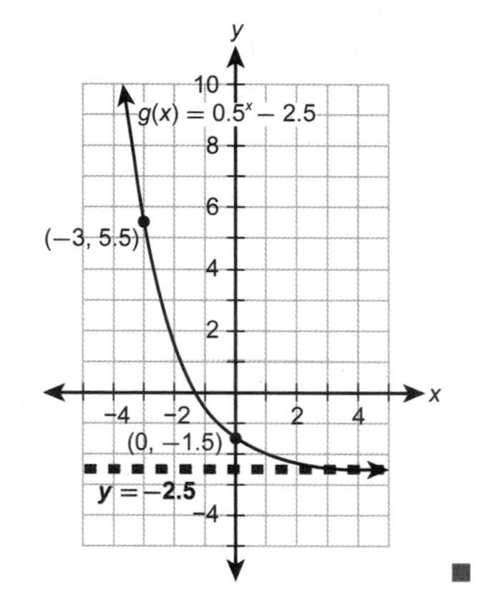

■

Using the Graph of a Function to Find an Equation for the Function

EXAMPLE 3

Find the equation of the function shown in the graph, given the equation of the parent function is $f(x) = 0.5^x$.

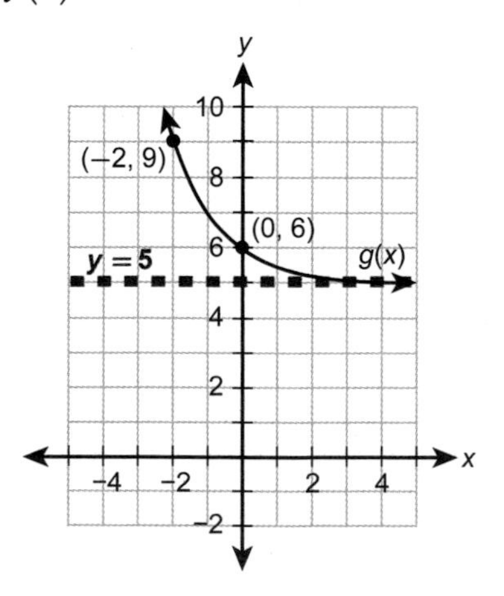

SOLUTION

The graph intersects the y-axis at the point (0, 6) and has asymptote $y = 5$, so $k = 5$.

The equation is $g(x) = 0.5^x + 5$.

CHECK

Substitute -2 for x and 9 for $g(x)$ to check if the ordered pair $(-2, 9)$ makes the equation true.

$$
\begin{aligned}
g(x) &\stackrel{?}{=} 0.5^x + 5 \\
\mathbf{9} &\stackrel{?}{=} 0.5^{(\mathbf{-2})} + 5 \\
9 &\stackrel{?}{=} \frac{1}{0.5^2} + 5 \\
9 &\stackrel{?}{=} \frac{1}{0.25} + 5 \\
9 &\stackrel{?}{=} 4 + 5 \\
9 &= 9 \checkmark
\end{aligned}
$$

The equation is correct. ■

Features of Exponential Functions

The key features of an exponential function include its intercepts and end behavior.

Using Technology to Graph Exponential Functions

With many graphing tools, you use a caret (^) to indicate that what follows is an exponent.

EXAMPLE 1

Use a technology tool to help you graph the function and label the intercepts.

A $f(x) = 1.8^x - 2.5$

SOLUTION

Enter the equation as

$$y = 1.8\text{^}x - 2.5.$$

This function has both an x- and a y-intercept. Zoom as needed to see both of them.

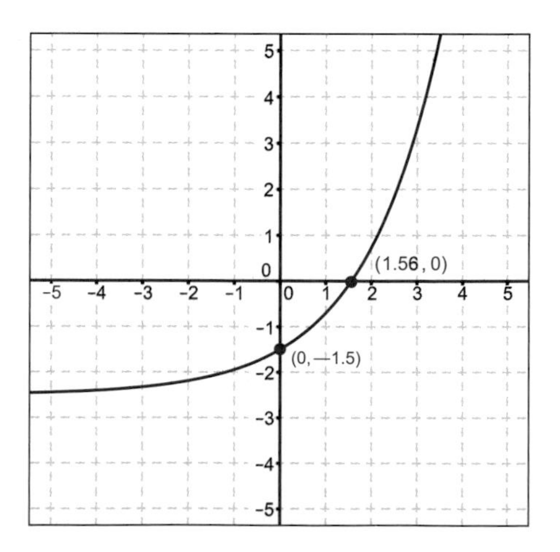

> **Think About It** For equations in the form $y = a \cdot b^x$, use an asterisk (*) to type the multiplication sign. Or use parentheses around the power: $y = a(b^x)$.

B $g(x) = -0.3^{x-1} + 2$

SOLUTION

Use parentheses around the exponent. Otherwise, it will appear that only x is the exponent.

Enter the equation as

$$y = -0.3\text{^}(x - 1) + 2.$$

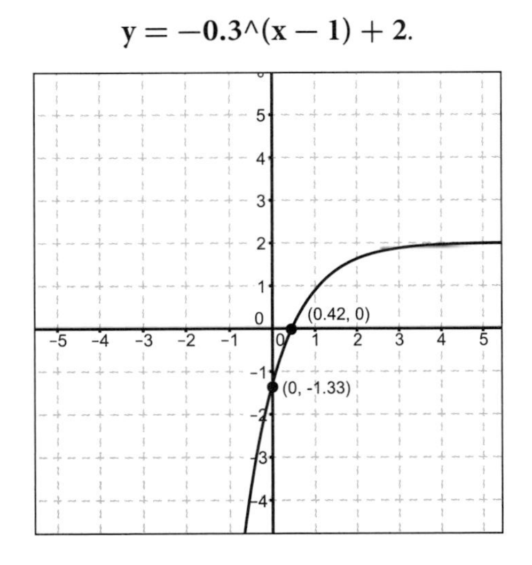

Another key feature in the graph of an exponential function is its asymptote. You can use the asymptote when describing the function's end behavior. ■

> **Think About It** The base of an exponential function is never negative. In Example 1B, the base of the power is 0.3. The negative sign indicates the opposite of the power: $g(x) = -1 \cdot 0.3^{x-1} + 2$.

Describing End Behavior

Definition

The **end behavior** of a function is how the function behaves when the domain values increase or decrease without bound.

▶ **Think About It** To increase or decrease without bound means to increase or decrease without a boundary, or to increase or decrease forever.

EXAMPLE 2

Describe the end behavior of the function.

A $f(x) = 1.8^x - 2.5$

SOLUTION

First look at how the outputs change as the inputs become smaller and smaller. In other words, look at how the graph changes as it continues forever to the left.

As the input values decrease, the output values gets closer to the asymptote, $y = -2.5$.

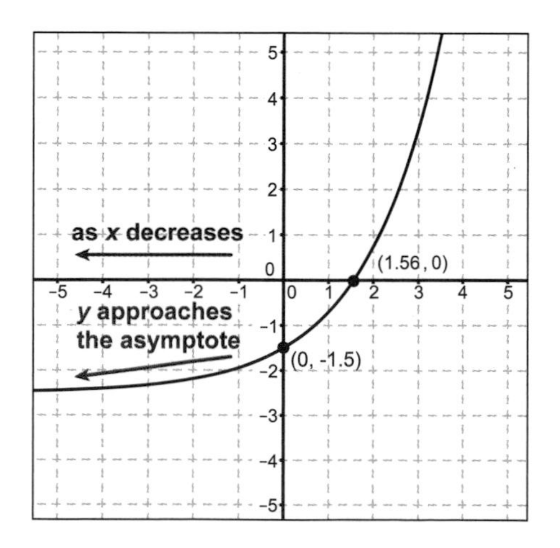

▶ **Remember** The asymptote of an exponential function is the line $y = k$.

Then look at how the outputs change as the inputs become larger and larger. In other words, look at how the graph changes as it continues forever to the right.

As the input values increase, the output values also continue to increase.

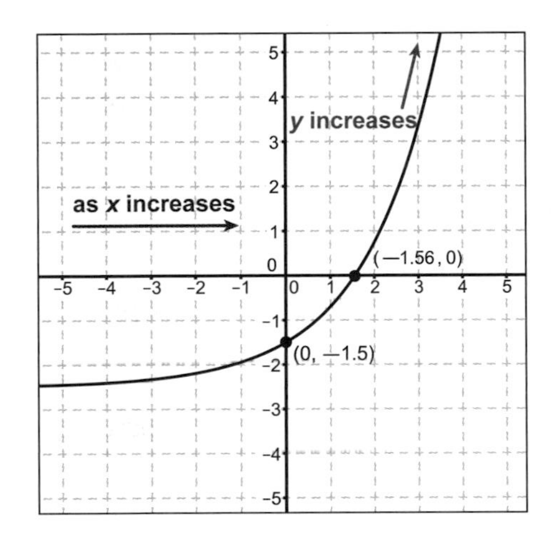

To fully describe the end behavior of a function, tell how it behaves in each direction. As x decreases without bound, $f(x)$ approaches the line $y = -2.5$. As x increases without bound, $f(x)$ increases without bound.

B $g(x) = -0.3^{x-1} + 2$

SOLUTION

As x decreases without bound, $f(x)$ decreases without bound. As x increases without bound, $f(x)$ approaches the line $y = 2$.

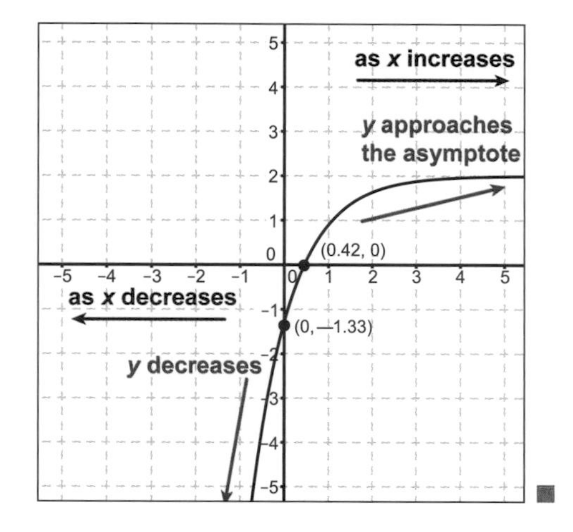

Interpreting Features of an Exponential Function

EXAMPLE 3

The function $P(n) = 4200 \cdot 0.986^n$ approximates a toad population n years after a population study concluded in 2010.

A Identify and interpret the intercepts in context of the situation.

SOLUTION

Sketch the general shape of the graph.

The value of b is 0.986. Because $b < 1$, the graph is an exponential decay function. Because $k = 0$, the asymptote is $y = 0$, and the graph does not have an x-intercept.

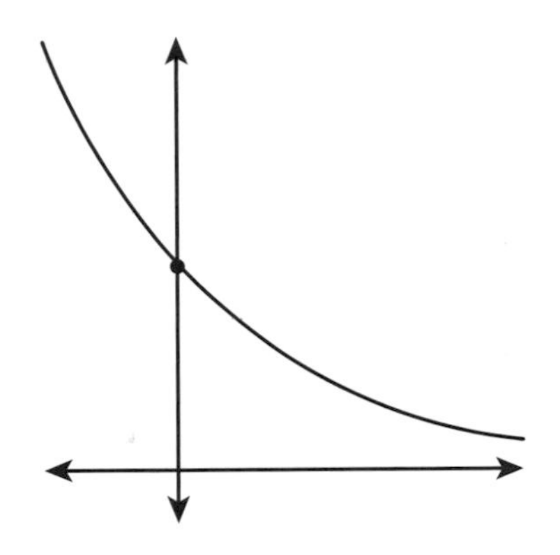

To find the y-intercept, substitute 0 for the input value, n.

$$\begin{aligned} P(\mathbf{0}) &= 4200 \cdot 0.986^{0} \\ &= 4200 \cdot 1 \\ &= 4200 \end{aligned}$$

The y-intercept is 4200. Therefore, the toad population in 2010, which was 0 years after the study concluded, was about 4200.

B Identify and interpret the asymptote in context of the situation.

SOLUTION

The asymptote is $y = 0$. As the years pass, the toad population approaches 0, or extinction. ■

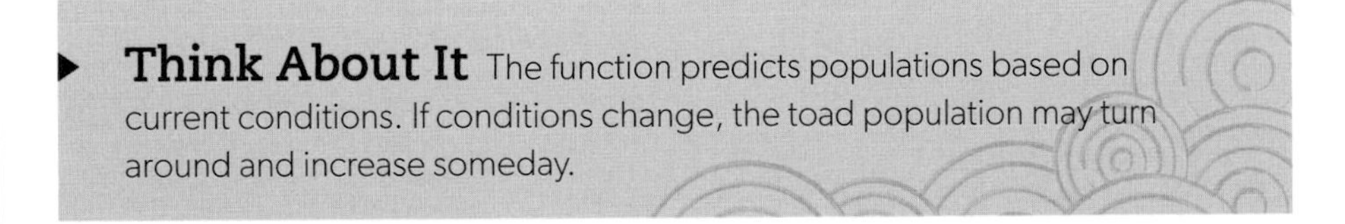

▸ **Think About It** The function predicts populations based on current conditions. If conditions change, the toad population may turn around and increase someday.

Average Rate of Change

Changes in a quantity may not occur at a steady rate.

Definition

The **average rate of change** in a quantity is the ratio of the change in the quantity to the change in time.

Finding Rates from a Table

EXAMPLE 1

The table shows the years Nick visited an amusement park and the admission fee he paid each year.

Year	2002	2008	2010	2014
Admission fee ($)	18	27	31	36

Between which two of Nick's visits did the rate of change in the admission fee increase the most?

SOLUTION

Find the slope between each consecutive pair of points.

Between 2002 and 2008: $\frac{27 - 18}{2008 - 2002} = \frac{9}{6} = 1.5 = \$1.50$ per year

Between 2008 and 2010: $\frac{31 - 27}{2010 - 2008} = \frac{4}{2} = 2 = \$2.00$ per year

Between 2010 and 2014: $\frac{36 - 31}{2014 - 2010} = \frac{5}{4} = 1.25 = \$1.25$ per year

The rate of change in the admission fee increased the most between 2008 and 2010, or between Nick's second and third visits. ■

▶ **Think About It** The actual changes in the yearly fee between 2002 and 2008 are unknown. It is known, however, that if those changes were evenly spaced out, there would be an increase of $1.50 per year.

You can also determine when the rate of change in the admission fee increased the most by graphing the ordered pairs.

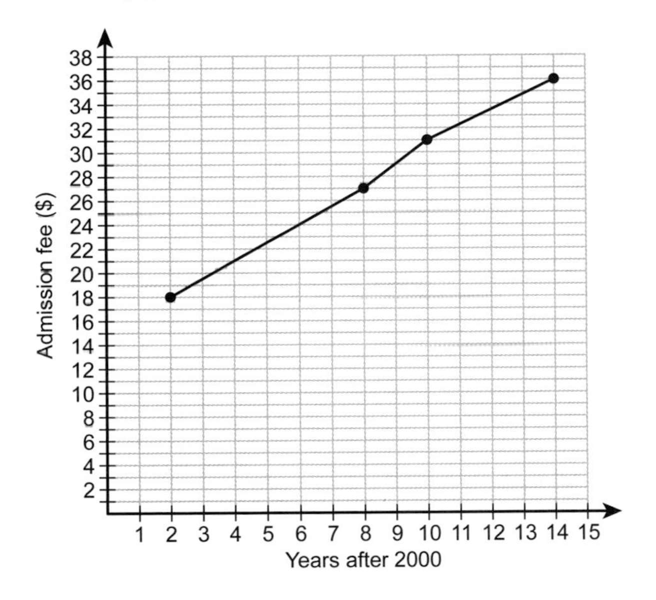

The steepest segment, or the one with the greatest slope, indicates the greatest rate of change. The steepest segment is the second segment. This segment joins the points with the data from Nick's second and third visits.

Finding Rates from a Graph

EXAMPLE 2

After a tank is filled with water, the number of liters in the tank is measured at the end of each of the following months. The graph shows these measurements.

A Describe the overall pattern of change in the amount of water.

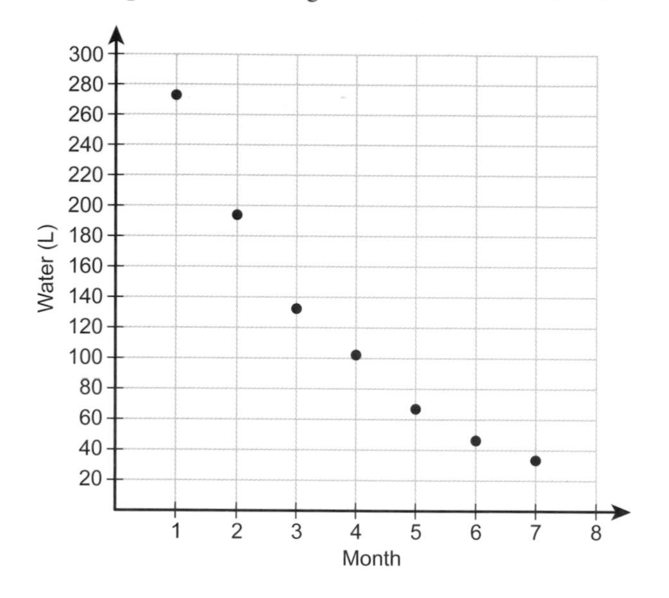

SOLUTION

The number of liters decreases every month. The amount of decrease is larger in the earlier months than the later months, so the amount of water is decreasing at a decreasing rate.

B Estimate the average rate of change between Month 1 and Month 4.

SOLUTION

After the first month, there are about 275 L of water in the tank. After the fourth month, there are about 100 L of water in the tank. Find the slope between (1, 275) and (4, 100).

$$\frac{100 - 275}{4 - 1} = \frac{-175}{3} = -58.\overline{3} \approx -58 \text{ L per month}$$

The average rate of change is about -58 L per month.

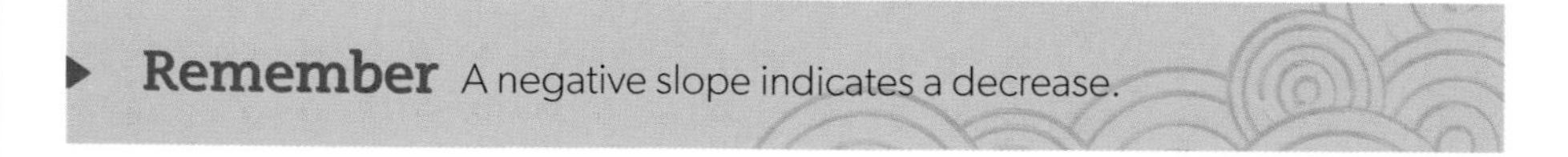

Remember A negative slope indicates a decrease.

C Compare the average rate of change between Month 5 and Month 7 to the average rate of change between Month 1 and Month 4.

> ▶ **Remember** If the rate of change were constant, the points would lie on a line.

SOLUTION

To estimate the average rate of change between Month 5 and Month 7, find the slope between (5, 65) and (7, 35).

$$\frac{35 - 65}{7 - 5} = \frac{-30}{2} = -15 = -15 \text{ L per month}$$

Both rates are decreases. Because 15 is about one-fourth of 58, the average rate of decrease between Month 5 and Month 7 is about one-fourth of what it is between Month 1 and Month 4.

You can sketch line segments in the graph for a visual comparison of the average rates of change.

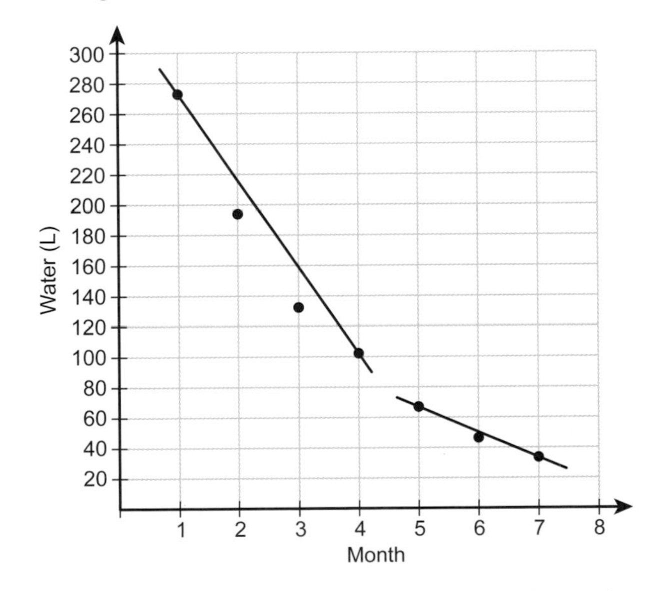

Notice that the segment representing the average rate of change between Month 5 and Month 7 is less steep than the segment representing the average rate of change between Month 1 and Month 4. ■

Average Rate of Change for Function Equations

EXAMPLE 3

Find the average rate of change of the function $f(x) = 2.2(1.5)^x$ from $x = 3$ to $x = 6$, rounded to the nearest hundredth.

SOLUTION

The average rate of change for function equations is the ratio of the change in $f(x)$ to the change in x.

Step 1 Find the value of $f(3)$ and $f(6)$.

$$f(3) = 2.2(1.5)^3 = 7.425 \qquad f(6) = 2.2(1.5)^6 = 25.059375$$

Step 2 Use the values calculated for $f(3)$ and $f(6)$ to determine the average rate of change from $x = 3$ to $x = 6$.

$$\frac{25.059375 - 7.425}{6 - 3} = \frac{17.634375}{3} = 5.878125$$

Rounding to the nearest hundredth, the average rate of change from $x = 3$ to $x = 6$ is approximately 5.88. ■

▶ **Think About It** If you were to find the average rate of change for the function $f(x) = 2.2(1.5)^x$ using different values of x, you would not always get the same average rate of change. This variance occurs because graphs of exponential functions are curved. The rate of change for linear functions, however, is constant.

Comparing Models

To determine whether a function that models a situation is linear or exponential, consider how the output values change over equal intervals.

If the output values change by equal differences, then the function is linear. If the output values change by equal factors, then the function is exponential.

Identifying a Function Type from a Verbal Description

EXAMPLE 1

Explain whether the best model for the situation is a linear function or an exponential function.

A An environmental scientist estimates that the number of people in a city who recycle on a regular basis is growing by about 20% per year.

SOLUTION
Each year, the number of people recycling on a regular basis will be about 1.2 times the number from the previous year. The value 1.2 is a common factor in this model, so the situation is best modeled by an exponential function.

B Jonah types an average of 38 words per minute.

SOLUTION
For any given minute, the total number of words Jonah typed is, on average, 38 more than the total number of words Jonah had typed a minute ago. The best model for the situation is a linear function. ■

Identifying a Function Type from a Table

EXAMPLE 2

Explain whether the best model for the situation is a linear function or an exponential function.

A The table shows the cost of catering an event with different numbers of people expected to attend.

Number of people	10	15	20	25	30
Cost ($)	270	342.5	415	487.5	560

SOLUTION

Subtracting consecutive costs reveals a common difference of $72.50. For every extra 5 people in attendance, the cost increases by $72.50. The situation is best modeled by a linear function.

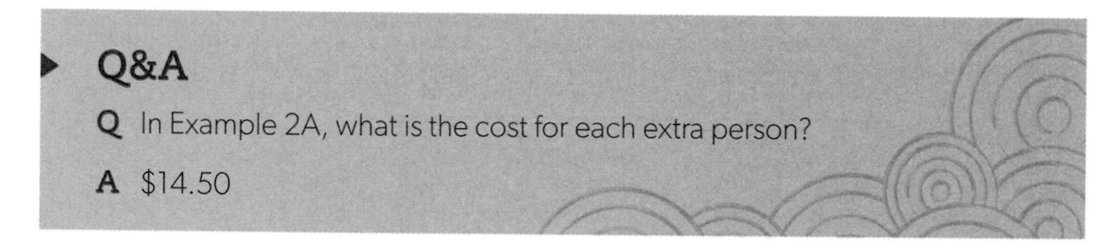

Q&A

Q In Example 2A, what is the cost for each extra person?

A $14.50

B The table shows the number of daily sit-ups Elisa plans to do each week.

Week	1	2	3	4	5	6
Number of daily sit-ups	20	30	45	68	101	152

SOLUTION

Dividing consecutive numbers of daily sit-ups reveals a common factor of 1.5 or a factor close to 1.5, so every week Elisa plans to increase her daily number of sit-ups by about 50%. The best model for the situation is an exponential function. ■

Multiple Representations

You can compare functions that are represented in tables, equations, or graphs.

Comparing Exponential Functions

EXAMPLE 1

Mrs. Cabrera purchases a painting and a lamp at an antique auction. The value of each item grows exponentially. The function $v(t) = 400 \cdot 1.03^t$ approximates the value (in dollars) of the painting t years after the auction. The table shows the value of the lamp at different years after the auction.

Year	0	1	2	3	4	25
Lamp value ($)	550	559	567	575	584	798

A Which item did Mrs. Cabrera pay more for? Explain your reasoning.

SOLUTION

The amount Mrs. Cabrera paid for each item is the y-intercept of each function.

Painting

Find $v(0)$.

$$\begin{aligned} v(0) &= 400 \cdot (1.03)^0 \\ &= 400 \cdot 1 \\ &= 400 \end{aligned}$$

Lamp

Look in the table to find the lamp value for Year 0: $550.

Mrs. Cabrera paid more for the lamp. She paid $400 for the painting and $550 for the lamp.

B Which item's value is growing at a faster rate?

SOLUTION

In $v(t) = 400 \bullet 1.03^t$, the base is 1.03, so the rate of growth is 3% per year. Find the rate of growth between consecutive years in the table.

$$\text{Year 0 to Year 1: } \frac{559 - 550}{550} = \frac{9}{550} \approx 0.01636 \approx 1.6\%$$

$$\text{Year 1 to Year 2: } \frac{567 - 559}{559} = \frac{8}{559} \approx 0.01431 \approx 1.4\%$$

$$\text{Year 2 to Year 3: } \frac{575 - 567}{567} = \frac{8}{567} \approx 0.01411 \approx 1.4\%$$

$$\text{Year 3 to Year 4: } \frac{584 - 575}{575} = \frac{9}{575} \approx 0.01565 \approx 1.6\%$$

The value of the lamp grows about 1.5% per year, so the painting's value is growing at the faster rate. ■

▶ Q&A

Q What is the value of each item 25 years after the auction?

A painting: \$838; lamp: \$798

EXAMPLE 2

Compare the behaviors of functions f and g.

$$f(x) = 4^x$$
$$g(x) = 50 \cdot 2^x$$

SOLUTION

Because each output is multiplied by 50, function g initially has the greater output values. However, the greater base in function f will lead to greater outputs for larger values of x. You can confirm this by graphing the functions or by making a table of values.

x	0	1	2	4	7	10
f(x)	1	4	16	256	**16,384**	**1,048,576**
g(x)	**50**	**100**	**200**	**400**	6400	51,200

■

▶ **Think About It** Graphing the functions reveals that value of function g is greater than the value of function f until $x \approx 5.64$.

Sequences and Modeling with Functions

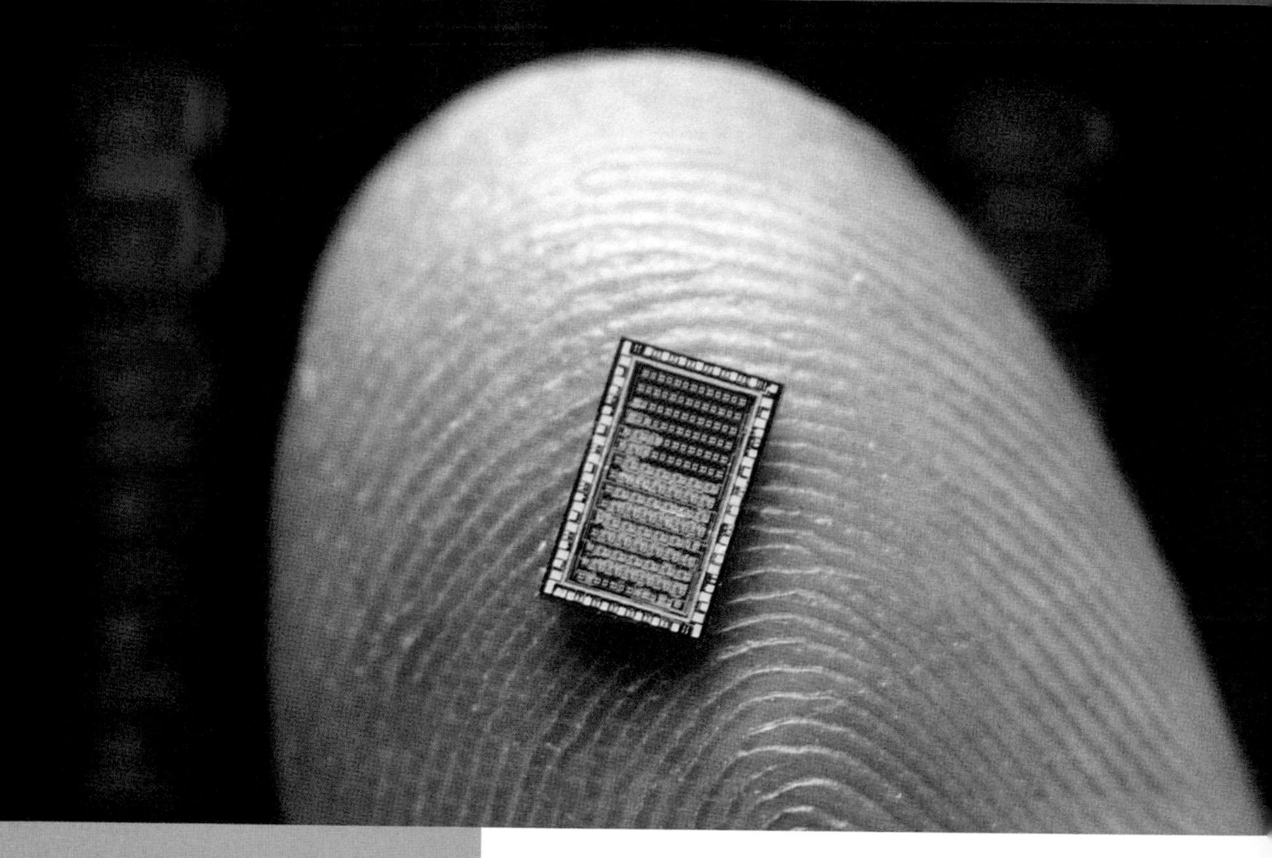

Topic List

- Sequences and Patterns
- Arithmetic Sequences
- Geometric Sequences
- Applications: Sequences
- Function Parameters
- Writing Function Equations

How many transistors can fit in a chip on the tip of your finger? Moore's law predicts that the number doubles every 2 years. Sequences like the one Gordon Moore predicted can help solve many real-world problems.

Sequences and Patterns

A sequence can be thought of as a list of numbers that follow a particular pattern.

Each number of the sequence is called a term. Subscripts are used to describe each term's position in the list.

$$a_1, a_2, a_3, \ldots, a_n, \ldots$$

For instance, in the sequence 3, 6, 9, 12, . . . , the value of a_1 is 3 because the first term is 3, $a_2 = 6$ because the second term is 6, and so on. The term a_n represents the nth term of the sequence.

Identifying Terms of a Sequence

A sequence can also be thought of as a function.

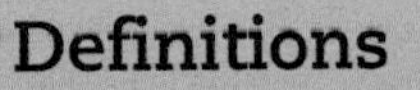

Definitions

A **sequence** is a function whose domain is the set of natural numbers.

The range of the sequence is the set of **terms**, or the values of the function.

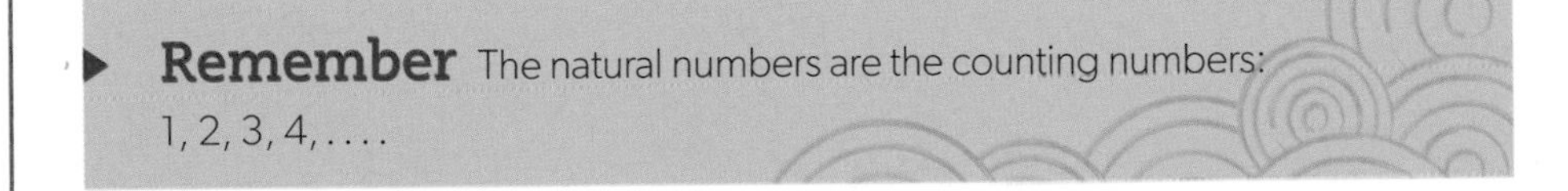

▶ **Remember** The natural numbers are the counting numbers: 1, 2, 3, 4, ...

EXAMPLE 1

Use the table of sequence values to answer the questions.

n	1	2	3	4	5	6	7
a_n	2	6	18	54	162	486	1458

A What is the third term of the sequence?

SOLUTION

The third term of the sequence is found when $n = 3$, so $a_3 = 18$.

B Which term in the sequence is 486?

SOLUTION

a_n is 486 when $n = 6$, so 486 is the sixth term of the sequence. ■

▶ **Think About It** You could write the *n*th element of the sequence as $a(n)$ instead of a_n, but you'll usually see the n written in subscript form.

Recursive Rules

Definition

A **recursive rule** is a rule for generating terms of a sequence that depends on one or more previous terms of the sequence.

EXAMPLE 2

A List the first four terms of the sequence.

$$a_1 = 8, \text{ and } a_n = a_{n-1} + 6 \text{ for } n \geq 2$$

SOLUTION

The first term is 8. Use this term and the recursive rule to generate the next three terms.

$$a_1 = 8$$
$$a_2 = a_{2-1} + 6 = a_1 + 6 = 8 + 6 = 14$$
$$a_3 = a_{3-1} + 6 = a_2 + 6 = 14 + 6 = 20$$
$$a_4 = a_{4-1} + 6 = a_3 + 6 = 20 + 6 = 26$$

The first four terms are 8, 14, 20, and 26.

▶ **Think About It** Because a_{n-1} represents the term just before a_n, each term in Example 2A can be found by adding 6 to the previous term.

B List the first four terms of the sequence.

$$b_1 = -2, \text{ and } b_n = (b_{n-1})^2 \text{ for } n \geq 2$$

SOLUTION

The first term is -2.

$$b_1 = -2$$
$$b_2 = (b_{2-1})^2 = (b_1)^2 = (-2)^2 = 4$$
$$b_3 = (b_{3-1})^2 = (b_2)^2 = 4^2 = 16$$
$$b_4 = (b_{4-1})^2 = (b_3)^2 = 16^2 = 256$$

The first four terms are -2, 4, 16, and 256.

List the first six terms of the Fibonacci sequence. The recursive rule for the Fibonacci sequence is:

$$f_1 = 1, f_2 = 1, \text{ and } f_n = f_{n-2} + f_{n-1} \text{ for } n \geq 3$$

SOLUTION

Use the rule when n is 3 or greater.

$$f_1 = 1$$

$$f_2 = 1$$

$$f_3 = f_{3-2} + f_{3-1} = f_1 + f_2 = 1 + 1 = 2$$

$$f_4 = f_{4-2} + f_{4-1} = f_2 + f_3 = 1 + 2 = 3$$

$$f_5 = f_{5-2} + f_{5-1} = f_3 + f_4 = 2 + 3 = 5$$

$$f_6 = f_{6-2} + f_{6-1} = f_4 + f_5 = 3 + 5 = 8$$

The first six terms of the Fibonacci sequence are 1, 1, 2, 3, 5, and 8. ■

Iterative Rules

Unlike a recursive rule, an iterative rule allows you to determine the nth term of a sequence, given the value of n.

Definition

An **iterative rule** is a rule that can be used to find the nth term of a sequence without calculating previous terms of the sequence.

To find a term using an iterative rule, evaluate the rule for the given domain value.

EXAMPLE 3

A Determine the fourth term of the sequence.

$$a_n = -n^3$$

SOLUTION

Substitute 4 for n.

$$a_{\mathbf{4}} = -\mathbf{4}^3 = -(4)^3 = -64$$

B Determine the 3rd, 8th, and 91st terms of the sequence.

$$a_n = -5n - 1$$

SOLUTION

Substitute 3, 8, and 91 for n.

$$a_{\mathbf{3}} = -5 \bullet \mathbf{3} - 1 = -15 - 1 = -16$$

$$a_{\mathbf{8}} = -5 \bullet \mathbf{8} - 1 = -40 - 1 = -41$$

$$a_{\mathbf{91}} = -5 \bullet \mathbf{91} - 1 = -455 - 1 = -456$$

The 3rd, 8th, and 91st terms are −16, −41, and −456. ■

Arithmetic Sequences

Sequences with a constant difference between consecutive terms have interesting properties and come up in many situations.

Finding Common Differences

Definitions

A sequence is an **arithmetic sequence** if the difference between consecutive terms is a constant.

$$d = a_n - a_{n-1}$$

The constant d is called the **common difference** of the sequence.

To find the common difference of a given sequence, select any term of the sequence and subtract it from the next consecutive term.

▶ **Think About It** If the differences between consecutive terms in a sequence are not equal, the sequence is not arithmetic.

EXAMPLE 1

For the arithmetic sequence, find the common difference.

A 14, 11, 8, 5, 2, . . .

SOLUTION

Find the difference between c_3 and c_2.

$$d = 8 - 11 = -3$$

The common difference is −3.

▶ **Think About It** What do the three dots following a list of numbers mean?

$$1, 2, 4, 8, 16, \ldots$$

The dots show that the sequence continues in the same pattern without end.

B −9, −7.5, −6, −4.5, −3, . . .

SOLUTION

Find the difference between a_2 and a_1.

$$d = -7.5 - (-9) = -7.5 + 9 = 1.5$$

The common difference is 1.5. ■

Writing and Using Recursive Rules for Arithmetic Sequences

Recursive Rule for an Arithmetic Sequence

The formula for the common difference $d = a_n - a_{n-1}$ can be rearranged to obtain the following recursive rule for arithmetic sequences:

$$a_n = a_{n-1} + d$$

any term (after first) ← a_n; a_{n-1} → previous term; d → common difference

When you define an arithmetic sequence recursively, you also need to provide the value for a_1.

EXAMPLE 2

For the sequence 12, −3, −18, −33, −48, . . . :

A Find a recursive rule.

SOLUTION

Begin by finding the common difference.

$$d = -3 - 12 = -15$$

Substitute −15 for d in the equation $m_n = m_{n-1} + d$. The recursive rule is $m_n = m_{n-1} - 15$.

The sequence starts with 12, so $m_1 = 12$.

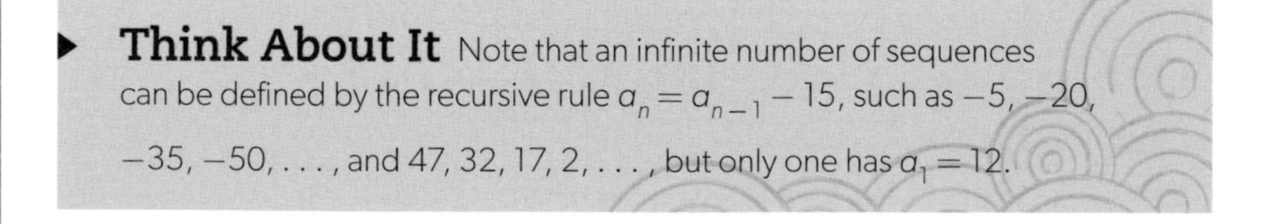

▶ **Think About It** Note that an infinite number of sequences can be defined by the recursive rule $a_n = a_{n-1} - 15$, such as −5, −20, −35, −50, . . . , and 47, 32, 17, 2, . . . , but only one has $a_1 = 12$.

B Use the recursive rule to find the next two terms in the sequence.

SOLUTION

Find the next two terms, m_6 and m_7.

$$\begin{aligned} m_6 &= m_{6-1} - 15 \\ &= m_5 - 15 \\ &= -48 - 15 = -63 \end{aligned} \qquad \begin{aligned} m_7 &= m_{7-1} - 15 \\ &= m_6 - 15 \\ &= -63 - 15 = -78 \end{aligned}$$

The next two terms of the sequence are -63 and -78. ■

Writing and Using Iterative Rules for Arithmetic Sequences

Using the recursive rule, you can see an iterative rule for jumping straight to the *n*th term in an arithmetic sequence.

$$a_1 = a_1 + 0d$$

$$a_2 = a_1 + d = a_1 + 1d$$

$$a_3 = a_2 + d = (a_1 + d) + d = a_1 + 2d$$

$$a_4 = a_3 + d = (a_1 + 2d) + d = a_1 + 3d$$

. . . and so on. Notice that each multiple of d is always 1 less than n.

Iterative Rule for an Arithmetic Sequence

The iterative rule for the *n*th term of an arithmetic sequence with first term a_1 and common difference d is

$$a_n = a_1 + (n - 1)d.$$

This rule makes it possible to find any term of an arithmetic sequence if you know the first term and the common difference.

EXAMPLE 3

For the sequence 16, 20, 24, 28, 32, . . . :

A Find an iterative rule.

SOLUTION

The first term is $f_1 = 16$, and the common difference is $d = 20 - 16 = 4$. Substitute 16 for f_1 and 4 for d in the rule $f_n = f_1 + (n - 1)d$, and then simplify:

$$\begin{aligned} f_n &= \mathbf{16} + (n - 1)\mathbf{4} \\ &= 16 + 4n - 4 \\ &= 12 + 4n \end{aligned}$$

The iterative rule is $f_n = 12 + 4n$.

B Use the iterative rule to find the 82nd term in the sequence.

SOLUTION

To find the 82nd term, substitute 82 for n in the rule.

$$f_{82} = 12 + 4 \bullet \mathbf{82} = 340$$

The 82nd term of the sequence is 340. ■

Sequences and Functions

The terms of an arithmetic sequence define a function. By determining the common difference and the first term of the sequence, you can write a function rule.

EXAMPLE 4

Use the sequence in the table to answer the questions.

n	1	2	3	4	5	6	7
a_n	4	7	10	13	16	19	22

A Write a function rule for the sequence.

SOLUTION

Find the common difference and the first term.

$$d = 7 - 4 = 3$$
$$a_1 = 4$$

Write and simplify the iterative rule for the sequence.

$a_n = a_1 + (n - 1)d$	Iterative Rule
$a_n = 4 + (n - 1)(3)$	Substitute $d = 3$ and $a_1 = 4$.
$a_n = 4 + 3n - 3$	Distributive Property
$a_n = 3n + 1$	Simplify.

The sequence can be described by the function $a_n = f(n) = 3n + 1$.

B Describe the domain and range of the function.

SOLUTION

The domain of the function is the set of natural numbers: $D = \{n \mid n = 1, 2, 3, 4...\}$. The range of the function represents the terms of the sequence: $R = \{a_n \mid a_n = 4, 7, 10, 13...\}$. ■

▶ **Think About It** Each term of a sequence depends on its location in the sequence, so each term, a_n, is a function of the term number, n.

EXAMPLE 5

Use the graph to answer the questions.

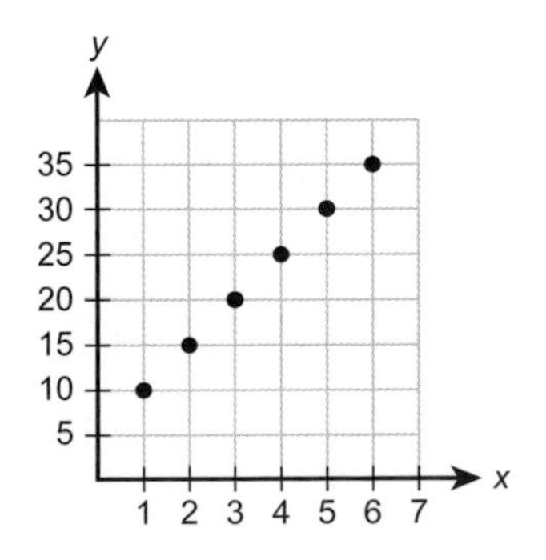

A Write a sequence for the graph. Express the sequence as a function.

SOLUTION

Write the points as ordered pairs: (1, 10), (2, 15), (3, 20), (4, 25), (5, 30), (6, 35).

▶ **Think About It** Each *x*-coordinate represents a term number, and each *y*-coordinate represents the corresponding term of the sequence.

Write and simplify the iterative rule for the sequence.

$$d = 15 - 10 = 5 \text{ and } a_1 = 10$$
$$a_n = 10 + (n - 1)(5)$$
$$a_n = 10 + 5n - 5$$
$$a_n = f(n) = 5n + 5$$

B Describe the domain and range of the sequence.

SOLUTION

The sequence can be described by the function $f(n) = 5n + 5$. The domain of the function is the set of natural numbers: $D = \{n \mid n = 1, 2, 3, 4 \ldots\}$. The range of the function is the set of the terms of the sequence: $R = \{a_n \mid a_n = 10, 15, 20, 25, \ldots\}$. ■

Graphing Arithmetic Sequences

EXAMPLE 6

Graph the arithmetic sequence in the coordinate plane.

A $a_n = -5 + 4\,(n - 1)$

SOLUTION

The domain is the set of positive integers. Make a table of some points and plot those points to get a partial graph.

▶ **Think About It** The graph of any arithmetic sequence will consist of discrete points that lie on a line.

n	$a_n = -5 + 4(n - 1)$	a_n
1	$a_1 = -5 + 4(\mathbf{1} - 1) = -5 + 4 \bullet 0 = -5 + 0$	−5
2	$a_2 = -5 + 4(\mathbf{2} - 1) = -5 + 4 \bullet 1 = -5 + 4$	−1
3	$a_3 = -5 + 4(\mathbf{3} - 1) = -5 + 4 \bullet 2 = -5 + 8$	3
4	$a_4 = -5 + 4(\mathbf{4} - 1) = -5 + 4 \bullet 3 = -5 + 12$	7
5	$a_5 = -5 + 4(\mathbf{5} - 1) = -5 + 4 \bullet 4 = -5 + 16$	11

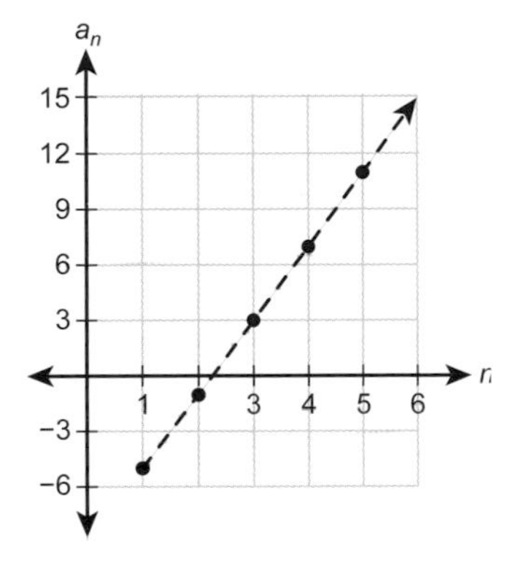

B $q_n = 12 + (-2)(n - 1)$

SOLUTION

Find the first five terms.

n	$q_n = 12 + (-2)(n - 1)$	q_n
1	$q_1 = 12 + (-2)(\mathbf{1} - 1) = 12 + (-2)(0) = 12 + 0$	12
2	$q_2 = 12 + (-2)(\mathbf{2} - 1) = 12 + (-2)(1) = 12 - 2$	10
3	$q_3 = 12 + (-2)(\mathbf{3} - 1) = 12 + (-2)(2) = 12 - 4$	8
4	$q_4 = 12 + (-2)(\mathbf{4} - 1) = 12 + (-2)(3) = 12 - 6$	6
5	$q_5 = 12 + (-2)(\mathbf{5} - 1) = 12 + (-2)(4) = 12 - 8$	4

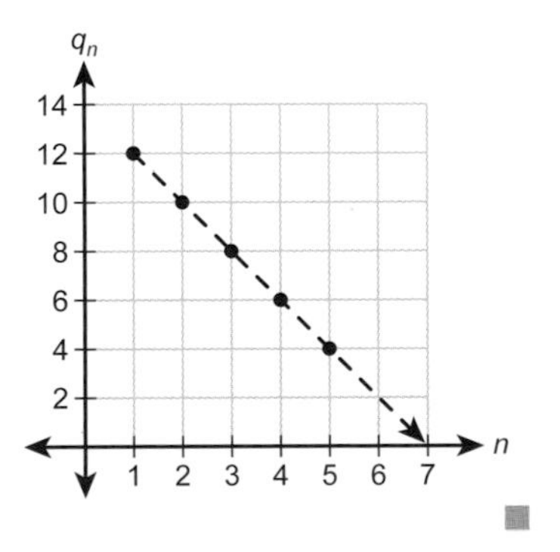

Converting Between Sequence Forms

EXAMPLE 7

An arithmetic sequence is defined recursively by $a_n = a_{n-1} + 7$, where $a_1 = 15$. Write an iterative rule for the sequence.

> ▶ **Think About It** An iterative rule is also known as an explicit rule. The terms *iterative rule* and *explicit rule* are used interchangeably.

SOLUTION

The first term is $a_1 = 15$. Because each term in the recursive rule is found by adding 7 to the previous term, the common difference is 7. Substitute 15 for a_1 and 7 for d in the rule $a_n = a_1 + (n - 1)d$ and simplify.

$$\begin{aligned} a_n &= \mathbf{15} + (n - 1)(\mathbf{7}) \\ &= 15 + 7n - 7 \\ &= 7n + 8 \end{aligned}$$

The explicit rule is $a_n = 7n + 8$.

CHECK

You can check your answer by making sure both rules produce the same sequence.

$a_n = a_{n-1} + 7, a_1 = 15$	$a_n = 7n + 8$
$a_1 = 15$	$a_1 = 7(1) + 8 = 15$
$a_2 = 15 + 7 = 22$	$a_2 = 7(2) + 8 = 22$
$a_3 = 22 + 7 = 29$	$a_3 = 7(3) + 8 = 29$
$a_4 = 29 + 7 = 36$	$a_4 = 7(4) + 8 = 36$ ■

EXAMPLE 8

An arithmetic sequence is defined by the rule $a_n = 4n + 13$. Write a recursive rule for the sequence.

SOLUTION

The common difference of the sequence is always the coefficient of n in the explicit rule.

$$d = 4$$

Calculate the first term of the sequence.

$$a_1 = 4(\mathbf{1}) + 13 = 17$$

Because each term is 4 more than the previous term, the recursive rule is $a_n = a_{n-1} + 4$, where $a_1 = 17$. ■

▶ **Remember** Check to be sure both rules produce the same sequence.

Geometric Sequences

Sequences for which consecutive terms have a constant ratio come up in many situations and have interesting properties.

Common Ratios

Definitions

A sequence is a **geometric sequence** if the ratio between consecutive terms is a constant.

$$r = \frac{a_n}{a_{n-1}}$$

The constant r is called the **common ratio** of the sequence.

▶ **Think About It** If the common ratio is negative, then the terms of the sequence alternate between positive and negative values.

EXAMPLE 1

Find the common ratio.

A 76, 38, 19, 9.5, 4.75, . . .

SOLUTION

To find the common ratio, select any term of the sequence except the first term. Then divide it by the previous term.

If you select 38, then $r = \frac{38}{76} = \frac{1}{2}$.

The common ratio is $\frac{1}{2}$.

B $-3, 9, -27, 81, -243, \ldots$

SOLUTION

To find the common ratio, select any term of the sequence except the first term. Then divide it by the previous term.

If you select -27, then $r = \frac{-27}{9} = -3$.

The common ratio is -3. ■

Recursive Rules for Geometric Sequences

Recursive Rule for a Geometric Sequence

The formula for the common ratio $r = \frac{a_n}{a_{n-1}}$ can be rearranged to obtain the following recursive rule for geometric sequences:

$$a_n = r \cdot a_{n-1}$$

any term (after first) ← a_n; r → common ratio; a_{n-1} → previous term

When you define a geometric sequence recursively, you also need to provide the value for a_1.

EXAMPLE 2

For the sequence $8, -16, 32, -64, 128, \ldots$:

A Find a recursive rule.

SOLUTION

Begin by finding the common ratio.

$$r = \frac{g_2}{g_1} = \frac{-16}{8} = -2$$

Substitute -2 for r in the equation $g_n = r \cdot g_{n-1}$.

The recursive rule is $g_n = -2 \cdot g_{n-1}$.

The sequence starts with 8, so $g_1 = 8$.

▶ **Think About It** In the sequence 5, 15, 45, 135, 405, . . . ,

$$a_1 = \text{given}$$
$$a_2 = 3a_1$$
$$a_3 = 3a_2$$
$$a_4 = 3a_3$$

and so on.

B Use the recursive rule to find the next two terms in the sequence.

SOLUTION

The next two terms are g_6 and g_7.

$$\begin{aligned} g_6 &= -2 \cdot g_{6-1} \\ &= -2 \cdot g_5 \\ &= -2 \cdot 128 = -256 \end{aligned} \qquad \begin{aligned} g_7 &= -2 \cdot g_{7-1} \\ &= -2 \cdot g_6 \\ &= -2 \cdot (-256) = 512 \end{aligned}$$

The next two terms of the sequence are −256 and 512. ■

Writing and Using Iterative Rules for Geometric Sequences

Using the recursive rule, you can see an iterative rule for jumping straight to the *n*th term in a geometric sequence.

$$a_1 = a_1 \cdot r^0$$
$$a_2 = a_1 \cdot r = a_1 \cdot r^1$$
$$a_3 = a_2 \cdot r = \left(a_1 \cdot r^1\right) \cdot r = a_1 \cdot r^2$$
$$a_4 = a_3 \cdot r = \left(a_1 \cdot r^2\right) \cdot r = a_1 \cdot r^3$$

. . . and so on. Notice that each power of r is always 1 less than n.

▶ **Think About It** Note that an infinite number of sequences can be defined by the recursive rule $a_n = -2 \cdot a_{n-1}$, such as −3, 6, −12, 24, . . . , and $\frac{1}{16}, -\frac{1}{8}, \frac{1}{4}, -\frac{1}{2}, \ldots$, but only one of the sequences with this recursive definition has $a_1 = 8$.

$$8, -16, 32, -64, \ldots$$

Iterative Rule for a Geometric Sequence

The iterative rule for the *n*th term of a geometric sequence with first term a_1 and common ratio *r* is

$$a_n = a_1 \bullet r^{n-1}.$$

This rule makes it possible to find any term of a geometric sequence, given the first term and the common ratio.

EXAMPLE 3

For the sequence $\frac{1}{64}, \frac{1}{16}, \frac{1}{4}, 1, 4, \ldots$:

A Find an iterative rule.

SOLUTION

Find the constant ratio.

$$r = a_2 \div a_1 = \frac{1}{16} \div \frac{1}{64} = \frac{1}{16} \bullet 64 = 4$$

Substitute $\frac{1}{64}$ for c_1 and 4 for *r* in the equation $a_n = a_1 \bullet r^{n-1}$ to obtain the iterative rule.

$$c_n = \frac{\mathbf{1}}{\mathbf{64}} \bullet \mathbf{4}^{n-1}$$

B Use the iterative rule to find the 10th term in the sequence.

SOLUTION

To find the 10th term, substitute 10 for *n*.

$$\begin{aligned} a_{\mathbf{10}} &= \frac{1}{64} \bullet 4^{\mathbf{10}-1} \\ &= \frac{1}{64} \bullet 4^9 \\ &= 4096 \end{aligned}$$ ■

Converting Between Sequence Forms

EXAMPLE 4

A geometric sequence is defined recursively by $a_n = -3a_{n-1}$, where $a_1 = -2$. Write an iterative rule for the sequence.

> **Remember** The terms *iterative rule* and *explicit rule* are used interchangeably.

SOLUTION

The first term is $a_1 = -2$, and the common ratio is -3. Substitute -2 for a_1 and -3 for r in the rule $a_n = a_1 \cdot r^{n-1}$.

$$a_n = \mathbf{-2 \cdot (-3)}^{n-1}$$

The explicit rule is $a_n = -2 \cdot (-3)^{n-1}$.

CHECK

You can check your answer by making sure both rules produce the same sequence.

$a_n = -3a_{n-1},\ a_1 = -2$	$a_n = -2 \cdot (-3)^{n-1}$
$a_1 = -2$	$a_1 = -2 \cdot (-3)^{1-1} = -2$
$a_2 = -3(-2) = 6$	$a_2 = -2 \cdot (-3)^{2-1} = 6$
$a_3 = -3(6) = -18$	$a_3 = -2 \cdot (-3)^{3-1} = -18$
$a_4 = -3(-18) = 54$	$a_4 = -2 \cdot (-3)^{4-1} = 54$ ■

EXAMPLE 5

A geometric sequence is defined by the rule $a_n = \frac{1}{125} \cdot (5)^{n-1}$. Write a recursive rule for the sequence.

SOLUTION

The common ratio of the sequence is the value raised to the $n - 1$ power in the explicit rule.

$$r = 5$$

Calculate the first term of the sequence.

$$a_1 = \frac{1}{125} \cdot (5)^{1-1} = \frac{1}{125}$$

The recursive rule is $a_n = 5a_{n-1}$, where $a_1 = \frac{1}{125}$. ■

▶ **Remember** Check to be sure both rules produce the same sequence.

Graphing Geometric Sequences

EXAMPLE 6

Graph the geometric sequence in the coordinate plane.

▶ **Think About It** The graph of any geometric sequence with a positive common ratio will consist of discrete points that lie on an exponential curve.

A $b_n = 1 \cdot 3^{n-1}$

SOLUTION

The domain is the set of positive integers. Make a table of some points and plot those points to get a partial graph.

n	$b_n = 1 \cdot 3^{n-1}$	b_n
1	$b_1 = 1 \cdot 3^{1-1} = 1 \cdot 3^0 = 1 \cdot 1$	1
2	$b_2 = 1 \cdot 3^{2-1} = 1 \cdot 3^1 = 1 \cdot 3$	3
3	$b_3 = 1 \cdot 3^{3-1} = 1 \cdot 3^2 = 1 \cdot 9$	9
4	$b_4 = 1 \cdot 3^{4-1} = 1 \cdot 3^3 = 1 \cdot 27$	27
5	$b_5 = 1 \cdot 3^{5-1} = 1 \cdot 3^4 = 1 \cdot 81$	81

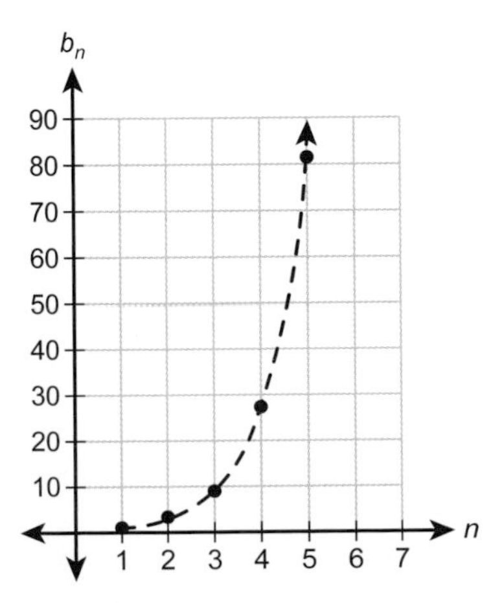

B $k_n = 32 \cdot \left(\frac{1}{2}\right)^{n-1}$

SOLUTION

n	$k_n = 32 \cdot \left(\frac{1}{2}\right)^{n-1}$	k_n
1	$k_1 = 32 \cdot \left(\frac{1}{2}\right)^{1-1} = 32 \cdot \left(\frac{1}{2}\right)^{0} = 32 \cdot 1$	32
2	$k_2 = 32 \cdot \left(\frac{1}{2}\right)^{2-1} = 32 \cdot \left(\frac{1}{2}\right)^{1} = 32 \cdot \frac{1}{2}$	16
3	$k_3 = 32 \cdot \left(\frac{1}{2}\right)^{3-1} = 32 \cdot \left(\frac{1}{2}\right)^{2} = 32 \cdot \frac{1}{4}$	8
4	$k_4 = 32 \cdot \left(\frac{1}{2}\right)^{4-1} = 32 \cdot \left(\frac{1}{2}\right)^{3} = 32 \cdot \frac{1}{8}$	4
5	$k_5 = 32 \cdot \left(\frac{1}{2}\right)^{5-1} = 32 \cdot \left(\frac{1}{2}\right)^{4} = 32 \cdot \frac{1}{16}$	2

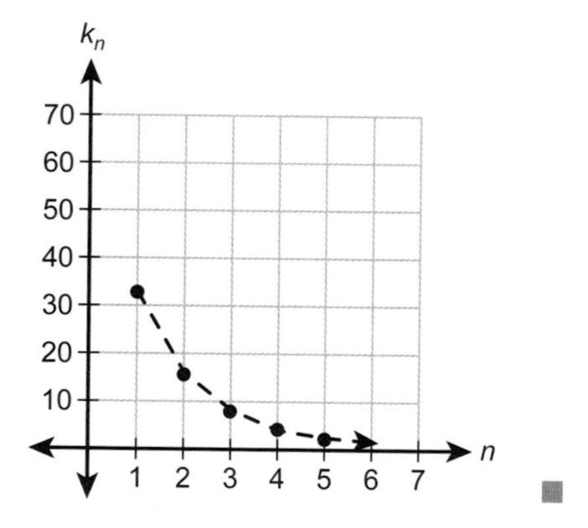

Applications: Sequences

You can use sequences to solve problems that involve number patterns.

A sequence may be arithmetic, geometric, or neither. For example, the sequence $1, -2, 3, -4, 5, \ldots$ is neither arithmetic nor geometric, but you can examine the pattern and predict that the 6th term is -6.

Determining Whether a Sequence Is Arithmetic, Geometric, or Neither

EXAMPLE 1

Decide whether the sequence is arithmetic, geometric, or neither.

▶ **Remember** In an arithmetic sequence, the difference between consecutive terms is the common difference.

In a geometric sequence, the ratio between consecutive terms is the common ratio.

A $-\frac{3}{2}, -\frac{3}{8}, -\frac{3}{32}, -\frac{3}{128}, \ldots$

SOLUTION

Is it arithmetic?

Test for a common difference by subtracting.

$$b_2 - b_1 = -\frac{3}{8} - \left(-\frac{3}{2}\right) = \frac{9}{8} \qquad b_3 - b_2 = -\frac{3}{32} - \left(-\frac{3}{8}\right) = \frac{9}{32}$$

There is no common difference, so it is not arithmetic.

Is it geometric?
Test for a common ratio by dividing.

$$b_2 \div b_1 = -\frac{3}{8} \div \left(-\frac{3}{2}\right) = -\frac{3}{8} \cdot \left(-\frac{2}{3}\right) = \frac{1}{4}$$

$$b_3 \div b_2 = -\frac{3}{32} \div \left(-\frac{3}{8}\right) = -\frac{3}{32} \cdot \left(-\frac{8}{3}\right) = \frac{1}{4}$$

$$b_4 \div b_3 = -\frac{3}{128} \div \left(-\frac{3}{32}\right) = -\frac{3}{128} \cdot \left(-\frac{32}{3}\right) = \frac{1}{4}$$

The common ratio is $\frac{1}{4}$. The sequence is geometric.

B 13, −8, −29, −50, . . .

SOLUTION
Is it arithmetic?
Test for a common difference by subtracting.

$$z_2 - z_1 = -8 - 13 = -21$$

$$z_3 - z_2 = -29 - (-8) = -21$$

$$z_4 - z_3 = -50 - (-29) = -21$$

The sequence is arithmetic.

C 6, 7, 9, 12, . . .

SOLUTION
Is it arithmetic?
Test for a common difference by subtracting.

$$t_2 - t_1 = 7 - 6 = 1 \qquad t_3 - t_2 = 9 - 7 = 2$$

There is no common difference, so it is not arithmetic.

Is it geometric?
Test for a common ratio by dividing.

$$t_2 \div t_1 = 7 \div 6 \approx 1.167 \qquad t_3 \div t_2 = 9 \div 7 \approx 1.286$$

There is no common ratio, so it is not geometric.

The sequence is neither arithmetic nor geometric. ■

EXAMPLE 2

Decide whether the sequence is arithmetic, geometric, or neither. Find the common difference or the common ratio, if there is one. Use the sequence to answer the question.

▶ **Think About It** To show that the test for a common difference or a common ratio fails, you only need to use two calculations. If the results are not the same, the test fails. However, to show that a common difference or a common ratio exists, you must test all the given numbers in the sequence.

A A display of soup cans in the grocery store is stacked so that the top layer has 1 can, the next layer is 2 by 2 and has 4 cans, the next layer is 3 by 3 and has 9 cans, and the next layer is 4 by 4 with 16 cans. How many cans are in the layer below that?

SOLUTION

Write the sequence of numbers.

$$1, 4, 9, 16, \ldots$$

Is it arithmetic?

Test for a common difference by subtracting.

$$4 - 1 = 3 \qquad 9 - 4 = 5$$

There is no common difference.

Is it geometric?

Test for a common ratio by dividing.

$$\frac{4}{1} = 4 \qquad \frac{9}{4} = 2.25$$

There is no common ratio.

The sequence is neither arithmetic nor geometric.

Use the pattern to find the next number in the sequence.

$$1^2 = 1 \qquad 2^2 = 4 \qquad 3^2 = 9 \qquad 4^2 = 16$$

The next layer will have $5^2 = 25$ cans.

B Suppose you find 1 penny on Monday, 2 pennies on Tuesday, 4 pennies on Wednesday, 8 pennies on Thursday, and 16 pennies on Friday. If this pattern continues, how many pennies will you find on Saturday?

SOLUTION

Write the sequence of numbers.

$$1, 2, 4, 8, 16, \ldots$$

Is it arithmetic?

Test for a common difference.

$$2 - 1 = 1 \qquad 4 - 2 = 2$$

There is no common difference.

Is it geometric?

Test for a common ratio.

$$\frac{2}{1} = 2 \qquad \frac{4}{2} = 2 \qquad \frac{8}{4} = 2 \qquad \frac{16}{8} = 2$$

The common ratio is 2, so the sequence is geometric.

Use the common ratio to find the next number in the sequence.

$$16 \bullet 2 = 32$$

The next number in the pattern is 32. You will find 32 pennies on Saturday.

C Makena adds \$15 every month to her savings jar. Every month, she counts the amount of money in the jar. What will her savings be after 6 months?

SOLUTION

Write the sequence of numbers.

$$15, 30, 45, 60, 75, \ldots$$

Is it arithmetic?

Test for a common difference.

$$30 - 15 = 15 \qquad 45 - 30 = 15 \qquad 60 - 45 = 15 \qquad 75 - 60 = 15$$

The common difference is \$15, so it is an arithmetic sequence.

Use the common difference to find the next number in the sequence.

$$75 + 15 = 90$$

After 6 months, Makena will have \$90. ■

Application: Money

EXAMPLE 3

Suppose someone offers to pay you 1 penny on the first day, 2 pennies the second day, and so on, doubling the number of pennies each day. (This pattern is the same pattern as in Example 2B.) What is the first day on which your pay would be at least \$10?

SOLUTION

Begin by changing \$10 to pennies. So the question is, on which day would you be paid at least 1000 pennies?

Step 1 Write what you know, and what you are looking for, in terms of the sequence rules.

You know the common ratio: $r = 2$. You know the first term: $a_1 = 1$.

You will be paid 1000 pennies on Day n, so you know the value of the nth term: $a_n = 1000$.

What you don't know is the value of n.

▶ **Remember** When you know one term of an a_n arithmetic or geometric sequence, use a recursive rule to find the next term.

For an arithmetic sequence:

$$a_n = a_{n-1} + d$$

For a geometric sequence:

$$a_n = r \cdot a_{n-1}$$

In both of these rules, a_n is any term after the first, called the nth term. The previous term is a_{n-1}. The common difference is d, and the common ratio is r.

Step 2 Substitute the known values into the iterative rule.

$a_n = a_1 \cdot r^{n-1}$	Iterative rule for a geometric sequence
$1000 = 1 \cdot 2^{n-1}$	Substitute.
$1000 = 2^{n-1}$	Simplify.

Step 3 Use the guess-and-check strategy to solve for n.

Try $n = 9$: $2^{\mathbf{9}-1} = 2^8 = 256$	too low
Try $n = 10$: $2^{\mathbf{10}-1} = 2^9 = 512$	too low
Try $n = 11$: $2^{\mathbf{11}-1} = 2^{10} = 1024$	too high

n is between 10 and 11. To determine whether you should round up or down, think about what you are looking for: The first day you earn at least 1000 pennies. On Day 10, your pay will be 512 pennies. On Day 11, your pay will be 1024 pennies, so the answer is Day 11. ■

Application: Population Growth

EXAMPLE 4

A small town had a population of 968 in 2000. By the next year, the population had grown to 1007. In 2002, there were 1047 people, and the next year there were 1089.

A What kind of sequence is this?

SOLUTION

Write the sequence of numbers.

$$968, 1007, 1047, 1089, \ldots$$

Step 1 Test for a common difference by subtracting.

$1007 - 968 = 39$ $\quad$ $1047 - 1007 = 40$ $\quad$ $1089 - 1047 = 42$

There is no common difference.

Step 2 Test for a common ratio by dividing.

$$\frac{1007}{968} \approx 1.04 \qquad \frac{1047}{1007} \approx 1.04 \qquad \frac{1089}{1047} \approx 1.04$$

There is a common ratio. This sequence is geometric.

Each year the population increases by about 4%.

▶ **Think About It** The ratios in example 4A aren't exactly equal to each other, but they are pretty close, so a geometric sequence is a reasonable model.

B If this pattern continues, what will the population be after 15 years?

SOLUTION

Use the iterative rule, $a_n = a_1 \cdot r^{n-1}$, with the values you know.

$a_n = a_1 \cdot r^{n-1}$

$a_{15} \approx 968 \cdot 1.04^{15-1}$ Substitute.

$a_{15} \approx 968 \cdot 1.04^{14}$ Simplify.

$a_{15} \approx 1676$ Use a calculator to approximate the value.

After 15 years, the population will be about 1676. ■

Application: Finance

EXAMPLE 5

The balance on a car loan is \$7600. The car owner makes a payment of \$200 every month.

A Write a sequence showing the balance for the first 5 months. What kind of sequence is this?

SOLUTION

The sequence is \$7600, \$7400, \$7200, \$7000, ... There is a common difference of −\$200, so this is an arithmetic sequence.

B When will the balance be less than \$600?

SOLUTION

Find the number of the term that is equal to \$600.

$$
\begin{aligned}
c_n &= c_1 + (n-1) \cdot d & \\
600 &= 7600 + (n-1) \cdot (-200) & \text{Substitute.} \\
600 &= 7600 - 200n + 200 & \text{Distribute } -200. \\
-7200 &= -200n & \text{Simplify.} \\
36 &= n & \text{Divide both sides by } -200.
\end{aligned}
$$

Notice that the first term, c_1, is \$7600, and the balance after 1 payment is c_2, or \$7400. So c_{36} is the balance after 35 payments, and $c_{36} = 600$. The balance will be less than \$600 after 36 payments. ■

Application: Physics

EXAMPLE 6

A ball is dropped from a height of 100 in. The ball bounces, each time reaching a lower and lower height. The height of each bounce is 80% of the height of the previous bounce.

> ▶ **Think About It** Because the height of each successive bounce is 80% of a positive number, the ball's bounce, in theory, will never reach a zero height. In practice, however, the ball loses energy and does eventually stop bouncing.

A What height, rounded to the nearest inch, will the ball reach after bouncing 4 times?

SOLUTION

In this situation, the first height in this geometric sequence is 100 in, so $f_1 = 100$. The second height will be 80% of 100 in., and so forth. The height, after bouncing 4 times, is the fifth height in the sequence, f_5.

Step 1 Write what you know, and what you are looking for, in sequence notation.

The common ratio is 80%, or 0.8, so $r = 0.8$, and you know $f_1 = 100$.

You are looking for the value of the fifth term, f_5.

Step 2 Find f_n when $n = 5$.

$f_n = f_1 \bullet r^{n-1}$

$f_5 = 100 \bullet 0.8^{5-1}$ Substitute.

$f_5 = 100 \bullet 0.8^4$ Simplify.

$f_5 = 40.96$ Use a calculator to evaluate.

After bouncing 4 times, the ball will reach a height of almost 41 in.

B How many bounces will it take for the ball to reach a height of less than 1 in.?

SOLUTION

You need to solve for n when the height f_n is 1 in.

$f_n = f_1 \bullet r^{n-1}$

$1 = 100 \bullet 0.8^{n-1}$ Substitute.

Use the guess-and-check strategy to solve for n.

Try $n = 23$: $100 \bullet 0.8^{23-1} = 100 \bullet 0.8^{22} \approx 0.7379$ too low

Try $n = 22$: $100 \bullet 0.8^{22-1} = 100 \bullet 0.8^{21} \approx 0.9223$ too low

Try $n = 21$: $100 \bullet 0.8^{21-1} = 100 \bullet 0.8^{20} \approx 1.153$ too high

n is between 21 and 22, but only whole number values make sense in this situation. Think about what you are looking for: the number of bounces it will take for the ball to reach a height of less than 1 in. Because $f_{21} > 1$, you want the bounce number that corresponds with f_{22}. The bounce number is 1 less than n, so the answer is 21 bounces ■

Actually, if you try this with a real ball, the ball would probably not bounce as many as 21 times. It would lose energy and stop bouncing before that.

Function Parameters

The parameters in a function can reveal specific details about the situation it represents.

Distinguishing Between Model Variables and Parameters

Definitions

In math modeling, a **model variable** takes on different values for a particular model.

A **model parameter** (or simply parameter) is a value that is held constant for a specific model.

Consider a linear function whose rule is written in slope-intercept form. The values m and b can be held constant, and thus are considered parameters, while the input variable x changes.

general equation $\quad f(x) = \mathbf{m}x + \mathbf{b}$

specific equation $\quad f(x) = -\mathbf{\frac{5}{2}}x + \mathbf{90}$

Now consider an exponential function. The values a and r can be held constant, and considered parameters, while the input variable n changes.

general equation $\quad g(n) = \boldsymbol{a} \cdot \boldsymbol{r}^{n-1}$

specific equation $\quad g(n) = \mathbf{24{,}000} \cdot \mathbf{(0.85)}^{n-1}$

▸ **Think About It** Function families are defined by their parameters.

Interpreting Parameters

EXAMPLE 1

The function $h(x) = -\frac{5}{2}x + 90$ represents the height of a container, in feet, as it is lowered from a building's rooftop x seconds after the process of lowering the container begins.

A What does the value $-\frac{5}{2}$ represent in this situation?

SOLUTION

The value $-\frac{5}{2}$ is the slope of the function. You could say that the container is being lowered 5 ft every 2 s. Alternatively, you could convert the fraction to a decimal $\left(-\frac{5}{2} = -2.5\right)$ and say that the container is being lowered 2.5 ft/s.

B What does the value 90 represent in this situation?

SOLUTION

The value 90 is the y-intercept of the function, or the value of the function when the input is 0. The input is the number of seconds after the lowering process begins, so $h(0)$ is the height of the container before it is lowered. Because the container is being lowered from a rooftop, $h(0)$ represents the height of the building. The building the container is being lowered from is 90 ft high. ■

EXAMPLE 2

The function $f(n) = 24{,}000 \cdot (0.85)^{n-1}$ represents the value of Reggie's car, in dollars, in the nth year he owns it.

A What does the value 24,000 represent in this situation?

SOLUTION

The function rule is written in a form that models a geometric sequence; 24,000 is the first term in the sequence. Reggie's car is worth $24,000 in the first year he owns it.

B What does the value 0.85 represent in this situation?

SOLUTION

Because 0.85 is the base of the power, it is the common ratio in the geometric sequence. For any given year, the value of Reggie's car is 85% of what it was the previous year. In other words, the value of Reggie's car is decreasing by 15% per year. ■

Choosing Parameters

Which variable or variables you choose to become a parameter in a function depends on the purpose of the function.

EXAMPLE 3

The function $t = hd$ can be used to determine the amount of money a person will earn for working h hours at d dollars per hour.

A Martina earns \$8.50/h and Sue earns \$9.10/h. Write the function, using function notation, that each woman can use to determine the total amount of money she will earn, given the number of hours she works.

SOLUTION

The number of hours that each woman will work will remain variable, and the amount earned per hour will become fixed for each woman. That is, h will be the input variable and d will become a parameter. Substitute 8.5 and 9.1 for d.

$$\text{Martina: } t(h) = 8.5h$$
$$\text{Sue: } t(h) = 9.1h$$

B Mr. Gardner's employees work either a part-time shift (24 h/wk) or a full-time shift (40 h/wk). Write the function, using function notation, that Mr. Gardner can use to determine the total amount of money an employee working each type of shift will earn, given the employee's hourly wage.

SOLUTION

The number of dollars per hour will remain variable, and the number of hours that an employee works will become fixed for each type of shift. That is, d will be the input variable and h will become a parameter. Substitute 24 and 40 for h.

$$\text{part-time shift: } t(d) = 24d$$
$$\text{full-time shift: } t(d) = 40d \quad \blacksquare$$

▶ **Think About It** If Martina works a full-time shift, she can either substitute 40 for h in the first function in Example 3A, or she can substitute 8.5 for d in the second function in Example 3B.

Writing Function Equations

You can use relationships, graphs, and tables of values to determine linear and exponential function equations for real-world situations.

Writing Linear Function Equations

Real-world situations are often described by the relationship between variables, presented in graphs or presented in tables. To model these situations with a linear function, determine the coordinates of two points that would lie on the graph of the function. Then use those points to determine the slope and y-intercept of the function.

▶ **Remember** The general slope-intercept form of a linear function is $f(x) = mx + b$, where m is the slope and b is the y-intercept.

EXAMPLE 1

A hot-air balloon is cruising at a certain altitude when it begins to descend at a constant rate. After 2 min, the balloon is 640 ft above the ground. After 5 min, the balloon is 520 ft above the ground. Write a linear function to model the height of the hot-air balloon t minutes after it began to descend.

SOLUTION

Define variables for the function.

$$t = \text{time (in minutes) since the balloon began its descent}$$
$$h(t) = \text{height (in feet) of the balloon after } t \text{ minutes}$$

Determine two ordered pairs from the problem situation.

$$(2, 640) \text{ and } (5, 520)$$

Determine the slope.

$$m = \frac{520 - 640}{5 - 2} = -40$$

Determine the y-intercept. Substitute either one of the **ordered pairs** and the **slope** into the equation $h(t) = mt + b$. Then solve for b.

$$\mathbf{640} = -\mathbf{40}(\mathbf{2}) + b$$
$$720 = b$$

The function $h(t) = -40t + 720$ gives the height of the balloon (in feet) t minutes after it began its descent. ■

EXAMPLE 2

Write a linear function to represent the situation shown in the graph.

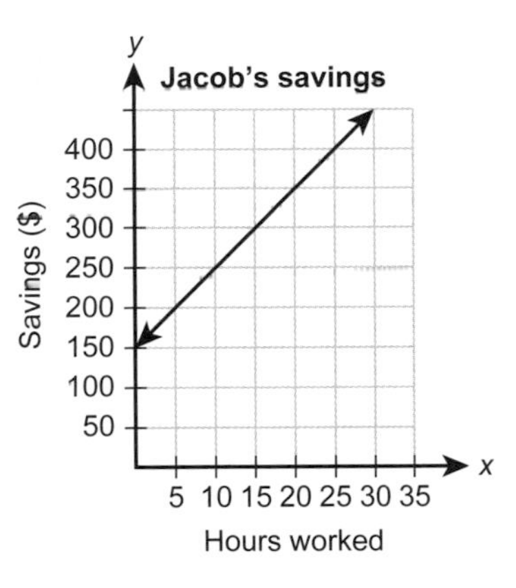

SOLUTION

Use two ordered pairs from the graph to determine the slope and y-intercept of the linear function.

$(5, 200)$ and $(10, 250)$	Determine two ordered pairs.
$m = \frac{250 - 200}{10 - 5} = 10$	Apply the slope formula.
$y = mx + b$	Slope-intercept form of a line
$200 = 10(5) + b$	Substitute $x = 5$, $y = 200$, and $m = 10$.
$150 = b$	Solve for b.

The function $f(x) = 10x + 150$ gives the total amount that Jacob has saved (in dollars) after working x hours. ■

▸ **Think About It** In Example 2, Jacob begins with $150 in savings and saves an additional $10 for each hour that he works.

EXAMPLE 3

The table shows the amount of profit (or loss) that the Drama Club will earn or lose if t tickets are sold for the fall play. Write a linear function to model the situation.

Tickets sold, t	0	50	100	150	200	250
Profit or loss ($), $A(t)$	−225	−100	25	150	275	400

SOLUTION

Use two ordered pairs from the table to determine the slope and y-intercept.

$(0, -225)$ and $(100, 25)$ — Determine two ordered pairs.

$m = \frac{25 - (-225)}{100 - 0} = 2.5$ — Apply the slope formula.

$A(t) = mt + b$ — General function form

$-225 = 2.5(0) + b$ — Substitute $t = 0$, $A(0) = -225$, and $m = 2.5$.

$-225 = b$ — Solve for b.

The function $A(t) = 2.5t - 225$ represents the amount of profit (or loss) the Drama Club will earn or lose if t tickets are sold. ■

Writing Exponential Function Equations

You can also model certain real-world situations by writing exponential functions. To model a situation with an exponential function, determine the coordinates of two consecutive points that would lie on the graph of the function. Divide these function values to determine the common ratio. Then determine the initial value of the function.

▶ **Remember** The general form of an exponential function is $f(x) = ab^x$, with base b, where $b > 0$ and $b \neq 1$, and initial value, a, where $a \neq 0$.

EXAMPLE 4

Wildlife experts have been studying the deer population in a region for the past several years. They have determined that the population is growing exponentially. Two years after the study began, the experts determined that 14,520 deer were in the region. After 3 years, an estimated 15,972 deer were in the region. Write an exponential function to model the number of deer in the region after t years.

SOLUTION

Define variables for the function.

$$t = \text{time (in years) since the study began}$$
$$P(t) = \text{population of deer after } t \text{ years}$$

Determine two ordered pairs from the problem situation.

$$(2, 14{,}520) \text{ and } (3, 15{,}972)$$

Since the t-values for the ordered pairs are $t = 2$ and $t = 3$, the function values are consecutive. Divide the function values to determine the common ratio, or base, of the function.

$$b = \frac{15{,}972}{14{,}520} = 1.1$$

Substitute either one of the **ordered pairs** and the **base** into the equation $P(t) = a(b)^t$. Use the ordered pair **(2, 14,520)**. Then solve for the initial value, a.

$$P(t) = a(b)^t$$
$$\mathbf{14{,}520} = a(\mathbf{1.1})^{\mathbf{2}}$$
$$14{,}520 = a(1.21)$$
$$12{,}000 = a$$

The function $P(t) = 12{,}000(1.1)^t$ models the population of deer in the region t years after the study began. ■

EXAMPLE 5

Write an exponential function to represent the situation shown in the graph.

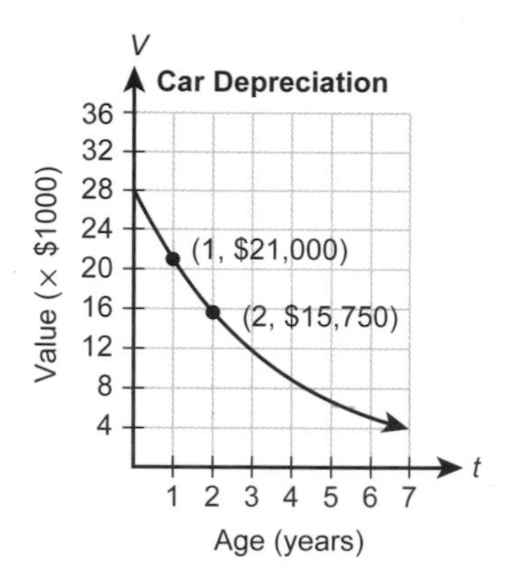

SOLUTION

Use two ordered pairs from the graph to determine the base and initial value of the function.

$(1, 21{,}000)$ and $(2, 15{,}750)$	Determine two consecutive ordered pairs.
$b = \dfrac{15{,}750}{21{,}000} = 0.75$	Divide consecutive function values.
$V(t) = a(b)^t$	General exponential function
$21{,}000 = a(0.75)^1$	Substitute $b = 0.75$, $V = 21{,}000$, and $t = 1$.
$21{,}000 = a(0.75)$	Simplify the power.
$28{,}000 = a$	Solve for a.

The function $V(t) = 28{,}000(0.75)^t$ represents the value (in dollars) of the car when it is t years old. ■

EXAMPLE 6

Jenna's savings account earns annual compound interest. The table shows the value of the account if she makes no other deposits or withdrawals after opening it. Write an exponential function to model the situation.

Years since opening the account, t	1	2	3	4
Value (\$), $V(t)$	1230	1260.75	1292.27	1324.58

SOLUTION

Use two ordered pairs from the graph to determine the base and initial value of the function.

$(1, 1230)$ and $(2, 1260.75)$	Determine two consecutive ordered pairs.
$b = \frac{1260.75}{1230} = 1.025$	Divide consecutive function values.
$V(t) = a(b)^t$	General exponential function
$1230 = a(1.025)^1$	Substitute $b = 1.025$, $V = 1230$, and $t = 1$.
$1230 = a(1.025)$	Simplify the power.
$1200 = a$	Solve for a.

The function $V(t) = 1200(1.025)^t$ represents the amount of money in Jenna's savings account after t years. ■

▶ **Think About It** In Example 3, Jenna's initial deposit to the savings account is \$1200. The account earns 0.025, or 2.5%, annual compound interest.

Systems of Equations

Topic List

- Graphs of Systems
- Approximating Solutions with Graphs
- Systems of Functions
- Substitution Method
- Linear Combination
- Linear Combination with Multiplication
- Justifying Linear Combination
- Applications: Systems of Linear Equations

Solving a system of equations is like finding the point at which two railroad lines meet. You are looking for a point that they share in common. Some systems are like a set of railroad ties that are parallel to each other and thus never meet, but most systems can be solved one way or another.

Graphs of Systems

Two equations in the same variables create a system of equations.

Using a Graph to Solve a System of Linear Equations

When both the equations in a system of equations are lines, it is a system of linear equations.

Definition

A **system of linear equations** is two or more linear equations with the same variables.

▶ **Think About It** Not all systems of equations are systems of linear equations.

EXAMPLE 1

Solve the system by graphing. Then check the solution algebraically.

$$x + 2y = 4$$
$$4x - 2y = 16$$

SOLUTION

Graph each line in the coordinate plane. The intersection of the two lines appears to be the point $(4, 0)$.

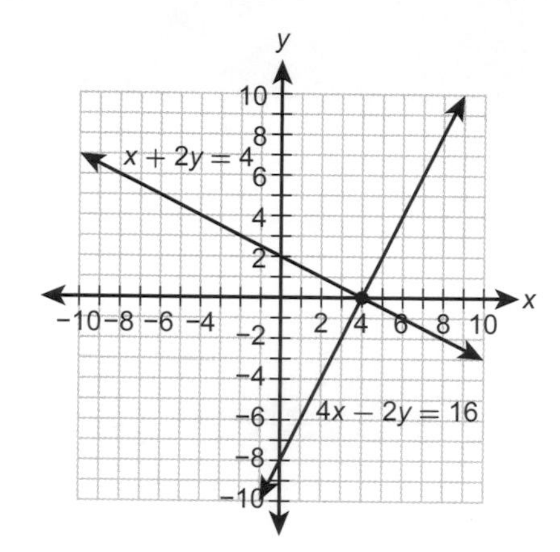

Check to determine whether $(4, 0)$ is a solution by substituting 4 for x and 0 for y in each equation.

$$\begin{aligned} x + 2y &= 4 \\ \mathbf{4} + 2 \cdot \mathbf{0} &\stackrel{?}{=} 1 \\ 4 &= 4 \checkmark \end{aligned} \qquad \begin{aligned} 4x - 2y &= 16 \\ 4 \cdot \mathbf{4} - 2 \cdot \mathbf{0} &\stackrel{?}{=} 16 \\ 16 &= 16 \checkmark \end{aligned}$$

The point $(4, 0)$ is the solution to the system of equations. ■

Classifying Systems of Linear Equations

A system of linear equations is **consistent** if it has exactly one solution or infinitely many solutions. A consistent system with exactly one solution is a **consistent independent** system. A consistent system with infinitely many solutions is a **consistent dependent** or a **coincident** system. Coincident linear systems contain equations whose graphs are the same line. When the lines of a system of linear equations are parallel, there is no solution to the system. A system of equations with no solution is an **inconsistent** system.

EXAMPLE 2

Classify the linear system as consistent independent, coincident, or inconsistent.

A

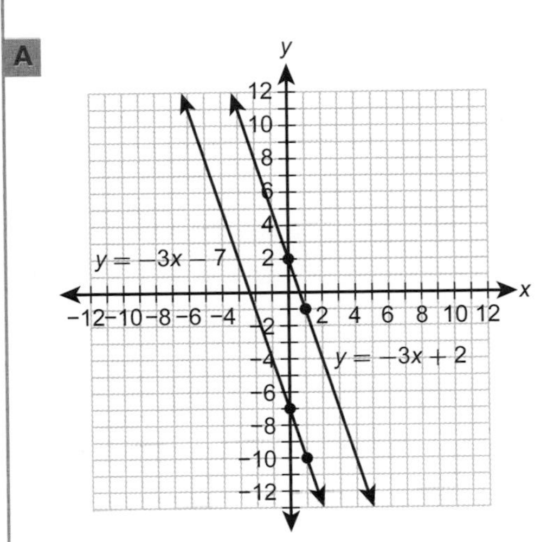

SOLUTION

The slope of both lines is -3, so the lines are parallel. The system is inconsistent.

B

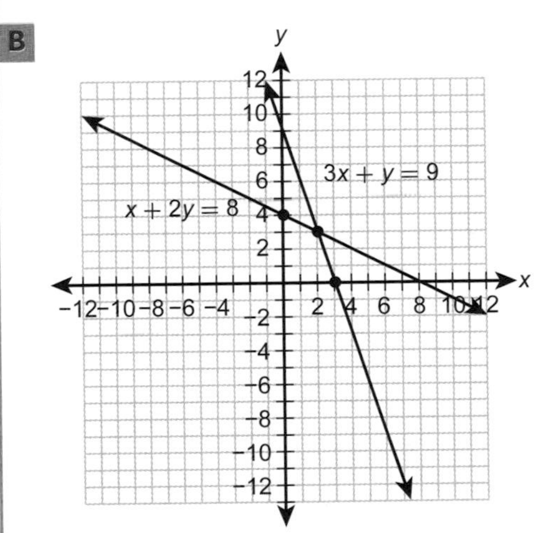

SOLUTION

The lines intersect at a single point. The system is consistent independent.

C

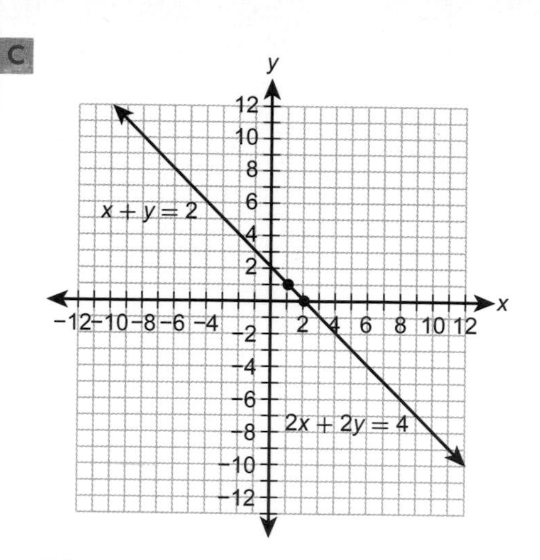

SOLUTION

The graphs are the same line. The system is coincident. ■

Approximating Solutions with Graphs

Sometimes a graph doesn't show you the exact coordinates of the point where two lines intersect.

Using a Graph to Estimate the Solution of a System

EXAMPLE 1

Estimate the coordinates of the solution of the system to the nearest tenth.

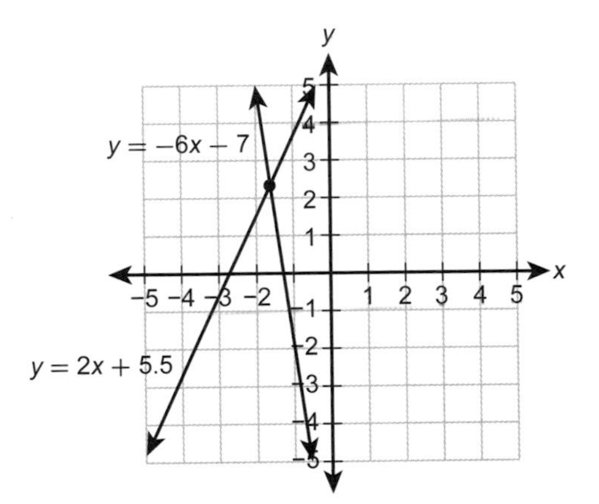

Q&A

Q In Example 1, what would be the coordinates if you were estimating to the nearest integer?

A $(-2, 2)$

SOLUTION

The x-coordinate is just greater than the halfway point between -1 and -2, so $x \approx -1.6$. The y-coordinate is just less than the halfway point between 2 and 3, so $y \approx 2.4$. An estimate of the solution is $(-1.6, 2.4)$.

CHECK

Substitute -1.6 for x and 2.4 for y in each equation

$$y = -6x - 7 \qquad\qquad y = 2x + 5.5$$
$$\mathbf{2.4} \stackrel{?}{=} -6 \cdot \mathbf{(-1.6)} - 7 \qquad \mathbf{2.4} \stackrel{?}{=} 2 \cdot \mathbf{(-1.6)} + 5.5$$
$$2.4 \approx 2.6 \checkmark \qquad\qquad 2.4 \approx 2.3 \checkmark$$

In both equations, the value on the left side is approximately equal to the value on the right side, so $(-1.6, 2.4)$ is a reasonable estimate of the solution. ■

EXAMPLE 2

Solve the system by graphing. Estimate the coordinates of the solution to the nearest integer.

$$y = -\frac{1}{3}x + 9$$
$$y = 3.5x$$

▶ **Remember** Because 3.5 is equivalent to $\frac{7}{2}$, the graph of $y = 3.5x$ has a rise of 7 and a run of 2.

SOLUTION

Graph each line, and locate the point of intersection.

The x-coordinate is nearest to 2 and the y-coordinate is nearest to 8. The estimate of the solution is $(2, 8)$.

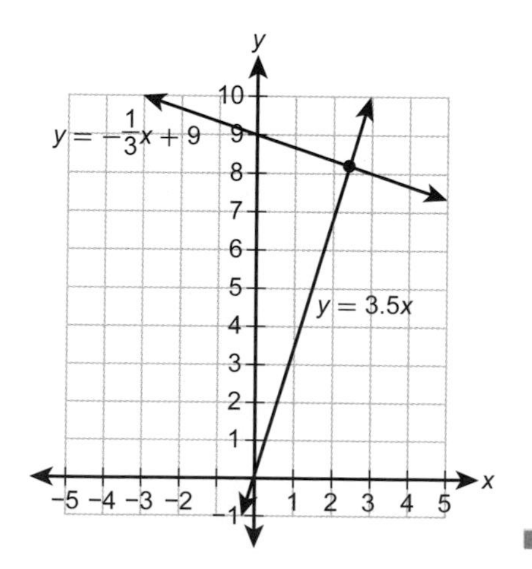

■

Using Technology to Solve a System

You can use a graphing tool to more accurately estimate a solution of a system of equations.

EXAMPLE 3

Use a graphing tool to solve the system. Round the coordinates of the solution to the nearest hundredth.

A $4x - 13y = -20$
$9x + 5y = 15$

SOLUTION

Enter both equations into a graphing tool. Use the tool's features to identify the coordinates of the intersection. Compare these screenshots from two graphing tools.

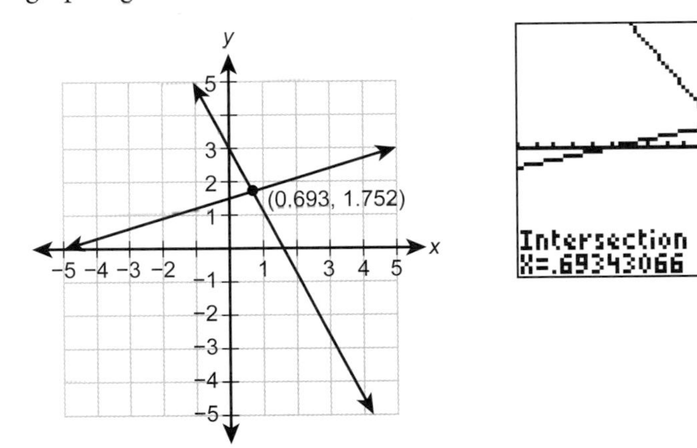

The estimate is $(0.69, 1.75)$.

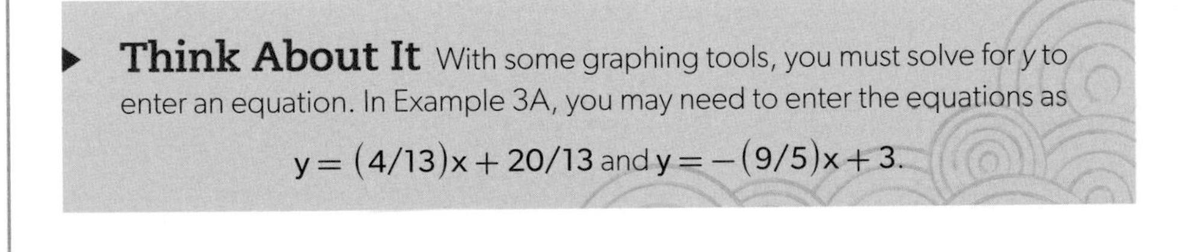

Think About It With some graphing tools, you must solve for y to enter an equation. In Example 3A, you may need to enter the equations as

$y = (4/13)x + 20/13$ and $y = -(9/5)x + 3$.

B $5x + 10y = 8$

$y = -\frac{1}{2}x + 6$

SOLUTION

Enter both equations into a graphing tool. The lines appear to be parallel.

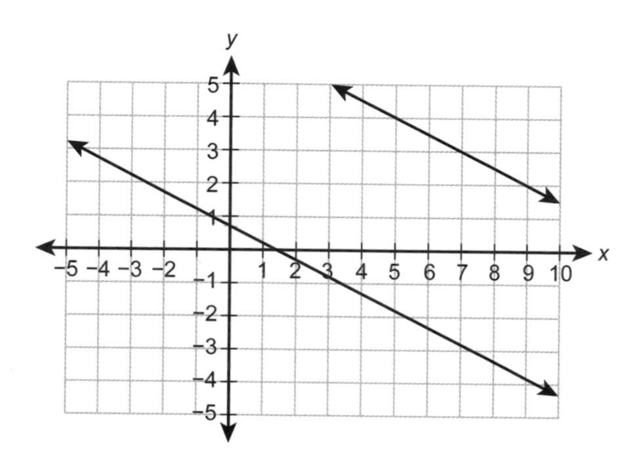

▶ **Remember** A system with no solutions is an inconsistent system.

Confirm that the lines are parallel by comparing their slopes. The first equation is in standard form, so $m = -\frac{A}{B} = -\frac{5}{10} = -\frac{1}{2}$. The second equation is in slope intercept form, so $m = -\frac{1}{2}$. The slopes are equal, so the lines will never intersect. The system has no solutions. ■

Systems of Functions

You can use graphs and tables to analyze the relationship between two functions.

Solving Systems of Functions by Graphing

A **linear function** is a function whose graph is a line. A **system of linear functions** is two or more linear functions with the same variables. The **solution** of a system of linear functions is the point or points, if they exist, where the graphs of the functions intersect.

EXAMPLE 1

Solve the system of linear functions by graphing.

$$\begin{cases} f(x) = x - 5 \\ g(x) = -x + 1 \end{cases}$$

▶ **Remember** In a function, the values of $f(x)$ depend on the values of x.

SOLUTION

Graph each line in the coordinate plane. The intersection of the two lines appears to be the point $(3, -2)$.

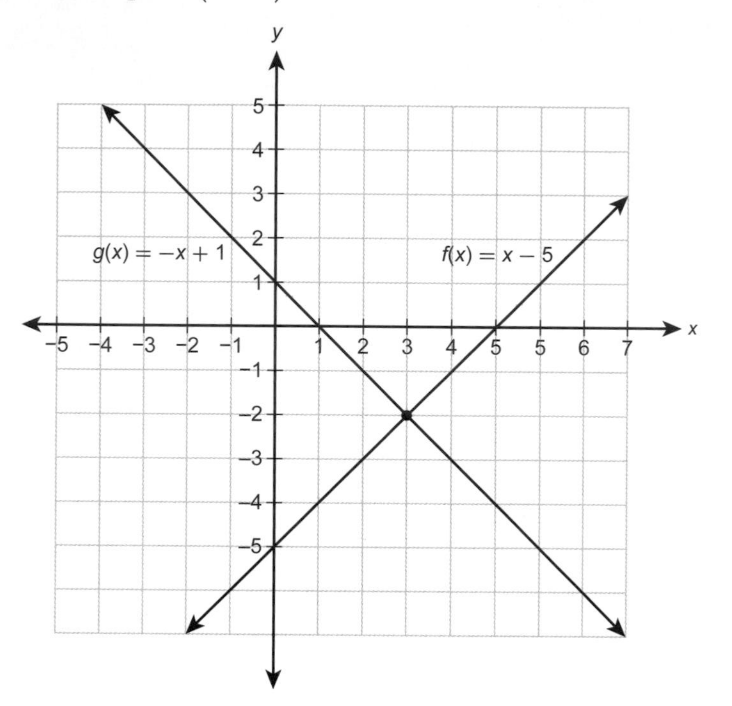

Check to determine whether $(3, -2)$ is a solution by substituting 3 for x, -2 for $f(x)$, and -2 for $g(x)$.

$$f(x) = x - 5 \qquad g(x) = -x + 1$$

$$\mathbf{-2 \stackrel{?}{=} 3 - 5} \qquad \mathbf{-2 \stackrel{?}{=} -3} + 1$$

$$-2 = -2\checkmark \qquad -2 = -2\checkmark$$

The point $(3, -2)$ is the solution of the system of functions. ■

Systems of linear functions are classified the same way systems of linear equations are classified. A system with exactly one solution is a consistent independent system. A system with infinitely many solutions is a consistent dependent, or coincident, system. Coincident linear systems contain functions whose graphs are the same line. When the lines of a system of linear functions are parallel, there is no solution to the system. A system of functions with no solutions is an inconsistent system.

Solving Systems of Functions Using Algebra

EXAMPLE 2

Solve the system of linear functions using algebra.

$$\begin{cases} f(x) = 2x - 11 \\ g(x) = -3x + 4 \end{cases}$$

SOLUTION

If you used graphing to solve the system, you would look for the point on the graph where $f(x) = g(x)$. To solve the system algebraically, set $f(x) = g(x)$ and then solve for x.

$f(x) = g(x)$	
$2x - 11 = -3x + 4$	
$5x - 11 = 4$	Add $3x$ to both sides.
$5x = 15$	Add 11 to both sides.
$x = 3$	Divide both sides by 5

Substitute $x = 3$ in either function and solve for $f(x)$ or $g(x)$.

$$\begin{aligned} f(\mathbf{3}) &= 2(\mathbf{3}) - 11 \\ &= 6 - 11 \\ &= -5 \end{aligned}$$

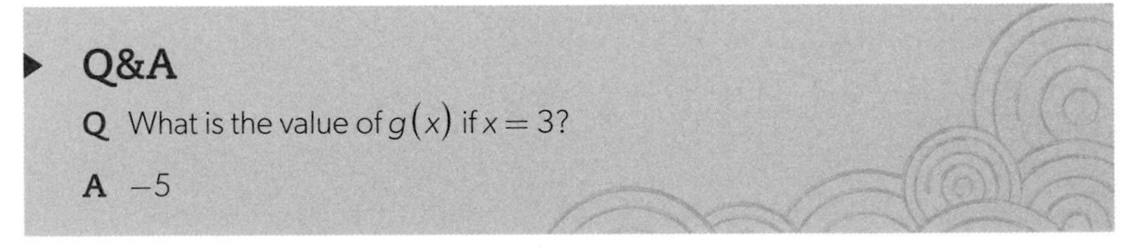

▶ Q&A

Q What is the value of $g(x)$ if $x = 3$?

A -5

So $(3, -5)$ is the solution of the system of functions. ■

Substitution Method

The substitution method is a way to solve a system of linear equations algebraically.

How to Use the Substitution Method for Solving a System of Equations

Step 1 Solve one of the equations for one of the variables.

Step 2 Substitute the expression obtained in Step 1 into the other equation. Solve the resulting equation.

Step 3 Substitute the value of the variable found in Step 2 into the equivalent equation from Step 1 and solve for the other variable.

▶ **Remember** Equivalent equations have the same solution. Use the properties of equality to write equivalent equations.

Using the Substitution Method to Solve a System of Equations

EXAMPLE 1

Solve the system.

$$4x + y = 14$$
$$x - 2y = 8$$

SOLUTION

Step 1 Solve the first equation for y. (You could also solve the second equation for x.)

$4x + y = 14$

$y = -4x + 14$ Subtract $4x$ from each side of the equation.

▶ **Think About It** Whenever possible, solve for a variable with a coefficient of 1 or −1.

Step 2 Substitute $-4x + 14$ for y in the second equation.

$x - 2y = 8$

$x - 2(\mathbf{-4x + 14}) = 8$ Substitute $-4x + 14$ for y.

$x + 8x - 28 = 8$ Distributive Property

$9x - 28 = 8$ Combine like terms.

$9x = 36$ Add 28 to each side.

$x = 4$ Divide each side by 9.

Step 3 Substitute 4 for x in the equivalent equation from Step 1.

$y = -4x + 14$

$y = -4 \cdot \mathbf{4} + 14$ Substitute 4 for x.

$y = -16 + 14$ Simplify.

$y = -2$

The solution to the system is $(4, -2)$.

CHECK

Substitute 4 for x and -2 for y into each original equation in the system.

$$\begin{aligned} 4x + y &= 14 \\ 4 \cdot \mathbf{4} + (\mathbf{-2}) &\stackrel{?}{=} 14 \\ 16 + (-2) &\stackrel{?}{=} 14 \\ 14 &= 14 \checkmark \end{aligned}$$

$$\begin{aligned} x - 2y &= 8 \\ \mathbf{4} - 2 \cdot (\mathbf{-2}) &\stackrel{?}{=} 8 \\ 4 + 4 &\stackrel{?}{=} 8 \\ 8 &= 8 \checkmark \end{aligned}$$

The solution $(4, -2)$ is correct. ■

Understanding What Happens when the Variables Disappear

You may sometimes eliminate a variable when using the substitution method, leaving either a statement that is always true (an identity) or a statement that is always false (a contradiction). If the statement is an identity, then the system is consistent and coincident. If the statement is a contradiction, then the system is inconsistent.

EXAMPLE 2

Solve the system.

A $-x + 5y = 3$
$-3x + 15y = 9$

SOLUTION

Step 1 Solve the first equation for x.

$-x + 5y = 3$

$-x = -5y + 3$ Subtract $5y$ from each side.

$x = 5y - 3$ Multiply each side by -1.

Step 2 Substitute $5y - 3$ for x in the second equation.

$-3x + 15y = 9$

$-3(\mathbf{5y - 3}) + 15y = 9$ Substitute $5y - 3$ for x.

$-15y + 9 + 15y = 9$ Distributive Property

$9 = 9$ Simplify.

Since the statement is an identity, the system is consistent and coincident. There are infinitely many solutions to the system. If you graph these lines, you will see that they have the same graph.

B $y = -5x + 10$
$5x + y = 3$

SOLUTION

Step 1 The first equation is already solved for y.

Step 2 Substitute $-5x + 10$ for y in the second equation.

$5x + y = 3$	
$5x + (\mathbf{-5x + 10}) = 3$	Substitute $-5x + 10$ for y.
$5x - 5x + 10 = 3$	Remove parentheses.
$10 \neq 3$	Simplify.

The final statement is a contradiction. The system is inconsistent, so there is no solution. Graph the equations to see that they are parallel and thus never intersect. ■

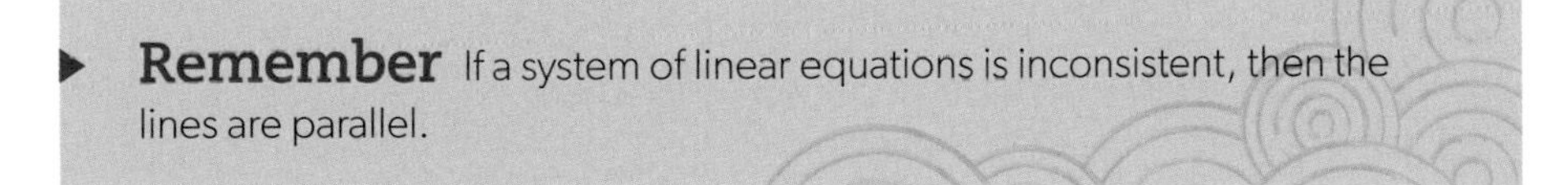

▶ **Remember** If a system of linear equations is inconsistent, then the lines are parallel.

Linear Combination

You can use the linear combination method to solve a system of linear equations algebraically.

How to Use the Linear Combination Method for Solving a System of Equations

Step 1 Add or subtract the equations to eliminate one of the variables.

Step 2 Solve the resulting equation for the remaining variable.

Step 3 Substitute the value of the variable found in Step 2 into either of the original equations to obtain the value of the other variable.

► **Think About It** The linear combination method is also called the elimination method.

Using the Linear Combination Method to Solve a System of Equations

EXAMPLE 1

Solve the system.

$$\begin{aligned} 2x + y &= 5 \\ -2x - 7y &= 13 \end{aligned}$$

SOLUTION

Step 1 Since the coefficients of the x terms, 2 and -2, are opposites, add the equations to eliminate x.

$$\begin{array}{r} 2x + y = 5 \\ +\ (-2x - 7y = 13) \\ \hline -6y = 18 \end{array}$$

Step 2 Solve the resulting equation for y.

$-6y = 18$

$y = -3$ Divide each side by -6.

Step 3 Substitute -3 for y in the first equation and solve for x. You could use either of the original equations for this step.

$2x + y = 5$

$2x + (-3) = 5$ Substitute -3 for y.

$2x = 8$ Add 3 to each side.

$x = 4$ Divide each side by 2.

The solution to the system is $(4, -3)$. ■

EXAMPLE 2

Solve the system.

$$\begin{aligned} 4x + 5y &= -5 \\ x + 5y &= 10 \end{aligned}$$

SOLUTION

Step 1 Since the coefficients of the y terms are equal, you can subtract the equations to eliminate y.

$$\begin{array}{r} 4x + 5y = \ \ -5 \\ -\ (\ \ x + 5y = \ \ \ 10) \\ \hline 3x \qquad = -15 \end{array}$$

Think About It When using subtraction, be sure to subtract every term in the second equation from the corresponding term in the first.

Step 2 Solve the resulting equation for x.

$3x = -15$

$x = -5$ Divide each side by 3.

Step 3 Substitute -5 for x in the second equation and solve for y. Remember that you can use either of the original equations for this step.

$x + 5y = 10$

$(-5) + 5y = 10$ Substitute -5 for x.

$5y = 15$ Add 5 to each side.

$y = 3$ Divide each side by 5.

The solution to the system is $(-5, 3)$. ■

Linear Combination with Multiplication

Sometimes you have to create equivalent equations before adding to eliminate a variable with linear combination.

How to Use the Linear Combination Method with Multiplication for Solving a System of Equations

Step 1 Multiply one or both of the equations by a constant so that one of the variables will be eliminated when the equations are added or subtracted.

Step 2 Add or subtract the equations to eliminate one of the variables.

Step 3 Solve the resulting equation for the remaining variable.

Step 4 Substitute the value for the variable found in Step 3 into either of the original equations to obtain the value of the other variable.

Using the Linear Combination Method with Multiplication to Solve a System of Equations

EXAMPLE 1

Solve the system.

$$\begin{aligned} 2x + 3y &= 2 \\ x + y &= 4 \end{aligned}$$

Remember You can multiply each side of an equation by the same nonzero number to create an equivalent equation.

SOLUTION

Step 1 Multiply the second equation by −2 on each side so that the coefficients of x will be opposites.

$$\begin{aligned} 2x + 3y &= 2 \\ -2(x + y &= 4) \end{aligned} \longrightarrow \begin{aligned} 2x + 3y &= 2 \\ -2(x + y) &= -2 \cdot 4 \end{aligned} \longrightarrow \begin{aligned} 2x + 3y &= 2 \\ -2x - 2y &= -8 \end{aligned}$$

Step 2 The x terms are opposites, so add the equations to eliminate x.

$$\begin{aligned} 2x + 3y &= 2 \\ +(-2x - 2y &= -8) \\ \hline y &= -6 \end{aligned}$$

Step 3 The equation is already solved for y.

Step 4 Substitute −6 for y in the original second equation and solve for x. Remember you could use either original equation for this step.

$$x + y = 4$$

$$x + (-6) = 4 \quad \text{Substitute } -6 \text{ for } y.$$

$$x = 10 \quad \text{Add 6 to each side.}$$

CHECK

Substitute 10 for x and −6 for y in each original equation in the system.

$$\begin{aligned} 2x + 3y &= 2 \\ 2 \cdot \mathbf{10} + 3 \cdot (\mathbf{-6}) &\stackrel{?}{=} 2 \\ 20 - 18 &\stackrel{?}{=} 2 \\ 2 &= 2 \checkmark \end{aligned} \qquad \begin{aligned} x + y &= 4 \\ \mathbf{10} - \mathbf{6} &\stackrel{?}{=} 4 \\ 4 &= 4 \checkmark \end{aligned}$$

The solution to the system is (10, −6). ■

Think About It When choosing a value to multiply by, pick a value that will allow you to add the equations. Adding equations is usually easier than subtracting.

EXAMPLE 2

Solve the system.

$$3x + 5y = 6$$
$$4x - 2y = 8$$

SOLUTION

Step 1 Multiply the first equation by 2 and the second equation by 5, which makes the y coefficients 10 and -10.

$$\begin{matrix} \mathbf{2}(3x + 5y = 6) \\ \mathbf{5}(4x - 2y = 8) \end{matrix} \longrightarrow \begin{matrix} \mathbf{2}(3x + 5y) = \mathbf{2} \bullet 6 \\ \mathbf{5}(4x - 2y) = \mathbf{5} \bullet 8 \end{matrix} \longrightarrow \begin{matrix} 6x + 10y = 12 \\ 20x - 10y = 40 \end{matrix}$$

Step 2 Add the equations to eliminate y.

$$\begin{array}{r} 6x + 10y = 12 \\ + \ (20x - 10y = 40) \\ \hline 26x \qquad = 52 \end{array}$$

Step 3 Solve the equation for x.

$$26x = 52$$
$$x = 2$$

Step 4 Substitute 2 for x in the original second equation and solve for y. Remember you could use either original equation for this step.

$4x - 2y = 8$	
$4 \bullet \mathbf{2} - 2y = 8$	Substitute 2 for x.
$8 - 2y = 8$	Simplify.
$-2y = 0$	Subtract 8 from each side.
$y = 0$	Divide each side by -2.

The solution to the system is $(2, 0)$. ■

Justifying Linear Combination

The properties of equality allow you to add or subtract two equations.

Combining Two Equations

The first step in solving a system of linear equations by the linear combination method is adding or subtracting the equations. The purpose is to eliminate one of the variables. But have you thought about why you are allowed to combine the equations through addition or subtraction?

Consider this system.

$$\begin{aligned} 2x + y &= 11 \\ x - y &= 1 \end{aligned}$$

The addition property of equality lets you add the same number to each side of an equation. Therefore, you can add 1 to each side of the first equation in the system to make a new equation.

$$2x + y \mathbf{+ 1} = 11 \mathbf{+ 1}$$

The second equation in the system tells you that $x - y$ and 1 are equivalent. By the substitution property of equality, you can substitute any occurrence of $x - y$ with 1 and any occurrence of 1 with $x - y$. Replace the 1 on the left side of the new equation with $x - y$.

$$2x + y + \mathbf{(x - y)} = 11 + 1$$

This new equation is the sum of the equations. Simplifying both sides of the equation gives $3x = 12$. You are used to seeing this addition performed vertically.

$$\begin{array}{r} 2x + y = 11 \\ +\ \ x - y = \ \ 1 \\ \hline 3x \qquad = 12 \end{array}$$

From here, solve to find that $x = 4$ and $y = 3$. The ordered pair $(4, 3)$ makes each equation in the system true. It also makes the sum of the equations true.

First equation	Second equation	Sum of equations
$2x + y = 11$	$x - y = 1$	$2x + y + (\mathbf{x - y}) = 11 + \mathbf{1}$
$2 \cdot \mathbf{4} + \mathbf{3} = 11$	$\mathbf{4} - \mathbf{3} = 1$	$2 \cdot \mathbf{4} + \mathbf{3} + \mathbf{4} - \mathbf{3} = 11 + 1$
$11 = 11$ ✓	$1 = 1$ ✓	$12 = 12$ ✓

Because $(4, 3)$ satisfies these equations, it follows that the graphs of these equations will all pass through the point $(4, 3)$.

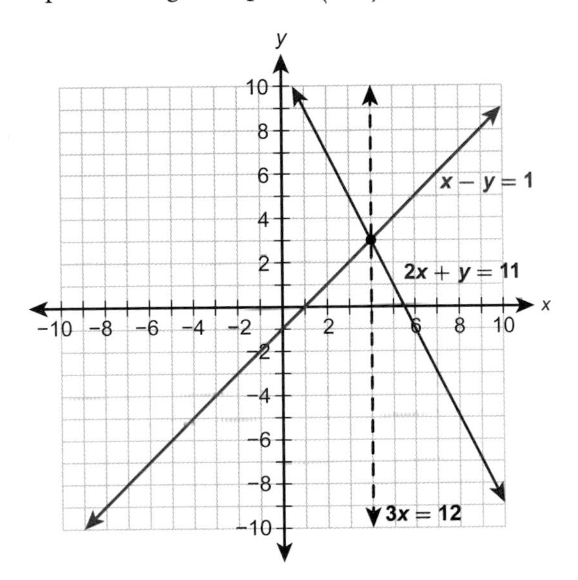

▸ **Think About It** The equation $3x = 12$ is equivalent to $x = 4$.

Applications: Systems of Linear Equations

Systems of linear equations can model many real-world situations.

Food Service

EXAMPLE 1

At a concession stand at a fair, a small cup of lemonade costs \$1.50 and a large cup costs \$2. The concession stand workers collected a total of \$6600 from the sale of lemonade. They sold twice as many large cups as small cups. How many cups of each size were sold?

SOLUTION

Step 1 Write a system of equations to model the problem.

Equation 1: Let s be the number of small cups of lemonade sold and l be the number of large cups of lemonade sold. You are told that twice as many large cups were sold.

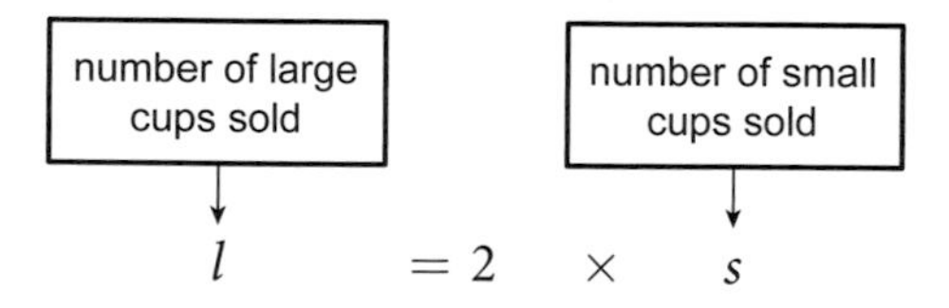

Equation 2: Total sales were \$6600 and you know the price of each type of cup, so you can write an equation to represent the total sales.

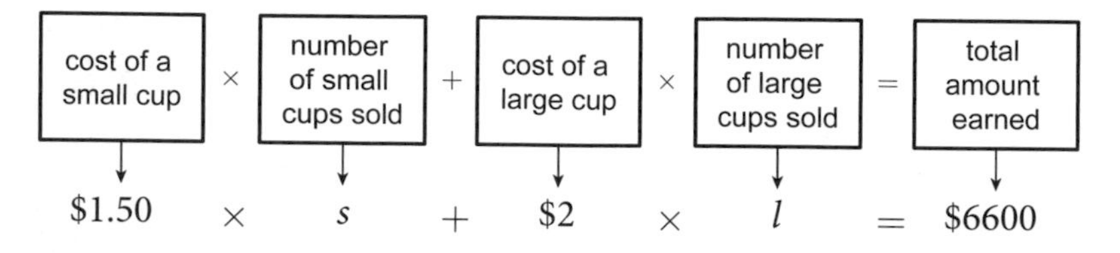

The system of equations is $\begin{matrix} l = 2s \\ 1.5s + 2l = 6600 \end{matrix}$.

Step 2 Solve the system of equations. Since the first equation is already solved for l, use the substitution method.

Substitute $2s$ for l in the second equation and solve for s.

$1.5s + 2l = 6600$	
$1.5s + 2 \cdot \mathbf{2s} = 6600$	Substitute $2s$ for l.
$1.5s + 4s = 6600$	Simplify.
$5.5s = 6600$	Combine like terms.
$s = 1200$	Divide each side by 5.5.

Of the total sales, 1200 small cups of lemonade were sold.

Substitute 1200 for s in the first equation and solve for l.

$l = 2s$	
$l = 2 \cdot \mathbf{1200}$	Substitute 1200 for s.
$l = 2400$	Multiply.

Of the total sales, 2400 large cups of lemonade were sold.

Step 3 Check. Substitute 1200 for s and 2400 for l in each equation in the system.

$$\begin{aligned} l &= 2s \\ \mathbf{2400} &\stackrel{?}{=} 2 \cdot \mathbf{1200} \\ 2400 &= 2400 \checkmark \end{aligned} \qquad \begin{aligned} 1.5s + 2l &= 6600 \\ 1.5 \cdot \mathbf{1200} + 2 \cdot \mathbf{2400} &\stackrel{?}{=} 6600 \\ 1800 + 4800 &\stackrel{?}{=} 6600 \\ 6600 &= 6600 \checkmark \end{aligned}$$

The solution is correct. ■

Cellular Phone Service

EXAMPLE 2

A cellular service plan for Company A has unlimited minutes for \$40/month and a text message rate of \$0.10/message. A cellular service plan for Company B has unlimited minutes for \$30/month and a text message rate of \$0.10/message. When is it cheaper to use Company B's plan?

SOLUTION

Step 1 Write a system of equations to model the problem. Let t be the number of text messages per month and let c be the total monthly cost.

Equation 1: This equation models the total cost per month for Company A.

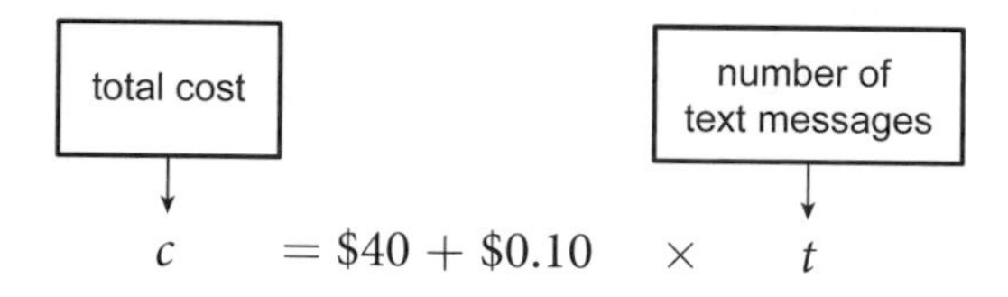

Equation 2: This equation models the total cost per month for Company B.

total cost

number of text messages

$$c = \$30 + \$0.10 \times t$$

The system of equations is $\begin{matrix} c = 40 + 0.10t \\ c = 30 + 0.10t \end{matrix}$ or $\begin{matrix} -0.10t + c = 40 \\ -0.10t + c = 30 \end{matrix}$.

Step 2 Solve the system of equations. Use the linear combination method and subtract the equations.

$$\begin{array}{r} -0.10t + c = 40 \\ -(-0.10t + c = 30) \\ \hline 0 \neq 10 \end{array}$$

Since the equation $0 \neq 10$ is false, the lines are parallel and there is no solution to the system. The cost is never the same for both services and it is always cheaper to use Company B's plan. ■

Mixture

EXAMPLE 3

Juan wants to make a juice drink that contains 80% orange juice and 20% grapefruit juice. How many cups of pure orange juice (100% orange juice) should be combined with a mix of 60% orange juice and 40% grapefruit juice to make 3 cups of the 80% orange juice-20% grapefruit juice mixture?

SOLUTION

Step 1 Write a system of equations to model the problem. The two unknowns in the problem are the number of cups of pure orange juice and the number of cups of the 60% orange juice-40% grapefruit juice mix. Let p represent the number of cups of pure orange juice and m represent the number of cups of the 60% orange juice-40% grapefruit juice mix.

Equation 1: This equation represents the total number of cups of Juan's juice mixture.

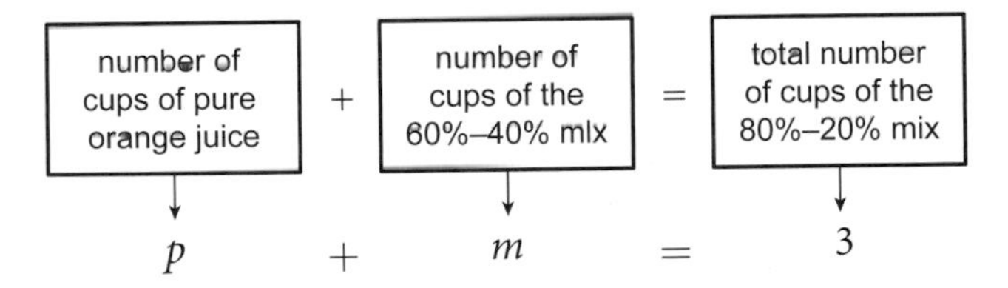

Equation 2: This equation represents the amount of orange juice in each juice.

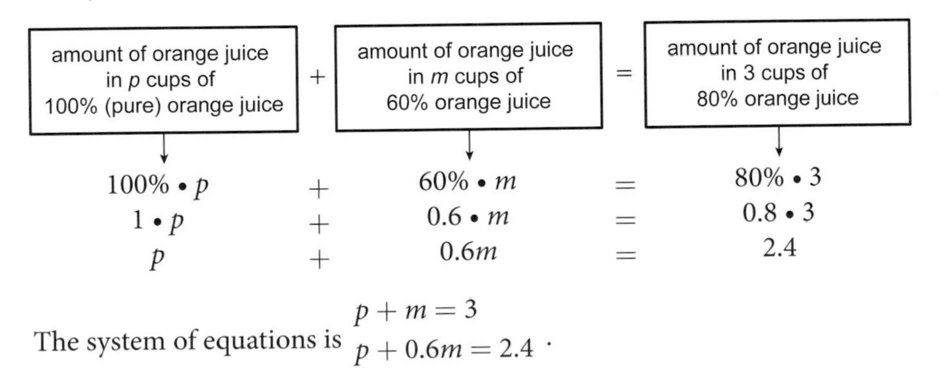

The system of equations is $\begin{array}{l} p+m=3 \\ p+0.6m=2.4 \end{array}$.

Step 2 Solve the system of equations.

Solve the first equation for p.

$$\begin{aligned} p + m &= 3 \\ p &= 3 - m \end{aligned}$$

Substitute $3 - m$ into the second equation for p.

$$\begin{aligned} p + 0.6m &= 2.4 \\ \mathbf{3 - m} + 0.6m &= 2.4 \\ -0.4m &= -0.6 \\ m &= 1.5 \end{aligned}$$

Substitute 1.5 for m into the equation.

$$\begin{aligned} p &= 3 - m \\ p &= 3 - \mathbf{1.5} \\ p &= 1.5 \end{aligned}$$

Combine 1.5 cups of pure orange juice and 1.5 cups of 60% orange juice-40% grapefruit juice mix to make 3 cups of the 80% orange juice-20% grapefruit juice mix.

Step 3 Check. Substitute 1.5 for p and 1.5 for m in each equation in the system.

$$\begin{aligned} p + m &= 3 \\ \mathbf{1.5} + \mathbf{1.5} &\stackrel{?}{=} 3 \\ 3 &= 3 \checkmark \end{aligned}$$

$$\begin{aligned} p + 0.6m &= 2.4 \\ \mathbf{1.5} + 0.6 \bullet \mathbf{1.5} &\stackrel{?}{=} 2.4 \\ 1.5 + 0.9 &\stackrel{?}{=} 2.4 \\ 2.4 &= 2.4 \checkmark \end{aligned}$$

The solution is correct. ■

Polynomials

Topic List

- Overview of Polynomials
- Adding and Subtracting Polynomials
- Multiplying Monomials
- Multiplying Polynomials by Monomials
- Multiplying Polynomials
- The FOIL Method
- Polynomials and Arithmetic
- Common Factors of Polynomials
- Factoring Perfect Squares
- Factoring Differences of Squares
- Factoring Quadratic Trinomials
- Finding Roots of a Polynomial

Square and rectangular tiles can help you visualize polynomials. Although the tiles may look like something that could have been designed by the Dutch painter Piet Mondrian, they can help you see how to add, subtract, and multiply polynomials.

Overview of Polynomials

Some expressions are monomials or polynomials.

Classifying Monomials

Definition

A **monomial** is a number, a variable, or the product of a number and one or more variables.

The exponents of the variables of monomials must be whole numbers. The **degree of a monomial** is the sum of the exponents of its variables. Some monomials, called constants, have no variable parts. The degree of a constant term c is equal to zero since c can be written as cx^0.

▶ **Remember** A value raised to the 0 power is equal to 1.

EXAMPLE 1

Determine whether each expression is a monomial. If it is not, explain why. If it is a monomial, determine its degree.

$$-25,\ 5x^{\frac{1}{2}},\ 3x,\ \frac{3}{y^2},\ 3x^2,\ -mn^2p^3$$

Remember A term is part of an expression that is added or subtracted. A term can be a number, a variable, or a combination of numbers and variables.

SOLUTION

Expression	Is it a monomial?	Degree
-25	Yes	0
$5x^{\frac{1}{2}}$	No, the exponent $\frac{1}{2}$ is not a whole number.	—
$3x$	Yes	1
$\frac{3}{y^2}$	No, the espression can be rewritten as $3y^{-2}$, and -2 is not a whole number.	—
$3x^2$	Yes	2
$-mn^2p^3$	Yes	6

■

Classifying Polynomials by the Number of Terms

Definition

A **polynomial** is a monomial or the sum or difference of two or more monomials.

Each monomial is a term of the polynomial. A polynomial with two terms is a **binomial**. A polynomial with three terms is a **trinomial**. The **degree of a polynomial** is equal to the degree of the monomial with the greatest degree.

EXAMPLE 2

Determine whether each expression is a polynomial. If it is not, explain why. If it is a polynomial, determine its degree.

$$7x, -9x^3yz + 3x^3 + \frac{1}{2}, 2x - x^{-2}, \frac{2}{a} + 3a^2 + a, 4$$

SOLUTION

Expression	Is it a polynomial?	Degree
$7x$	Yes	1
$-9x^3yz + 3x^3 + \frac{1}{2}$	Yes	5
$2x - x^{-2}$	No, the term $-x^{-2}$ has an exponent that is not a whole number.	—
$\frac{2}{a} + 3a^2 + a$	No, the term $\frac{2}{a}$ is not a monomial since it has a variable in the denominator.	—
4	Yes	0

■

Writing a Polynomial in Standard Form

A polynomial is in **standard form** when every term is simplified and its terms are listed by decreasing degree.

EXAMPLE 3

Write $21y - 3y^2 + 4 + y^3$ in standard form.

SOLUTION

Determine the degree of each term, and then list the terms by decreasing degree.

$21y$	$-3y^2$	$+4$	$+y^3$
degree 1	degree 2	degree 0	degree 3

The polynomial written in standard form is $y^3 - 3y^2 + 21y + 4$. ■

Classifying Polynomials

You can classify a polynomial by the number of terms it has or by its degree. Polynomials of certain degrees have special names.

Name	Degree	Example (in simplified form)
constant	0	10
linear	1	$3x - 2$
quadratic	2	$x^2 + 4x + 4$
cubic	3	$-2x^3 + x^2 + 5$
quartic	4	$5x^4 + 7x$
quintic	5	$-8x^5 + 6x^4 + 2x^3 + 8x^2 + 3x - 11$

A polynomial of nth degree can be written in the form

$$a_n x^n + a_{n-1} x^{n-1} + \ldots + a_1 x + a_0$$

where a_n denotes the coefficient of the term with a power of n, a_{n-1} denotes the coefficient of the next term of the polynomial with a power of $n - 1$, and so on. For example, the polynomial $6x^5 + 3x^4 - 2x^3 + 6x^2 + 3$ has the following coefficients:

a_n	a_{n-1}	a_{n-2}	a_{n-3}	a_{n-4}	a_{n-5}
a_5	a_4	a_3	a_2	a_1	a_0
6	3	−2	6	0	3

Notice that the coefficient of a term may be the same as another term or may equal zero.

EXAMPLE 4

A Classify the polynomial $3c + 1$ by its degree and number of terms.

SOLUTION

The polynomial $3c + 1$ has two terms, and the greatest degree of its terms is 1. It is a linear binomial.

B Classify the polynomial $8b^3 + 2b^2 - 5b + 6$ by its degree.

SOLUTION

The degree of the term with the greatest degree is 3, so the polynomial is cubic. ■

Application: Geometry

EXAMPLE 5

The height of a ball (in feet) t seconds after being thrown into the air can be modeled by the polynomial $-16t^2 + v_0t + h_0$. Classify the polynomial in the variable t by its number of terms and by its degree.

SOLUTION

The polynomial $-16t^2 + v_0t + h_0$ has three terms, so it is a trinomial. The degree of the term with the greatest degree is 2, so the polynomial is a quadratic trinomial. ■

Adding and Subtracting Polynomials

You can add and subtract polynomials with like terms.

Adding Polynomials

Combine like terms to add polynomials.

▶ **Remember** Like terms have the same variables raised to the same powers.

EXAMPLE 1

Add.

A $\left(2a^2 + a + 1\right) + (3a - 6)$

SOLUTION

You can add polynomials vertically or horizontally.

Vertically Align like terms in the same column and add the coefficients of the variables.

$$\begin{array}{r} 2a^2 + a + 1 \\ + 3a - 6 \\ \hline 2a^2 + 4a - 5 \end{array}$$

▶ **Remember** To combine like terms, add or subtract the coefficients and keep the variable part the same.

Horizontally Use the commutative and associative properties to rewrite the sum with like terms grouped together. Then simplify by combining like terms.

$(2a^2 + a + 1) + (3a - 6) = 2a^2 + a + 1 + 3a - 6$	Associative Property
$= 2a^2 + (a + 3a) + (1 - 6)$	Commutative and Associative Properties of Addition
$= 2a^2 + 4a + (-5)$	Combine like terms.
$= 2a^2 + 4a - 5$	Simplify.

B $(4x^4 + 2x^3 - x^2 + 7) + (10x^4 + 8x^2 - 3)$

SOLUTION

Combine the like terms.

$$\begin{aligned}(4x^4 + 2x^3 - x^2 + 7) + (10x^4 + 8x^2 - 3) &= 4x^4 + 2x^3 - x^2 + 7 + 10x^4 + 8x^2 - 3\\ &= (4x^4 + 10x^4) + 2x^3 + (-x^2 + 8x^2) + (7 - 3)\\ &= 14x^4 + 2x^3 + 7x^2 + 4 \blacksquare\end{aligned}$$

Subtracting Polynomials

Subtraction and addition are inverse operations. To subtract polynomials, you can rewrite the problem as an addition problem. You could also use the distributive property to subtract polynomials.

EXAMPLE 2

Subtract.

A $(5x + 6) - (x + 2)$

SOLUTION

You can subtract polynomials vertically or horizontally.

Vertically Align like terms in the same column, and rewrite the problem as an addition problem.

Subtraction		**Addition**
$\begin{array}{r} 5x+6 \\ -(x+2) \\ \hline \end{array}$	$\longrightarrow$	$\begin{array}{r} 5x+6 \\ +(-x-2) \\ \hline 4x+4 \end{array}$

Horizontally Use the distributive property to remove the parentheses. Then group like terms together and simplify by combining like terms.

$(5x+6)-(x+2)=5x+6-x-2$	Distributive Property
$=(5x-x)+(6-2)$	Commutative and Associative Properties of Addition
$=4x+4$	Combine like terms.

▶ **Think About It** Remember to distribute −1 to each term when changing a subtraction problem to an addition problem.

B $\left(12a^2+3ab-4b^2\right)-\left(8a^2-ab-5b^2\right)$

SOLUTION

$$\begin{aligned}\left(12a^2+3ab-4b^2\right)-\left(8a^2-ab-5b^2\right)&=12a^2+3ab-4b^2-8a^2+ab+5b^2\\&=\left(12a^2-8a^2\right)+(3ab+ab)+\left(-4b^2+5b^2\right)\\&=4a^2+4ab+b^2\end{aligned}$$ ■

Application: Geometry

EXAMPLE 3

Use the triangle to solve.

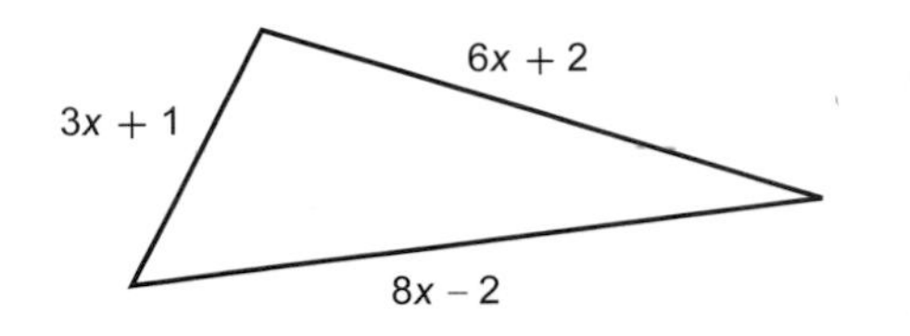

A Express the perimeter of the triangle as a polynomial.

SOLUTION

The perimeter of a triangle is the sum of the lengths of its sides.

$P = (3x + 1) + (6x + 2) + (8x - 2)$	Write the perimeter as the sum of the side lengths.
$= 3x + 1 + 6x + 2 + 8x - 2$	Associative Property
$= (3x + 6x + 8x) + (1 + 2 - 2)$	Commutative and Associative Properties of Addition
$= 17x + 1$	Combine like terms.

The perimeter of the triangle is $17x + 1$ units.

B Find the perimeter of the triangle when $x = 1$, 2, and 3.4.

SOLUTION

Substitute each value of x into the polynomial $17x + 1$.

$x = 1$

$$\begin{aligned} 17x + 1 &= 17 \bullet \mathbf{1} + 1 \\ &= 17 + 1 \\ &= 18 \end{aligned}$$

When $x = 1$, the perimeter of the triangle is 18 units.

$x = 2$

$$\begin{aligned} 17x + 1 &= 17 \bullet \mathbf{2} + 1 \\ &= 34 + 1 \\ &= 35 \end{aligned}$$

When $x = 2$, the perimeter of the triangle is 35 units.

$x = 3.4$

$$\begin{aligned} 17x + 1 &= 17 \bullet \mathbf{3.4} + 1 \\ &= 57.8 + 1 \\ &= 58.8 \end{aligned}$$

When $x = 3.4$, the perimeter of the triangle is 58.8 units. ■

Multiplying Monomials

Every monomial has a coefficient and most have factors that are powers of variables. Multiplying two monomials means multiplying the coefficients and multiplying the variable powers.

When you multiply two powers with the same base, you can use the product of powers property to simplify the product.

Product of Powers Property

If a is a real number and m and n are integers, then

$$a^m \bullet a^n = a^{m+n}.$$

Simplifying the Product of Powers

EXAMPLE 1

Use the product of powers property to simplify the product.

A $4^2 \bullet 4^5$

SOLUTION

$4^2 \bullet 4^5 = 4^{2+5}$ Product of Powers Property

$= 4^7$ Simplify.

CHECK

$$4^2 \cdot 4^5 \stackrel{?}{=} 4^7$$
$$16 \cdot 1024 \stackrel{?}{=} 16{,}384$$
$$16{,}384 = 16{,}384 \checkmark$$

The solution is correct.

B $x^3 \cdot x \cdot x^4$

SOLUTION

$x^3 \cdot x \cdot x^4 = \left(x^3 \cdot x^1\right) \cdot x^4$ Associative Property of Multiplication

$= x^{3+1} \cdot x^4$ Product of Powers Property

$= x^4 \cdot x^4$ Simplify.

$= x^{4+4}$ Product of Powers Property

$= x^8$ Simplify. ■

Multiplying Monomials

To multiply two monomials, use the commutative and associative properties of multiplication to get the constant factors together and each variable power together. Once you have all the like variables together, use the product of powers property to simplify.

EXAMPLE 2

Find the product.

A $3x^3 \cdot 2x^5$

SOLUTION

$3x^3 \cdot 2x^5 = (3 \cdot 2)\left(x^3x^5\right)$ Commutative and Associative Properties of Multiplication

$= 6\left(x^3x^5\right)$ Multiply.

$= 6x^{3+5}$ Product of Powers Property

$= 6x^8$ Simplify.

B $-5ab^4 \bullet ab$

SOLUTION

$-5ab^4 \bullet ab = -5\left(a^1a^1\right)\left(b^4b^1\right)$	Commutative and Associative Properties of Multiplication
$= -5a^{1+1}b^{4+1}$	Product of Powers Property
$= -5a^2b^5$	Simplify.

C $\frac{1}{2}x^3y^2z \bullet 2x^5y$

SOLUTION

$\frac{1}{2}x^3y^2z \bullet 2x^5y = \left(\frac{1}{2} \bullet 2\right)\left(x^3x^5\right)\left(y^2y^1\right)z$	Commutative and Associative Properties of Multiplication
$= 1x^{3+5}y^{2+1}z$	Product of Powers Property
$= x^8y^3z$	Simplify. ■

Application: Geometry

EXAMPLE 3

Use the figure to solve.

A Express the area of the rectangle as a monomial.

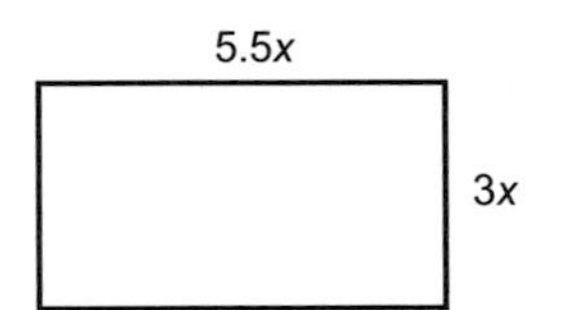

SOLUTION

The area of a rectangle is the product of its length and width.

$A = lw$

$= \mathbf{5.5x \bullet 3x}$	Substitute 5.5x for l and 3x for w.
$= (5.5 \bullet 3)\left(x^1x^1\right)$	Commutative and Associative Properties of Multiplication
$= 16.5\left(x^1x^1\right)$	Multiply.
$= 16.5\,x^{1+1}$	Product of Powers Property
$= 16.5x^2$	Simplify.

The area of the rectangle is $16.5x^2$ units^2.

B Find the area when x is 3 in., 5 km, and 7.9 cm.

SOLUTION

Substitute the given values for x into the monomial $16.5x^2$.

$x = 3$ in.

$$\begin{aligned} 16.5x^2 &= 16.5 \bullet (\mathbf{3\ in.})^2 \\ &= 16.5 \bullet 9\ \text{in}^2 \\ &= 148.5\ \text{in}^2 \end{aligned}$$

When x is 3 in., the area of the rectangle is $148.5\ \text{in}^2$.

$x = 5$ km

$$\begin{aligned} 16.5x^2 &= 16.5 \bullet (\mathbf{5\ km})^2 \\ &= 16.5 \bullet 25\ \text{km}^2 \\ &= 412.5\ \text{km}^2 \end{aligned}$$

When x is 5 km, the area of the rectangle is is $412.5\ \text{km}^2$.

$x = 7.9$ cm

$$\begin{aligned} 16.5x^2 &= 16.5 \bullet (\mathbf{7.9\ cm})^2 \\ &= 16.5 \bullet 62.41\ \text{cm}^2 \\ &= 1029.765\ \text{cm}^2 \end{aligned}$$

When x is 7.9 cm, the area of the rectangle is $1029.765\ \text{cm}^2$. ■

Multiplying Polynomials by Monomials

Use the distributive property to multiply a polynomial by a monomial.

You have used the distributive property to multiply a binomial by a monomial: $a(b + c) = ab + ac$. The distributive property is true for any number of terms inside the parentheses: $a(b + c + d) = ab + ac + ad$. You can also use the distributive property when the order of the factors is reversed: $(b + c)a = ba + ca$.

Multiplying a Polynomial by a Monomial

How to Multiply a Polynomial by a Monomial

Step 1 Use the distributive property to multiply the monomial by each term of the polynomial.

Step 2 Multiply each set of monomials. Use the product of powers property when necessary.

Remember The product of powers property states $a^m \cdot a^n = a^{m+n}$.

EXAMPLE 1

Find the product.

A $4x(x + 3)$

SOLUTION

$4x(x + 3) = 4x \cdot x + 4x \cdot 3$ — Distributive Property

$= 4x^2 + 12x$ — Multiply. Use the product of powers property for the first term.

B $7y(3y^3 - 4y^2 - y)$

SOLUTION

$7y(3y^3 - 4y^2 - y) = 7y \cdot 3y^3 + 7y \cdot (-4y^2) + 7y \cdot (-y)$ — Distributive Property

$= 21y^4 - 28y^3 - 7y^2$ — Multiply. Use the product of powers property.

C $(21ab^3 + 5ab^2 - 3ab - 7)a^2b$

SOLUTION

$(21ab^3 + 5ab^2 - 3ab - 7)a^2b$

$= 21ab^3 \cdot a^2b + 5ab^2 \cdot a^2b - 3ab \cdot a^2b - 7 \cdot a^2b$ — Distributive Property

$= 21a^1a^2b^3b^1 + 5a^1a^2b^2b^1 - 3a^1a^2b^1b^1 - 7a^2b^1$ — Commutative Property of Multiplication

$= 21a^3b^4 + 5a^3b^3 - 3a^3b^2 - 7a^2b$ — Product of Powers Property ■

Application: Area

EXAMPLE 2

Write a polynomial that represents the area of the shaded region.

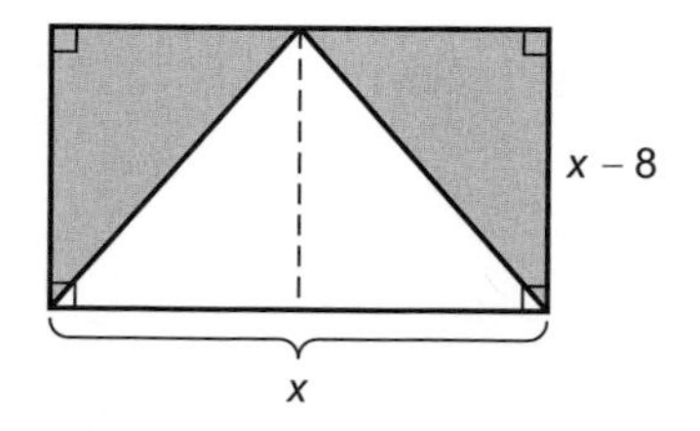

SOLUTION

Find the area of the shaded region by subtracting the area of the white triangle from the area of the rectangle.

Step 1 Find the area of the white triangle.

$A = \frac{1}{2}bh$

$= \frac{1}{2}x(x - 8)$	The base of the triangle is x and the height is $x - 8$.
$= \frac{1}{2}x \bullet x - \frac{1}{2}x \bullet 8$	Distributive Property
$= \frac{1}{2}x^2 - 4x$	Simplify.

The area of the triangle is $\frac{1}{2}x^2 - 4x$ units^2.

Step 2 Find the area of the rectangle.

$A = lw$

$= x(x - 8)$	The length of the rectangle is x and the width is $x - 8$.
$= x \bullet x - x \bullet 8$	Distributive Property
$= x^2 - 8x$	Simplify.

The area of the rectangle is $x^2 - 8x$ units^2.

Step 3 Find the area of the shaded region.

area of the shaded region = area of rectangle − area of white triangle

$= \left(x^2 - 8x\right) - \left(\frac{1}{2}x^2 - 4x\right)$	
$= x^2 - 8x - \frac{1}{2}x^2 + 4x$	Distributive Property
$= x^2 - \frac{1}{2}x^2 - 8x + 4x$	Commutative Property of Addition
$= \frac{1}{2}x^2 - 4x$	Simplify.

The area of the shaded region is $\frac{1}{2}x^2 - 4x$ units^2. ■

Multiplying Polynomials

Using the distributive property to multiply polynomials is similar to multiplying a polynomial by a monomial.

How to Use the Distributive Property to Multiply Two Polynomials

Step 1 Use the distributive property to multiply each term of the first polynomial by the second polynomial.

Step 2 Use the distributive property to multiply the monomials by each term of the polynomial.

Step 3 Multiply each set of monomials.

Step 4 If necessary, combine like terms to simplify.

Multiplying a Binomial by a Binomial

EXAMPLE 1

Multiply $(3x + 2)(x - 5)$.

▶ **Remember** A binomial is a polynomial with two terms.

SOLUTION

Use the distributive property. Think of $(x - 5)$ as a single value.
Multiply $3x$ by $(x - 5)$ and 2 by $(x - 5)$.

$(3x + 2)(\boldsymbol{x - 5}) = 3x(\boldsymbol{x - 5}) + 2(\boldsymbol{x - 5})$	Distributive Property
$= 3x \cdot x + 3x \cdot (-5) + 2 \cdot x + 2 \cdot (-5)$	Distributive Property
$= 3x^2 - 15x + 2x - 10$	Multiply the monomials.
$= 3x^2 - 13x - 10$	Combine like terms. ■

Squaring a Binomial

When you multiply two binomials and both factors are equivalent, you are squaring the binomial. In the diagram, each side of the square has a side length of $a + b$. Use the diagram to see that $(a + b)^2 = a^2 + 2ab + b^2$.

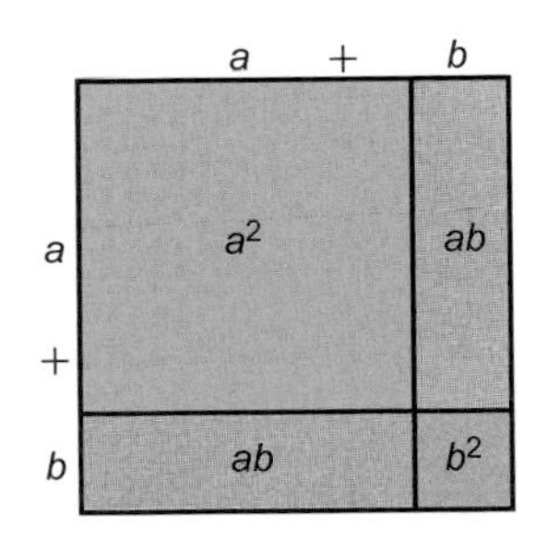

Square of a Binomial

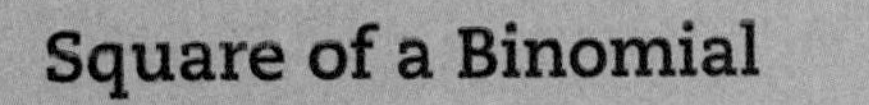

$$(a + b)^2 = a^2 + 2ab + b^2$$

EXAMPLE 2

Expand $(2x + 1)^2$.

SOLUTION

Use the pattern $(a + b)^2 = a^2 + 2ab + b^2$ to square the binomial.

$(a + b)^2 = a^2 + 2ab + b^2$

$(\mathbf{2x} + \mathbf{1})^2 = (\mathbf{2x})^2 + 2 \bullet \mathbf{2x} \bullet \mathbf{1} + \mathbf{1}^2$ Substitute $2x$ for a and 1 for b.

$= 2x \bullet 2x + 4x + 1$ Multiply the monomials.

$= 4x^2 + 4x + 1$ Multiply. ■

Multiplying a Polynomial by a Polynomial

EXAMPLE 3

Find the product.

A $(a - 4)(2a^2 + 3a - 7)$

SOLUTION

$(a - 4)(\mathbf{2a^2 + 3a - 7}) = a(\mathbf{2a^2 + 3a - 7}) - 4(\mathbf{2a^2 + 3a - 7})$ Distributive Property

$= a \bullet 2a^2 + a \bullet 3a + a \bullet (-7) - 4 \bullet 2a^2 - 4 \bullet 3a - 4 \bullet (-7)$ Distributive Property

$= 2a^3 + 3a^2 - 7a - 8a^2 - 12a + 28$ Multiply the monomials.

$= 2a^3 - 5a^2 - 19a + 28$ Combine like terms.

B $\left(x^2 + 6x + 9\right)\left(2x^2 - x - 1\right)$

SOLUTION

$$\begin{aligned}
\left(x^2 + 6x + 9\right)\left(\mathbf{2x^2 - x - 1}\right) &= x^2\left(\mathbf{2x^2 - x - 1}\right) + 6x\left(\mathbf{2x^2 - x - 1}\right) && \text{Distributive Property} \\
&\quad + 9\left(\mathbf{2x^2 - x - 1}\right) \\
&= x^2 \cdot 2x^2 + x^2 \cdot (-x) + x^2 \cdot (-1) && \text{Distributive Property} \\
&\quad + 6x \cdot 2x^2 + 6x \cdot (-x) + 6x \cdot (-1) \\
&\quad + 9 \cdot 2x^2 + 9 \cdot (-x) + 9 \cdot (-1) \\
&= 2x^4 - x^3 - x^2 + 12x^3 - 6x^2 - 6x && \text{Multiply the monomials.} \\
&\quad + 18x^2 - 9x - 9 \\
&= 2x^4 + 11x^3 + 11x^2 - 15x - 9 && \text{Combine like terms.}
\end{aligned}$$

C $(x + 1)(x - 1)(5x + 2)$

SOLUTION

First multiply $(x + 1)(x - 1)$. Then multiply the product by $(5x + 2)$.

Step 1

$$\begin{aligned}
(x + 1)(\mathbf{x - 1}) &= x(\mathbf{x - 1}) + 1(\mathbf{x - 1}) && \text{Distributive Property} \\
&= x \cdot x + x \cdot (-1) + 1 \cdot x + 1 \cdot (-1) && \text{Distributive Property} \\
&= x^2 - x + x - 1 && \text{Multiply the monomials.} \\
&= \mathbf{x^2 - 1} && \text{Combine like terms.}
\end{aligned}$$

Step 2

$$\begin{aligned}
\left(\mathbf{x^2 - 1}\right)(\mathbf{5x + 2}) &= \mathbf{x^2}(\mathbf{5x + 2}) - \mathbf{1}(\mathbf{5x + 2}) && \text{Distributive Property} \\
&= x^2 \cdot 5x + x^2 \cdot 2 - 1 \cdot 5x - 1 \cdot 2 && \text{Distributive Property} \\
&= 5x^3 + 2x^2 - 5x - 2 && \text{Multiply the monomials.}
\end{aligned}$$

■

Application: Area

EXAMPLE 4

A garden is bordered on three sides by a tiled walkway.

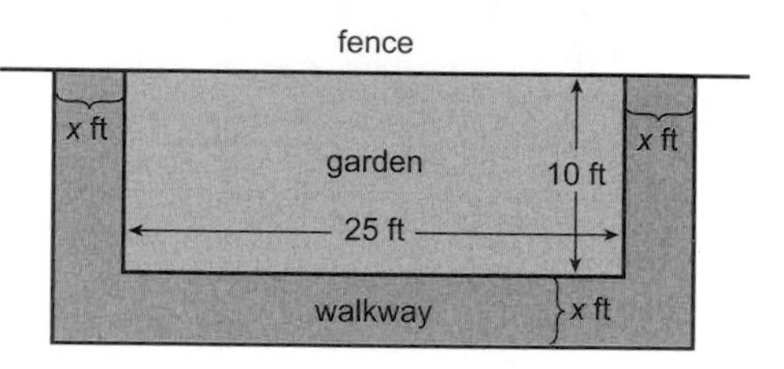

A Write a polynomial that represents the total area of the garden and the walkway.

SOLUTION

Step 1 Write expressions for the outer length and width of the walkway.

The length of the walkway is $x + 25 + x = 2x + 25$.

The width of the walkway is $x + 10$.

Step 2 Use the formula for the area of a rectangle.

$A = lw$

$= \mathbf{(2x + 25)(x + 10)}$ — Substitute $(2x + 25)$ for l and $(x + 10)$ for w.

$= 2x(x + 10) + 25(x + 10)$ — Distributive Property

$= 2x^2 + 20x + 25x + 250$ — Multiply.

$= 2x^2 + 45x + 250$ — Combine like terms.

The total area of the garden and the walkway is $2x^2 + 45x + 250$ ft^2.

B If the walkway is 3 ft wide, what is the total area of the garden and the walkway?

SOLUTION

$A = 2x^2 + 45x + 250$	Write the expression found in Example 4A.
$= 2 \cdot \mathbf{3}^2 + 45 \cdot \mathbf{3} + 250$	Substitute 3 for x.
$= 2 \cdot 9 + 45 \cdot 3 + 250$	Evaluate 3^2.
$= 18 + 135 + 250$	Multiply.
$= 403$	Add.

The total area of the garden and the walkway is 403 ft^2. ■

The FOIL Method

When you use the distributive property to multiply two binomials, you are multiplying each term in the first binomial by each term in the second binomial. The FOIL method helps you organize the steps used to multiply two binomials.

Using the FOIL Method to Multiply a Binomial by a Binomial

The letters of the word *FOIL* stand for **F**irst, **O**uter, **I**nner, and **L**ast. These words tell you which terms to multiply.

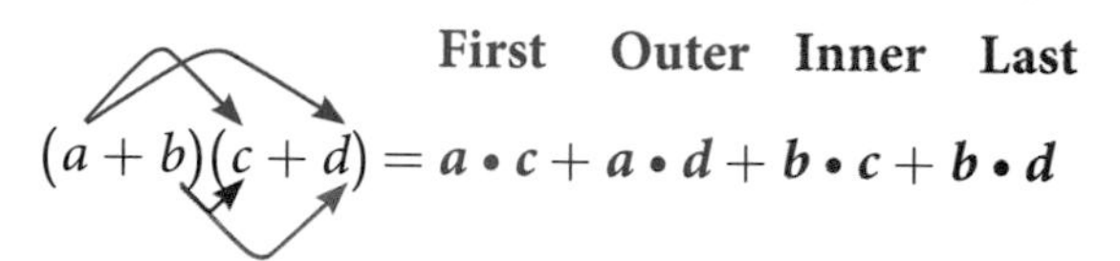

EXAMPLE 1

Multiply.

A $(x + 9)(3x - 4)$

SOLUTION

	First Outer Inner Last	
$(x + 9)(3x - 4)$	$= \mathbf{x \cdot 3x + x \cdot (-4) + 9 \cdot 3x + 9 \cdot (-4)}$	FOIL
	$= 3x^2 - 4x + 27x - 36$	Multiply.
	$= 3x^2 + 23x - 36$	Combine like terms.

B $(\sqrt{a}-2)(\sqrt{a}+4)$

▸ **Remember** $\sqrt{a}\cdot\sqrt{a}=\sqrt{a^2}$
$=a$

SOLUTION

	First	Outer	Inner	Last	
$(\sqrt{a}-2)(\sqrt{a}+4)=$	$\sqrt{a}\cdot\sqrt{a}$	$+\sqrt{a}\cdot 4$	$+(-2)\cdot\sqrt{a}$	$+(-2)\cdot 4$	FOIL

$$=a+4\sqrt{a}-2\sqrt{a}-8 \quad \text{Multiply.}$$

$$=a+(4-2)\sqrt{a}-8 \quad \text{Combine like terms.}$$

$$=a+2\sqrt{a}-8 \quad \text{Simplify.}$$

■

Using the FOIL Method to Multiply Conjugate Binomials

Conjugate binomials, $(a+b)$ and $(a-b)$, are two binomials with the same terms but opposite signs.

Conjugate Binomials

For any real numbers a and b,

$$(a+b)(a-b)=a^2-b^2.$$

EXAMPLE 2

A Prove that $(a+b)(a-b)=a^2-b^2$.

SOLUTION

$(a+b)(a-b)=a\cdot a+a\cdot(-b)+b\cdot a+b\cdot(-b)$	FOIL
$=a^2-ab+ba-b^2$	Multiply the monomials.
$=a^2-ab+ab-b^2$	Commutative Property of Multiplication
$=a^2-b^2$	Additive Inverse Property

B Multiply $(5x - 7)(5x + 7)$.

SOLUTION

Use the pattern $(a + b)(a - b) = a^2 - b^2$ to find the product.

$$(\boldsymbol{a} - \boldsymbol{b})(\boldsymbol{a} + \boldsymbol{b}) = \boldsymbol{a}^2 - \boldsymbol{b}^2$$

$$(\mathbf{5x} - \mathbf{7})(\mathbf{5x} + \mathbf{7}) = (\mathbf{5x})^2 - \mathbf{7}^2 \quad \text{Substitute } 5x \text{ for } a \text{ and } 7 \text{ for } b.$$

$$= 5x \cdot 5x - 7 \cdot 7 \quad \text{Multiply the monomials.}$$

$$= 25x^2 - 49 \quad \text{Simplify.}$$ ■

Cubing a Binomial

You know a pattern for squaring a binomial. There is also a pattern for cubing a binomial.

EXAMPLE 3

Find the product.

A $(x + y)^3$

SOLUTION

$$(x + y)^3 = (x + y)(x + y)(x + y)$$

Step 1 Use FOIL to expand $(x + y)(x + y)$.

$$(x + y)(x + y) = x \cdot x + x \cdot y + y \cdot x + y \cdot y \quad \text{FOIL}$$

$$= x^2 + xy + yx + y^2 \quad \text{Multiply the monomials.}$$

$$= x^2 + xy + xy + y^2 \quad \text{Commutative Property of Multiplication}$$

$$= x^2 + 2xy + y^2 \quad \text{Combine like terms.}$$

Step 2 Use the distributive property to multiply the product found in Step 1 by $(x+y)$.

$(x+y)(\mathbf{x^2+2xy+y^2}) = x(\mathbf{x^2+2xy+y^2}) + y(\mathbf{x^2+2xy+y^2})$	Distributive Property
$= x \cdot x^2 + x \cdot 2xy + x \cdot y^2 + y \cdot x^2 + y \cdot 2xy + y \cdot y^2$	Distributive Property
$= x^3 + 2x^2y + xy^2 + x^2y + 2xy^2 + y^3$	Multiply the monomials.
$= x^3 + 3x^2y + 3xy^2 + y^3$	Combine like terms.

The expression $(x+y)^3$ is a perfect cube, and $(x+y)^3 = x^3 + 3x^2y + 3xy^2 + y^3$.

You can use this fact to find any perfect cube.

B $(a+3)^3$

SOLUTION

Use the perfect cube pattern: $(x+y)^3 = x^3 + 3x^2y + 3xy^2 + y^3$.

$(\mathbf{x}+\mathbf{y})^3 = \mathbf{x}^3 + 3\mathbf{x}^2\mathbf{y} + 3\mathbf{x}\mathbf{y}^2 + \mathbf{y}^3$	
$(\mathbf{a}+\mathbf{3})^3 = \mathbf{a}^3 + 3\mathbf{a}^2 \cdot \mathbf{3} + 3\mathbf{a} \cdot \mathbf{3}^2 + \mathbf{3}^3$	Substitute a for x and 3 for y.
$= a^3 + 9a^2 + 27a + 27$	Simplify. ■

Polynomials and Arithmetic

Polynomials can be added, subtracted, multiplied, and divided just like real numbers can. When you add, subtract, or multiply polynomials, you always end up with a polynomial result, which is not always true when dividing polynomials.

Closure

Definition

A set is closed under an operation if the result of the operation on any two elements of the set is also an element of the set.

For instance, the set of even numbers is closed under addition. If you add any two even numbers, the sum is also an even number.

Think About It A **counterexample** is an example that shows that a statement is false. You need only a single counterexample to show that a statement is false.

EXAMPLE 1

Determine whether the set is closed under subtraction. If so, explain why; if it is not closed, give a counterexample.

A the set of positive integers

SOLUTION

The set of positive integers is not closed under subtraction. For instance, $6 - 9 = -3$ and -3 is not a positive integer.

B the set of even integers

SOLUTION

The set of even integers is closed under subtraction. An even integer can be written as $2x$, where x is an integer. Subtract two even integers $2p$ and $2q$: $2p - 2q = 2(p - q)$. The value $(p - q)$ is an integer, so $2 \cdot (p - q)$ is an integer as well. The set of even integers is closed under subtraction. ■

Operations Under Which Polynomials Are Closed

The set of polynomials is closed under addition, subtraction, and multiplication.

▶ **Remember** A **polynomial** is a monomial or the sum of monomials. The variables in polynomials must have whole-number exponents. Also, a constant without a variable, such as -4, is considered a polynomial because it is a monomial.

▶ **Remember** The **degree of a monomial** is the sum of the exponents of its variable factors. The **degree of a polynomial** is the degree of the monomial with the greatest degree.

EXAMPLE 2

Explain why the set of polynomials is closed under addition.

SOLUTION

Start with a simple case—the addition of two binomials of degree 1: $(ax + b) + (cx + d)$ where a, b, c, and d are all integers.

$$\begin{aligned}(ax + b) + (cx + d) &= (ax + cx) + (b + d)\\ &= (a + c)x + (b + d)\end{aligned}$$

The values $(a + c)$ and $(b + d)$ are integers, so the result of adding two binomials, $(ax + b) + (cx + d)$, is also a polynomial.

Expanding this argument, you can use like terms to simplify the sum of any polynomials. Consider the sum of the polynomials

$$\left(ax^3 + bx^2 + cx + d\right) + \left(px^3 + qx^2 + rx + s\right).$$

The result of this sum is a polynomial.

$$(a + p)x^3 + (b + q)x^2 + (c + r)x + (d + s) \blacksquare$$

Common Factors of Polynomials

When every term of a polynomial shares a common monomial factor, you can factor out the common factor from all the terms.

Identifying the Greatest Common Monomial Factor

The greatest common factor of the expression $18 + 27$ is 9, since 9 is the greatest factor that evenly divides 18 and 27.

Finding the greatest common monomial factor of polynomials with variables is similar to finding the greatest common factor of numerical expressions.

How to Find the Greatest Common Monomial Factor

Step 1 Write each term of the polynomial as the product of its prime factors, and look for the smallest power of each prime factor common to each term.

Step 2 Multiply the common factors found in Step 1.

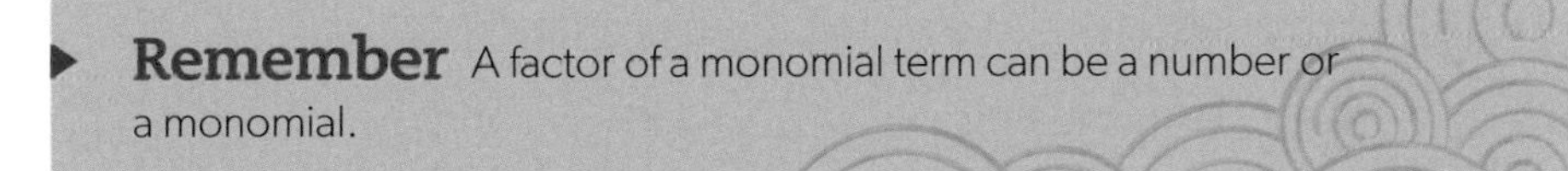

Remember A factor of a monomial term can be a number or a monomial.

EXAMPLE 1

Find the greatest common monomial factor of the terms of the polynomial.

A $8x^5 + 12x^2$

SOLUTION

Step 1

$$8x^5 = 2^3 \cdot x^5$$

$$12x^2 = 2^2 \cdot 3 \cdot x^2$$

Step 2 Multiply 2^2 and x^2. The greatest common monomial factor is $4x^2$.

B $15a^3b + 25a^2bc - 100a^5b^4c^2$

SOLUTION

Step 1

$$15a^3b = 3 \cdot 5 \cdot a^3 \cdot b$$

$$25a^2bc = 5^2 \cdot a^2 \cdot b \cdot c$$

$$100a^5b^4c^2 = 2^2 \cdot 5^2 \cdot a^5 \cdot b^4 \cdot c^2$$

Step 2 Multiply 5, a^2, and b: $5 \cdot a^2 \cdot b = 5a^2b$. The greatest common monomial factor is $5a^2b$. ■

Factoring Out the Greatest Common Monomial Factor

Since 9 is the greatest common factor of the expression $18 + 27$, you can use the distributive property to factor it out.

$$18 + 27 = 9(2 + 3)$$

EXAMPLE 2

Factor the polynomial $14a^3b + 7a^2b^2 + 49ab^3$.

SOLUTION

Step 1 Find the greatest common monomial factor.

$$14a^3b = 2 \bullet 7 \bullet a^3 \bullet b$$
$$7a^2b^2 = 7 \bullet a^2 \bullet b^2$$
$$49ab^3 = 7^2 \bullet a \bullet b^3$$

The greatest common monomial factor is $7ab$.

Step 2 Rewrite each term of the polynomial as a product of the greatest common monomial factor.

$$14a^3b + 7a^2b^2 + 49ab^3 = \mathbf{7ab} \bullet 2a^2 + \mathbf{7ab} \bullet ab + \mathbf{7ab} \bullet 7b^2$$

▶ **Think About It** You can check your work by multiplying the greatest common monomial factor by the new polynomial to get the original polynomial.

Step 3 Use the distributive property to factor out the greatest common monomial factor.

$$7ab \bullet 2a^2 + 7ab \bullet ab + 7ab \bullet 7b^2 = 7ab\left(2a^2 + ab + 7b^2\right) \blacksquare$$

You can also divide each term of a polynomial by its greatest common monomial factor to factor out the greatest common monomial factor.

EXAMPLE 3

Factor the polynomial $12xy^4 - 21x^2y^5z + 36xy^3$.

SOLUTION

Step 1 Find the greatest common monomial factor.

$$12xy^4 = 2^2 \bullet 3 \bullet x \bullet y^4$$
$$21x^2y^5z = 3 \bullet 7 \bullet x^2 \bullet y^5 \bullet z$$
$$36xy^3 = 2^2 \bullet 3^2 \bullet x \bullet y^3$$

The greatest common monomial factor is $3xy^3$.

Step 2 Factor out the greatest common monomial factor. Divide each term of the polynomial by the greatest common monomial factor.

$$\frac{12xy^4 - 21x^2y^5z + 36xy^3}{\mathbf{3xy^3}} = \frac{12xy^4}{3xy^3} - \frac{21x^2y^5z}{3xy^3} + \frac{36xy^3}{3xy^3}$$

$$= 4x^{(1-1)}y^{(4-3)} - 7x^{(2-1)}y^{(5-3)}z + 12x^{(1-1)}y^{(3-3)}$$

$$= 4y - 7xy^2z + 12$$

Step 3 Multiply the greatest common monomial factor by the result in Step 2.

$$12xy^4 - 21x^2y^5z + 36xy^3 = 3xy^3\left(4y - 7xy^2z + 12\right)$$ ■

Factoring Out a Binomial Factor

EXAMPLE 4

Factor $7x(x+3) - 5(x+3)$.

SOLUTION

Notice that both terms of the polynomial contain the binomial factor $(x+3)$.

Step 1 To factor out the common binomial factor, divide each term by the common binomial factor.

$$\frac{7x\mathbf{(x+3)} - 5\mathbf{(x+3)}}{\mathbf{(x+3)}} = \frac{7x(x+3)}{(x+3)} - \frac{5(x+3)}{(x+3)}$$

$$= 7x - 5$$

Step 2 Multiply the common binomial factor by the result in Step 1.

$$7x(x+3) - 5(x+3) = (x+3)(7x-5)$$ ■

Application: Geometry

EXAMPLE 5

A rectangle has an area of $6x + 4$ ft^2 and a width of 2 ft. What is the length of the rectangle?

SOLUTION

$A = lw$	Write the formula for the area of a rectangle.
$\mathbf{6x + 4 = l \cdot 2}$	Substitute 2 for w and $6x + 4$ for A.
$\underbrace{(3x + 2)}_{l} \cdot \underbrace{2}_{w} = l \cdot 2$	Factor 2 from $6x + 4$.

The length of the rectangle is $3x + 2$ ft. ■

Factoring Perfect Squares

When you square a binomial, the result is a perfect square trinomial. You can use this perfect square pattern to work the other way and find the squared binomial for a given trinomial.

When you expand the square of a binomial, you get a perfect square trinomial because it can be written as the square of a binomial rather than the product of two different binomials. You can use the patterns of perfect squares to help you factor perfect square trinomials.

▶ **Remember** The pattern for squaring a binomial is

$$(a+b)^2 = a^2 + 2ab + b^2.$$

Identifying a Perfect Square

Perfect Square Trinomial Patterns
$a^2 + 2ab + b^2 = (a+b)^2$
$a^2 - 2ab + b^2 = (a-b)^2$

Note that for a trinomial to be a perfect square, the first and last terms have to be perfect squares and the middle term has to equal twice the square root of the first and third terms.

EXAMPLE 1

Determine whether the expression is a perfect square trinomial.

A $x^2 - 4x + 4$

SOLUTION

Try to write the polynomial in the form $a^2 + 2ab + b^2$ or $a^2 - 2ab + b^2$.

Substitute x for a and 2 for b.

$$x^2 - 4x + 4 = x^2 - 2 \bullet x \bullet 2 + 2^2$$

The trinomial $x^2 - 4x + 4$ is a perfect square.

B $x^2 - 1$

SOLUTION

Since there is no x term, the polynomial $x^2 - 1$ is not a perfect square.

C $x^2 + 7x + 25$

SOLUTION

To write the trinomial in the form $a^2 + 2ab + b^2$, substitute x for a and 5 for b. The middle term $2ab$ must then be $2 \bullet x \bullet 5$ or $10x$. Since the middle term is $7x$, the trinomial is not a perfect square.

D $4x^2 + 12x - 100$

SOLUTION

When you square a binomial, the sign of the constant term is always positive. Since the constant in the trinomial $4x^2 + 12x - 100$ has a negative sign, the trinomial is not a perfect square. ■

Factoring a Perfect Square

EXAMPLE 2

Factor the trinomial.

A $x^2 + 4x + 4$

SOLUTION

Write the polynomial in the form $a^2 + 2ab + b^2$.

$x^2 + 4x + 4 = \mathbf{x^2 + 2 \cdot x \cdot 2 + 2^2}$ Substitute x for a and 2 for b.

$= \mathbf{(x + 2)^2}$ Use the pattern for $(a + b)^2$.

B $4x^2 - 20xy + 25y^2$

SOLUTION

$4x^2 - 20xy + 25y^2 = \mathbf{(2x)^2 - 2 \cdot 2x \cdot 5y + (5y)^2}$ Substitute $2x$ for a and $5y$ for b.

$= \mathbf{(2x - 5y)^2}$ Use the pattern for $(a - b)^2$.

C $4x^2 - \frac{4}{3}x + \frac{1}{9}$

SOLUTION

$4x^2 - \frac{4}{3}x + \frac{1}{9} = \mathbf{(2x)^2 - 2 \cdot 2x \cdot \frac{1}{3} + \left(\frac{1}{3}\right)^2}$ Substitute $2x$ for a and $\frac{1}{3}$ for b.

$= \mathbf{\left(2x - \frac{1}{3}\right)^2}$ Use the pattern for $(a - b)^2$. ■

Factoring Differences of Squares

You can use a pattern to factor a difference of squares.

Conjugate binomials, $(a + b)$ and $(a - b)$, are two binomials with the same terms but opposite signs. The product of conjugate binomials, $a^2 - b^2$, is called the difference of squares.

Identifying a Difference of Squares

EXAMPLE 1

Determine whether the expression is the difference of squares.

A $x^2 - 1$

SOLUTION

Try to write the polynomial in the form $a^2 - b^2$.

Since $x^2 - 1 = x^2 - 1^2$, it is the difference of squares.

▶ **Think About It** The word *difference* in the phrase *difference of squares* means one square term is subtracted from the other square term.

B $x^2 + 1$

SOLUTION

Since the terms are added, the binomial is the sum of two squares, not the difference of two squares.

C $x^4 - 9$

SOLUTION

Try to write the polynomial in the form $a^2 - b^2$. Use the power of a power property of exponents to rewrite x^4.

Since $x^4 - 9 = \left(x^2\right)^2 - 3^2$, it is the difference of squares. ■

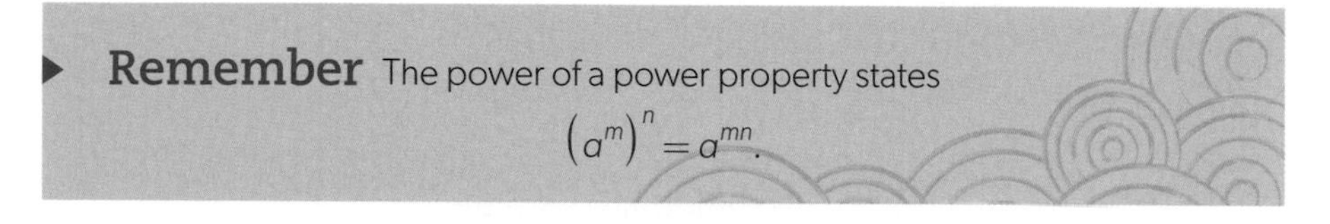

▸ **Remember** The power of a power property states $\left(a^m\right)^n = a^{mn}$.

Factoring the Difference of Two Squares

You can use the sum and difference pattern to help you factor any binomial that is the difference of squares.

Difference of Squares Pattern

$$a^2 - b^2 = (a + b)(a - b)$$

EXAMPLE 2

Completely factor the difference of squares.

A $144x^2 - z^2$

SOLUTION

First write the polynomial in the form $a^2 - b^2$. Then apply the difference of squares pattern.

$144x^2 - z^2 = (\mathbf{12x})^2 - \mathbf{z}^2$	Substitute $12x$ for a and z for b.
$= (\mathbf{12x} + \mathbf{z})(\mathbf{12x} - \mathbf{z})$	Difference of squares pattern

B $p^{12} - q^{20}$

SOLUTION

$p^{12} - q^{20} = \left(p^6\right)^2 - \left(q^{10}\right)^2$ Power of a Power Property

$= \left(p^6 + q^{10}\right)\left(p^6 - q^{10}\right)$ Difference of squares pattern

The binomial $p^6 - q^{10}$ is also a difference of squares, so the expression can be factored further.

$\left(p^6 + q^{10}\right)\left(p^6 - q^{10}\right) = \left(p^6 + q^{10}\right)\left[\left(p^3\right)^2 - \left(q^5\right)^2\right]$ p^6 and q^{10} are perfect squares.

$= \left(p^6 + q^{10}\right)\left(p^3 + q^5\right)\left(p^3 - q^5\right)$ Difference of squares pattern

C $4x^2 - \frac{4}{9}$

SOLUTION

$4x^2 - \frac{4}{9} = (2x)^2 - \left(\frac{2}{3}\right)^2$ Substitute $2x$ for a and $\frac{2}{3}$ for b.

$= \left(2x + \frac{2}{3}\right)\left(2x - \frac{2}{3}\right)$ Difference of squares pattern ■

▶ **Think About It** Always look for perfect squares when a binomial has a minus sign and even powers of variables.

Application: Geometry

EXAMPLE 3

A picture frame is created by cutting a 4.5 in. square piece from a square piece of plywood.

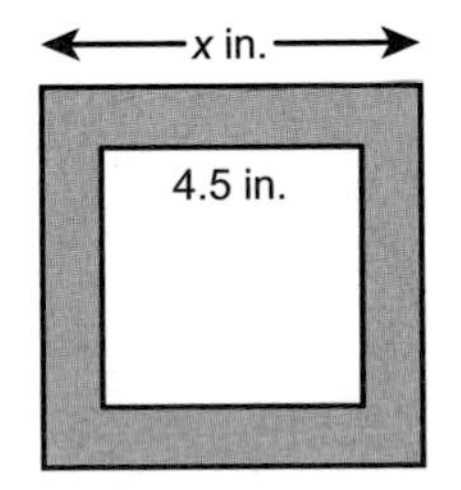

A Write a polynomial expression that represents the area of the picture frame after the square piece is removed.

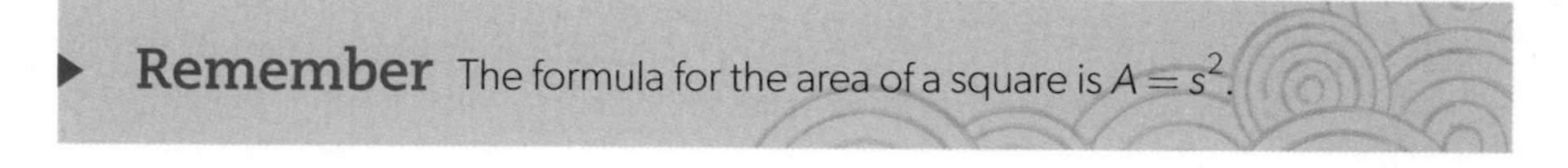

SOLUTION

Find the area of the original piece of plywood and subtract the area of the piece that was removed.

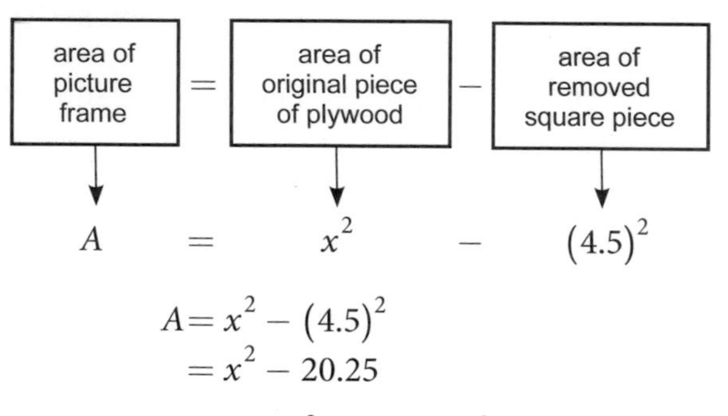

$$A = x^2 - (4.5)^2$$
$$= x^2 - 20.25$$

The area of the picture frame is $x^2 - 20.25$ in^2.

B Write the area as the difference of squares.

SOLUTION

Factor the binomial found in Example 3A.

$x^2 - 20.25 = \boldsymbol{x}^2 - (\mathbf{4.5})^2$	Substitute x for a and 4.5 for b.
$= (x + 4.5)(x - 4.5)$	Difference of squares pattern ■

Factoring Quadratic Trinomials

You learned how to multiply two binomials using the distributive property and the FOIL method. You can reverse this process to factor a trinomial into two binomial factors.

The trinomial $x^2 + bx + c$ can be factored into the product $(x + d)(x + e)$ if $d + e = b$ and $de = c$.

Factoring $x^2 + bx + c$

If $c > 0$ and $b > 0$, then the product can be written as $(x + \blacksquare)(x + \blacksquare)$.

If $c > 0$ and $b < 0$, then the product can be written as $(x - \blacksquare)(x - \blacksquare)$.

If $c < 0$, then the product can be written as $(x + \blacksquare)(x - \blacksquare)$.

Factoring Trinomials of the Form $x^2 + bx + c$

EXAMPLE 1

Factor the trinomial.

A $x^2 + 5x + 6$

SOLUTION

Find two binomials whose product is $x^2 + 5x + 6$. Both the x term and the constant term are positive, so the binomials will have the form $(x + \blacksquare)(x + \blacksquare)$.

The coefficient of the x term is 5 and the constant term is 6, so you need to find two positive factors of 6 whose sum is 5.

Positive factors of 6	Sum of the factors
1, 6	7
2, 3	**5**

The factors 2 and 3 have a sum of 5, so $x^2 + 5x + 6 = (x + 2)(x + 3)$.

CHECK

$x^2 + 5x + 6 \stackrel{?}{=} (x + 2)(x + 3)$

$x^2 + 5x + 6 \stackrel{?}{=} x \cdot x + x \cdot 3 + 2 \cdot x + 2 \cdot 3$ FOIL

$x^2 + 5x + 6 \stackrel{?}{=} x^2 + 3x + 2x + 6$ Simplify.

$x^2 + 5x + 6 = x^2 + 5x + 6$ ✓ Combine like terms.

The answer is correct.

▶ **Think About It** Use the FOIL method to check your answer when factoring.

B $x^2 - 7x - 8$

SOLUTION

The constant term is negative, so the factors have opposite signs.

The binomials will have the form $(x + \blacksquare)\ (x - \blacksquare)$.

The coefficient of the x term is -7 and the constant term is -8, so you need to find two factors of -8 whose sum is -7.

Factors of −8	Sum of the factors
$-1, 8$	7
$1, -8$	**-7**
$-2, 4$	2
$2, -4$	-2

The factors 1 and -8 have a sum of -7, so $x^2 - 7x - 8 = (x + 1)(x - 8)$.

▸ **Think About It** If the sign of c (the constant term) is negative, the factors will have opposite signs.

C $x^2 + 6x - 27$

SOLUTION

The constant term is negative, so the binomials will have the form $(x + ■)(x - ■)$.

The coefficient of the x term is 6 and the constant term is -27, so you need to find two factors of -27 whose sum is 6.

Factors of −27	Sum of the factors
$-1, 27$	26
$1, -27$	-26
$-3, 9$	**6**
$3, -9$	-6

The factors -3 and 9 have a sum of 6, so $x^2 + 6x - 27 = (x + 9)(x - 3)$.

D $x^2 - 9x + 20$

SOLUTION

The x term is negative and the constant term is positive, so the factors will have the same sign as the x term. The binomials will have the form $(x - \blacksquare)(x - \blacksquare)$.

The coefficient of the x term is -9 and the constant term is positive 20, so you need to find two negative factors of 20 whose sum is -9.

Positive factors of 9	Sum of the factors
$-1, -20$	-21
$-2, -10$	-12
$-4, -5$	**-9**

The factors -4 and -5 have a sum of -9, so $x^2 - 9x + 20 = (x - 4)(x - 5)$. ■

Prime Polynomials

Just as a prime number cannot be broken down into the product of two other numbers, a prime polynomial cannot be broken down into the product of two other polynomials.

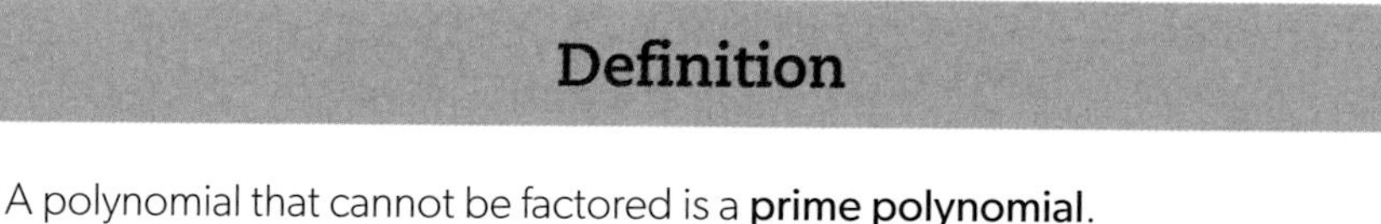

Definition

A polynomial that cannot be factored is a **prime polynomial**.

In this course:

- All polynomials have rational coefficients.
- A polynomial is factorable if you can write it as the product of at least two other polynomials with rational coefficients.

EXAMPLE 2

Factor $x^2 + 8x + 9$.

SOLUTION

Both the x term and the constant term are positive, so the binomials will have the form $(x + ■)(x + ■)$.

The coefficient of the x term is 8 and the constant term is 9, so you need to find two positive factors of 9 whose sum is 8.

Positive factors of 9	Sum of the factors
1, 9	10
3, 3	6

Since there are no factors of 9 whose sum is 8, the trinomial is prime. ■

Finding a Value to Make a Polynomial Factorable

EXAMPLE 3

Find the value of k, for $k > 0$, that makes the polynomial factorable.

A $x^2 + kx + 7$

SOLUTION

Both the x term and the constant term are positive, so the binomials will have the form $(x + ■)(x + ■)$.

The only factors of 7 are 1 and 7, so the only possible factorization is $(x + 1)(x + 7)$.

$$(x + 1)(x + 7) = x^2 + 7x + x + 1 \cdot 7 \qquad \text{FOIL}$$

$$= x^2 + \mathbf{8}x + 7 \qquad \text{Combine like terms.}$$

So $k = 8$.

B $x^2 - kx + 10$

SOLUTION

The x term is negative and the constant is positive, so the binomials will have the form $(x - \blacksquare)(x - \blacksquare)$.

The factor pairs of 10 are 1 and 10, and 2 and 5. The possible factorizations are $(x - 1)(x - 10)$ and $(x - 2)(x - 5)$.

$$\begin{aligned}(x - 1)(x - 10) &= x^2 - 10x - x - 1 \bullet (-10) \\ &= x^2 - \mathbf{11}x + 10\end{aligned}$$

$$\begin{aligned}(x - 2)(x - 5) &= x2 - 5x - 2x - 2 \bullet (-5) \\ &= x^2 - \mathbf{7}x + 10\end{aligned}$$

So $k = 11$ or $k = 7$. ■

Finding Roots of a Polynomial

Use the zero product property to find the roots of a polynomial.

Zero Product Property

For any real numbers a and b, if $ab = 0$, then $a = 0$ or $b = 0$ or both $a = 0$ and $b = 0$.

▶ **Think About It** For any real number a, $a \cdot 0 = 0$. You can also say for any real numbers a and b, if $a = 0$ or $b = 0$, then $ab = 0$. The zero product property is the converse of this statement.

You can use the zero product property to solve polynomial equations in which one side of the equation is a factored polynomial and the other side of the equation is equal to zero. The solutions to a polynomial equation of this form are called the **roots of the polynomial**.

Solving Polynomial Equations

EXAMPLE 1

Find the roots.

A $x^2 + 5x - 6 = 0$

SOLUTION

Factor the left side of the equation. Then use the zero product property to find the solutions.

$x^2 + 5x - 6 = 0$			
$(x + 6)(x - 1) = 0$			Factor.
$x + 6 = 0$	or	$x - 1 = 0$	Zero Product Property
$x + 6 - 6 = 0 - 6$		$x - 1 + 1 = 0 + 1$	Solve each equation for x.
$x = -6$		$x = 1$	Simplify.

The roots of the polynomial are -6 and 1.

CHECK

You can check your solutions by substituting each root into the equation for x.

$x^2 + 5x - 6 = 0$	$x^2 + 5x - 6 = 0$
$(-6)^2 + 5 \bullet (-6) - 6 \stackrel{?}{=} 0$	$1^2 + 5 \bullet 1 - 6 \stackrel{?}{=} 0$
$36 - 30 - 6 \stackrel{?}{=} 0$	$1 + 5 - 6 \stackrel{?}{=} 0$
$0 = 0$ ✓	$0 = 0$ ✓

The solutions are correct.

B $x^2 + 6x = -9$

SOLUTION

To use the zero product property, one side of the equation must equal 0.

The first step in solving the equation $x^2 + 6x = -9$ is to write an equivalent equation in which one side of the equation is equal to 0.

$x^2 + 6x = -9$	
$x^2 + 6x + 9 = -9 + 9$	Add 9 to each side of the equation.
$x^2 + 6x + 9 = 0$	Simplify.

Now solve the polynomial equation.

$$x^2 + 6x + 9 = 0$$

$(x + 3)(x + 3) = 0$ Perfect squares pattern

The factors are the same, so this equation has only one solution.

$x + 3 = 0$ Solve the equation for x.

$x = -3$ Subtract 3 from both sides of the equation.

The root of the polynomial is −3.

C $2x^3 - 7x^2 - 15x = 0$

SOLUTION

Factor the polynomial.

$$2x^3 - 7x^2 - 15x = 0$$

$x(2x^2 - 7x - 15) = 0$ Factor out the common monomial x.

$x(2x + 3)(x - 5) = 0$ Factor the trinomial.

$x = 0$ or $2x + 3 = 0$ or $x - 5 = 0$ Zero Product Property

$2x = -3$ $x = 5$ Solve each equation for x.

$x = -\frac{3}{2}$ Simplify.

The roots of the polynomial are 0, $-\frac{3}{2}$, and 5. ■

Finding the Zeros of a Polynomial Function

A zero of a function $f(x)$ is a solution to the equation $f(x) = 0$. The zeros of the function are the x-intercepts of the graph of the function.

▶ **Remember** The x-intercept of a graph is the x-coordinate of the point where the graph intersects the x-axis.

EXAMPLE 2

Use the zeros of the polynomial function $f(x) = 25x^2 - 9$ to find the x-intercepts of the function.

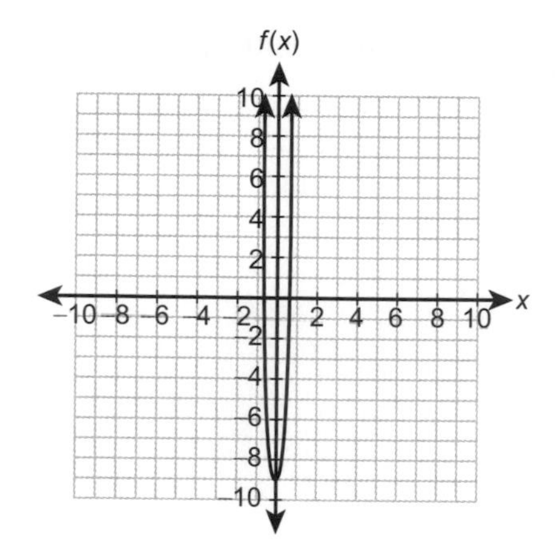

SOLUTION

On the graph, the x-intercepts appear to be about halfway between 0 and 1 and about halfway between 0 and -1. The zeros of the polynomial function are the values of x where $f(x) = 0$. Set the function equal to zero and solve to find the exact values of the x-intercepts. Factor the right side of the equation. Then use the zero product property.

$0 = 25x^2 - 9$ — Set the function equal to 0.

$0 = (5x - 3)(5x + 3)$ — Difference of squares pattern

$5x - 3 = 0$ or $5x + 3 = 0$ — Zero Product Property

$5x = 3$ $\quad 5x = -3$ — Solve each equation for x.

$x = \frac{3}{5}$ $\quad x = -\frac{3}{5}$ — Simplify.

The zeros are $\frac{3}{5}$ and $-\frac{3}{5}$, so the x-intercepts are $\frac{3}{5}$ and $-\frac{3}{5}$. ■

Application: Measurement

EXAMPLE 3

A rectangular fishpond is surrounded by a border with a uniform width of x feet. The length of the fishpond, including the border, is 12 ft and the width, including the border, is 10 ft. The area of the fishpond is 48 ft^2. What are the length and width of the fishpond?

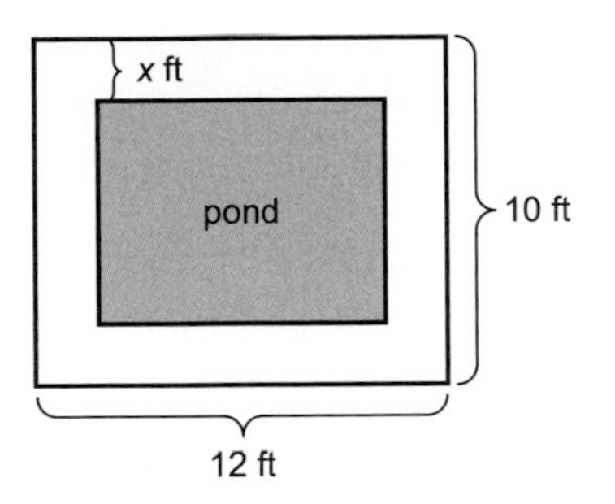

SOLUTION

Use the diagram to help you write an equation to solve the problem.

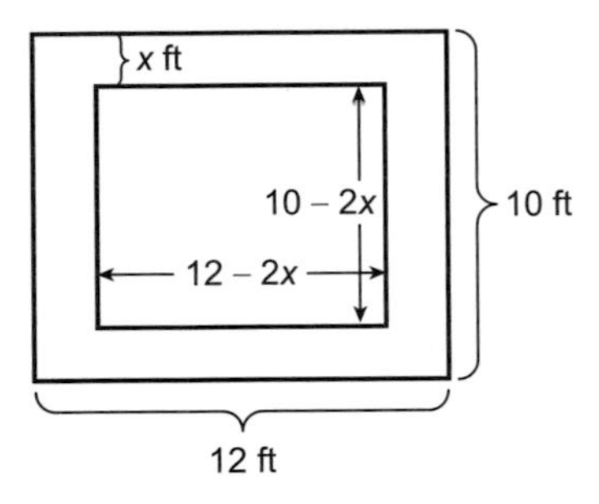

The length of the fishpond is $12 - x - x = 12 - 2x$.

The width of the fishpond is $10 - x - x = 10 - 2x$.

Use the formula for the area of a rectangle to write an equation that represents the area of the fishpond.

$A = lw$	
$\mathbf{48 = (12 - 2x)(10 - 2x)}$	Substitute 48 for A, $12 - 2x$ for l, and $10 - 2x$ for
$48 = 120 - 24x - 20x + 4x^2$	Multiply the two binomials using the FOIL method.
$48 = 120 - 44x + 4x^2$	Combine like terms.
$0 = 72 - 44x + 4x^2$	Subtract 48 from each side.

Now factor the polynomial and solve for x using the zero product property to find the zeros.

$$4x^2 - 44x + 72 = 0$$

$$4(x^2 - 11x + 18) = 0 \qquad \text{Factor out the common monomial 4.}$$

$$4(x - 9)(x - 2) = 0 \qquad \text{Factor the trinomial.}$$

Set each binomial equal to zero and solve for x.

$$x - 9 = 0 \quad \text{or} \quad x - 2 = 0$$

$$x = 9 \qquad\qquad x = 2$$

The zeros of the function are 9 and 2.

The length and width of the fishpond are $12 - 2x$ and $10 - 2x$, respectively. If you substitute 9 into each expression to find the length and width, the values are negative, so 9 is not a valid solution.

$$12 - 2x = 12 - 2 \bullet \mathbf{9} \quad \text{and} \quad 10 - 2x = 10 - 2 \bullet \mathbf{9}$$

$$= 12 - 18 \qquad\qquad = 10 - 18$$

$$= -6 \qquad\qquad = -8$$

Substitute 2 into the expressions to find the length and width of the fishpond.

$$12 - 2x = 12 - 2 \bullet \mathbf{2} \quad \text{and} \quad 10 - 2x = 10 - 2 \bullet \mathbf{2}$$

$$= 12 - 4 \qquad\qquad = 10 - 4$$

$$= 8 \qquad\qquad = 6$$

The length of the fishpond is 8 ft and the width is 6 ft. ■

Quadratic Equations

Topic List

- Solving Perfect Square Equations
- Completing the Square
- The Quadratic Formula
- Solving Quadratic Equations
- Formulas with Quadratics
- Applications: Area Problems

Balls, pumpkins, and even water jets can behave like projectiles. Whether you're trying to hit a target or design a cool water feature, understanding quadratic polynomial equations can help.

Solving Perfect Square Equations

Some of the simplest quadratic equations involve perfect squares.

An equation of the form $ax^2 + bx + c = 0$, where $a \neq 0$, is a quadratic equation in standard form. There are different methods for solving a quadratic equation, and the values of a, b, and c determine which method is most appropriate.

▶ **Remember** A quadratic polynomial is a polynomial of degree 2.

Solving by Taking the Square Root of Each Side

To solve a perfect square equation, take the square root of both sides of the equation.

EXAMPLE 1

Solve $x^2 = 4$.

SOLUTION

$$x^2 = 4$$

$$|x| = \sqrt{4}$$

$$x = \sqrt{4} \quad \text{or} \quad x = -\sqrt{4}$$

$$x = 2 \quad \text{or} \quad x = -2$$

The equation is true when $x = 2$ or $x = -2$. The solution set is $\{2, -2\}$. ■

Example 1 suggests a property that can make solving quadratic equations a bit simpler.

Square Root Property

If $x^2 = a$, then $x = \pm\sqrt{a}$.

EXAMPLE 2

Solve the equation.

A $16x^2 = 9$

SOLUTION

$16x^2 = 9$

$x^2 = \frac{9}{16}$ Divide each side by 16.

$x = \pm\sqrt{\frac{9}{16}}$ Take the square root of each side.

$x = \pm\frac{3}{4}$ Simplify.

The solution set is $\left\{\frac{3}{4}, -\frac{3}{4}\right\}$.

CHECK

$$16x^2 = 9 \qquad 16x^2 = 9$$

$$16\left(\frac{3}{4}\right)^2 \stackrel{?}{=} 9 \qquad 16\left(-\frac{3}{4}\right)^2 \stackrel{?}{=} 9$$

$$\cancel{16} \cdot \frac{9}{\cancel{16}} \stackrel{?}{=} 9 \qquad \cancel{16} \cdot \frac{9}{\cancel{16}} \stackrel{?}{=} 9$$

$$9 = 9 \checkmark \qquad 9 = 9 \checkmark$$

The solution set $\left\{\frac{3}{4}, -\frac{3}{4}\right\}$ is correct.

B $(x-6)^2 = 4$

SOLUTION

$(x-6)^2 = 4$

$(x-6) = \pm\sqrt{4}$ Take the square root of each side.

$x - 6 = \pm 2$ Simplify.

$x = 6 \pm 2$

The expression 6 ± 2 means that there are two answers: $6 + 2$ and $6 - 2$. The solution set is $\{8, 4\}$.

C $5t^2 - 3 = 4$

SOLUTION

$5t^2 - 3 = 4$

$5t^2 = 7$ Add 3 to each side.

$t^2 = \frac{7}{5}$ Divide each side by 5.

$t = \pm\sqrt{\frac{7}{5}}$ Take the square root of each side.

$t = \pm\frac{\sqrt{35}}{5}$ Rationalize the denominator.

The solution set is $\left\{\frac{\sqrt{35}}{5}, -\frac{\sqrt{35}}{5}\right\}$. ■

▶ **Remember** To rationalize a denominator, multiply the numerator and denominator of the expression by the radical in the denominator of the expression.

Identifying and Using Perfect Square Factoring Patterns

Some quadratic equations have perfect squares hidden in a trinomial. If you know the factoring pattern, you can use it to simplify and solve equations that look complicated at first.

Perfect Square Trinomial Patterns

$$a^2 + 2ab + b^2 = (a + b)^2$$
$$a^2 - 2ab + b^2 = (a - b)^2$$

When you are solving a quadratic equation, you may need to start by factoring one side of the equation.

EXAMPLE 3

Solve $x^2 + 16x + 64 = 49$.

SOLUTION

The left side is a perfect square trinomial.

$x^2 + 16x + 64 = 49$	
$x^2 + 2 \bullet x \bullet 8 + 8^2 = 49$	Write the polynomial in the form $a^2 + 2ab + b^2$.
$(x + 8)^2 = 49$	Perfect square trinomial pattern
$(x + 8) = \pm\sqrt{49}$	Take the square root of each side.
$x = -8 \pm 7$	Subtract 8 from both sides and simplify.

The solutions are $-8 + 7$ and $-8 - 7$. The solution set is $\{-1, -15\}$.

CHECK

$$x^2 + 16x + 64 = 49$$
$$(-1)^2 + 16 \bullet (-1) + 64 \stackrel{?}{=} 49$$
$$1 - 16 + 64 \stackrel{?}{=} 49$$
$$49 = 49 \checkmark$$

$$x^2 + 16x + 64 = 49$$
$$(-15)^2 + 16 \bullet (-15) + 64 \stackrel{?}{=} 49$$
$$225 - 240 + 64 \stackrel{?}{=} 49$$
$$49 = 49 \checkmark$$

The solution set $\{-1, -15\}$ is correct. ■

Application: Geometry

EXAMPLE 4

The surface area S of a cube is equal to the sum of the areas of the 6 square faces that form the cube. If each face has side length s, then the formula $S = 6s^2$ can be used to find the surface area of a cube. The surface area of the cube shown is 1350 units^2. What is the value of x?

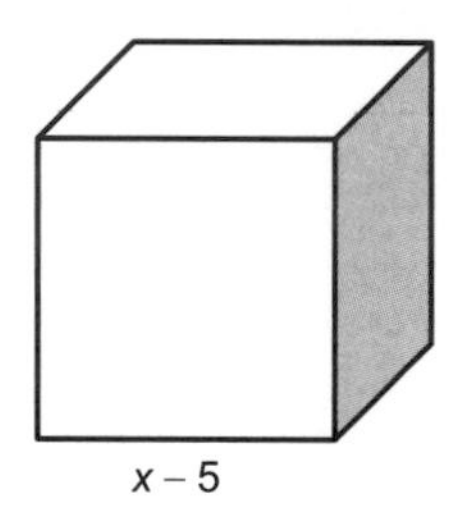

SOLUTION

Substitute the given information into the formula and isolate the perfect square to solve.

$$S = 6s^2$$

$$\mathbf{1350} = 6(x - 5)^2 \qquad \text{Substitute 1350 for } S \text{ and } (x - 5) \text{ for } s.$$

$$225 = (x - 5)^2 \qquad \text{Divide each side by 6.}$$

$$\pm\sqrt{225} = x - 5 \qquad \text{Take the square root of each side.}$$

$$5 \pm 15 = x \qquad \text{Add 5 to both sides and simplify.}$$

The solutions are -10 and 20. Since a side length cannot be a negative value, the only value of x is 20 units. ■

Completing the Square

You can write any quadratic equation as a perfect square equation.

In a perfect square trinomial, the constant term is always equal to the square of half the coefficient of the x term, as shown in the examples.

$$(x+5)^2 = x^2 + 10x + 25 = x^2 + \mathbf{10}x + \left(\frac{\mathbf{10}}{2}\right)^2$$

$$(x-4)^2 = x^2 - 8x + 16 = x^2 - \mathbf{8}x + \left(\frac{\mathbf{-8}}{2}\right)^2$$

You can use this fact to turn a quadratic expression into a perfect square trinomial.

Completing the Square

Complete the square by finding the number that should be added to each expression to change it into a perfect square trinomial.

Definition

Completing the square is the process of transforming an expression of the form $x^2 + bx$ into a perfect square trinomial by adding the term $\left(\frac{b}{2}\right)^2$ to it.

▶ **Think About It** The last term in a perfect square trinomial is always positive.

EXAMPLE 1

Find the number that should be added to the expression $x^2 + 14x$ to change it into a perfect square trinomial.

SOLUTION

Take half of 14 and square the result.

$$\left(\frac{14}{2}\right)^2 = 7^2 = 49$$

The number is 49.

CHECK

Determine whether $x^2 + 14x + 49$ is a perfect square trinomial.

$$x^2 + 14x + 49 = (x + 7)(x + 7) = (x + 7)^2 \checkmark$$

The number 49 makes the expression a perfect square trinomial. ■

Solving a Quadratic Equation by Completing the Square

Completing the square makes it possible to write any quadratic equation as a perfect square equation. Use the following steps to solve any quadratic equation by completing the square.

How to Use Completing the Square to Solve a Quadratic Equation

Step 1 Write the equation in the form $x^2 + bx = c$.

Step 2 Add $\left(\frac{b}{2}\right)^2$ to each side of the equation and simplify.

Step 3 Factor the perfect square trinomial and solve for x.

EXAMPLE 2

Transform the equation into a perfect square equation and solve.

A $4x^2 = 3 + 4x$

SOLUTION

Step 1 Write the equation in the form $x^2 + bx = c$ by subtracting $4x$ from each side of the equation and then dividing each side by 4.

$$4x^2 = 3 + 4x$$

$$4x^2 - 4x = 3 \qquad \text{Subtract } 4x \text{ from each side.}$$

$$x^2 - x = \frac{3}{4} \qquad \text{Divide each side by 4.}$$

Step 2 Add $\left(\frac{-1}{2}\right)^2$ to each side.

$$x^2 - x = \frac{3}{4}$$

$$x^2 - x + \left(\frac{-1}{2}\right)^2 = \frac{3}{4} + \frac{1}{4} \qquad \text{Add } \left(\frac{-1}{2}\right)^2 = \frac{1}{4} \text{ to each side.}$$

$$x^2 - x + \left(\frac{-1}{2}\right)^2 = 1 \qquad \text{Simplify.}$$

Step 3 Factor the perfect square trinomial and solve for x.

$$x^2 - x + \left(\frac{-1}{2}\right)^2 = 1$$

$$\left(x - \frac{1}{2}\right)^2 = 1 \qquad \text{Factor the perfect square trinomial.}$$

$$\left(x - \frac{1}{2}\right) = \pm\sqrt{1} \qquad \text{Take the square root of each side.}$$

$$x = \frac{1}{2} \pm 1 \qquad \text{Add } \frac{1}{2} \text{ to each side and simplify.}$$

The solution set is $\left\{\frac{3}{2}, -\frac{1}{2}\right\}$.

> **Remember** Before you complete the square, the coefficient of the squared term must be 1.

▶ **Think About It** Do not multiply out the $\left(\frac{b}{2}\right)^2$ term on the left side. That way, the trinomial is easier to factor and you are less likely to make a mistake.

B $x^2 + 20x + 8 = 0$

SOLUTION

Step 1

$x^2 + 20x + 8 = 0$

$x^2 + 20x = -8$ Subtract 8 from each side.

Step 2

$x^2 + 20x + \mathbf{10^2} = -8 + \mathbf{100}$ Add $\left(\frac{20}{2}\right)^2 = 10^2 = 100$ to each side.

$x^2 + 20x + 10^2 = 92$ Simplify.

Step 3

$(x + 10)^2 = 92$ Factor the perfect square trinomial.

$x + 10 = \pm\sqrt{92}$ Take the square root of each side.

$x + 10 = \pm 2\sqrt{23}$ Simplify.

$x = -10 \pm 2\sqrt{23}$ Subtract 10 from each side.

The solution set is $\left\{-10 + 2\sqrt{23}, -10 - 2\sqrt{23}\right\}$. ■

▶ **Think About It** Sometimes quadratic equations have solutions that are irrational numbers.

Application: Art

EXAMPLE 3

An 8 in. by 10 in. painting is framed so that the total area of the painting with the frame is 100 in^2. Find the width of the frame to the nearest hundredth of an inch.

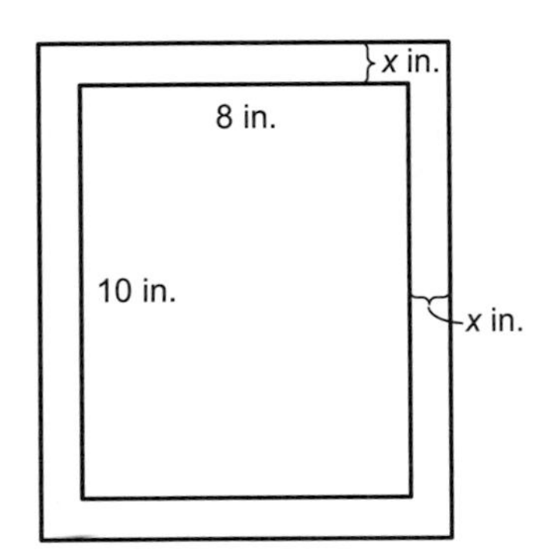

SOLUTION

Use the problem-solving plan.

Step 1 ***Identify*** Find the width of the frame.

Step 2 ***Strategize*** The length and width of the frame is x inches. Write the length and width of the painting, with the frame, in terms of x.

The total width in inches is $8 + x + x = 8 + 2x$.

The total length in inches is $10 + x + x = 10 + 2x$.

Step 3 ***Set Up*** Use the length and width to write and solve an equation for the area.

$A = lw$	Area equals length times width.
$100 = (10 + 2x)(8 + 2x)$	Substitute $(10 + 2x)$ for l and $(8 + 2x)$ for w.

Step 4 ***Solve***

$$100 = (10 + 2x)(8 + 2x)$$

$$100 = 80 + 36x + 4x^2 \quad \text{Multiply the binomials.}$$

$$25 = 20 + 9x + x^2 \quad \text{Divide each side by 4.}$$

$$5 = 9x + x^2 \quad \text{Subtract 20 from each side.}$$

$$5 = x^2 + 9x \quad \text{Commutative Property of Addition}$$

$$5 + \mathbf{\frac{81}{4}} = x^2 + 9x + \left(\mathbf{\frac{9}{2}}\right)^2 \quad \text{Add } \left(\frac{9}{2}\right)^2 = \frac{81}{4} \text{ to each side.}$$

$$\frac{101}{4} = \left(x + \frac{9}{2}\right)^2 \quad \text{Factor the perfect square trinomial and simplify.}$$

$$\pm\sqrt{\frac{101}{4}} = \left(x + \frac{9}{2}\right) \quad \text{Take the square root of each side.}$$

$$-\frac{9}{2} \pm \frac{\sqrt{101}}{2} = x \quad \text{Subtract } \frac{9}{2} \text{ from each side.}$$

$$-\frac{9}{2} + \frac{\sqrt{101}}{2} = x \text{ or } -\frac{9}{2} - \frac{\sqrt{101}}{2} = x \quad \text{Simplify.}$$

$$0.5249 \approx x \qquad -9.5249 \approx x$$

The width of the frame must be positive, so you can disregard the negative solution. The width is about 0.52 in.

Step 5 ***Check***

$$(10 + 2x)(8 + 2x) = 100$$

$$(10 + 2 \bullet \mathbf{0.52})(8 + 2 \bullet \mathbf{0.52}) \stackrel{?}{=} 100$$

$$11.04 \bullet 9.04 \stackrel{?}{=} 100$$

$$99.80 \approx 100 \checkmark$$

The approximate solution is accurate. ■

The Quadratic Formula

You can solve any quadratic equation in standard form using the quadratic formula.

Use completing the square on the standard form of a quadratic equation, $ax^2 + bx + c = 0$, to derive the **quadratic formula**.

$$ax^2 + bx + c = 0$$

$$ax^2 + bx = -c$$ Subtract c from each side.

$$x^2 + \frac{b}{a}x = -\frac{c}{a}$$ Divide each side by a.

$$x^2 + \frac{b}{a}x + \left(\frac{b}{2a}\right)^2 = -\frac{c}{a} + \frac{b^2}{4a^2}$$ Add $\left(\frac{b}{2a}\right)^2 = \frac{b^2}{4a^2}$ to each side.

$$x^2 + \frac{b}{a}x + \left(\frac{b}{2a}\right)^2 = -\frac{4ac}{4a^2} + \frac{b^2}{4a^2}$$ Multiply $\frac{c}{a}$ by $\frac{4a}{4a}$ to get a common denominator.

$$x^2 + \frac{b}{a}x + \left(\frac{b}{2a}\right)^2 = \frac{b^2 - 4ac}{4a^2}$$ Simplify.

$$\left(x + \frac{b}{2a}\right)^2 = \frac{b^2 - 4ac}{4a^2}$$ Factor the perfect square trinomial.

$$\left(x + \frac{b}{2a}\right) = \pm\sqrt{\frac{b^2 - 4ac}{4a^2}}$$ Take the square root of each side.

$$x + \frac{b}{2a} = \pm\frac{\sqrt{b^2 - 4ac}}{2a}$$ Simplify.

$$x = -\frac{b}{2a} \pm \frac{\sqrt{b^2 - 4ac}}{2a}$$ Subtract $\frac{b}{2a}$ from each side.

$$x = \frac{-b \pm \sqrt{b^2 - 4ac}}{2a}$$ Simplify.

Using the Quadratic Formula

The Quadratic Formula

For a quadratic equation written in standard form, $ax^2 + bx + c = 0$, where $a \neq 0$, the solutions of the equation can be found using the quadratic formula.

$$x = \frac{-b \pm \sqrt{b^2 - 4ac}}{2a}$$

To use the quadratic formula, write the quadratic equation you are trying to solve in standard form, and then identify the values of a, b, and c.

EXAMPLE 1

Solve the equation. Estimate irrational solutions to the nearest tenth.

A $x^2 + 9x - 22 = 0$

SOLUTION

Since the equation is in standard form, identify a, b, and c: $a = 1$, $b = 9$, and $c = -22$.

$$x = \frac{-b \pm \sqrt{b^2 - 4ac}}{2a}$$

$$x = \frac{-9 \pm \sqrt{9^2 - 4 \bullet 1 \bullet (-22)}}{2 \bullet 1}$$ Substitute values for a, b, and c.

$$x = \frac{-9 \pm \sqrt{81 - (-88)}}{2}$$ Simplify the radicand.

$$x = \frac{-9 \pm \sqrt{169}}{2}$$ Simplify.

$$x = \frac{-9 \pm 13}{2}$$ Evaluate the square root.

$$x = \frac{-9 + 13}{2} \text{ or } x = \frac{-9 - 13}{2}$$ Write $x = \frac{-9 \pm 13}{2}$ as two equations.

$$x = \frac{4}{2} \qquad x = \frac{-22}{2}$$ Simplify each numerator.

$$x = 2 \qquad x = -11$$ Divide.

The solution set is $\{2, -11\}$.

B $x^2 + 3x = 5$

SOLUTION

Write the equation in standard form by subtracting 5 from each side.

$$x^2 + 3x = 5$$

$$x^2 + 3x - 5 = 0 \qquad \text{Subtract 5 from each side.}$$

Identify a, b, and c: $a = 1$, $b = 3$, and $c = -5$.

$$x = \frac{-b \pm \sqrt{b^2 - 4ac}}{2a}$$

$$x = \frac{-3 \pm \sqrt{3^2 - 4 \bullet 1 \bullet (-5)}}{2 \bullet 1} \qquad \text{Substitute values for } a, b, \text{ and } c.$$

$$x = \frac{-3 \pm \sqrt{9 - (-20)}}{2} \qquad \text{Simplify the radicand.}$$

$$x = \frac{-3 \pm \sqrt{29}}{2} \qquad \text{Simplify.}$$

$$x = \frac{-3 + \sqrt{29}}{2} \approx 1.2 \text{ or } x = \frac{-3 - \sqrt{29}}{2} \approx -4.2 \qquad \text{Write } x = \frac{-3 \pm \sqrt{29}}{2} \text{ as two equations.}$$

The solution set is $\{1.2, -4.2\}$. ■

Using the Discriminant

The **discriminant** is the radicand $b^2 - 4ac$ in the quadratic formula. If you know the value of the discriminant, you can determine how many solutions the equation has and whether the solutions are rational, irrational, or nonreal.

Using the Discriminant to Determine the Number of Solutions

The equation, $ax^2 + bx + c = 0$, where $a \neq 0$, has

- Two rational solutions if $b^2 - 4ac > 0$ and $b^2 - 4ac$ is a perfect square.
- Two irrational solutions if $b^2 - 4ac > 0$ and $b^2 - 4ac$ is not a perfect square.
- One rational solution if $b^2 - 4ac = 0$
- No real solutions if $b^2 - 4ac < 0$.

▶ **Remember** A number is a perfect square if it can be written as the square of a rational number.

EXAMPLE 2

Use the discriminant to determine the number and type of solutions the equation has.

A $2x^2 + 13x + 15 = 0$

SOLUTION

Identify a, b, and c: $a = 2$, $b = 13$, and $c = 15$.

$$b^2 - 4ac = 13^2 - 4 \bullet 2 \bullet 15 = 169 - 120 = 49$$

The discriminant, 49, is positive and is a perfect square, so the equation has two rational solutions.

B $x^2 - \frac{1}{2}x + \frac{1}{16} = 0$

SOLUTION

Identify a, b, and c: $a = 1$, $b = -\frac{1}{2}$, and $c = \frac{1}{16}$.

$$b^2 - 4ac = \left(-\frac{1}{2}\right)^2 - 4 \bullet 1 \bullet \frac{1}{16} = \frac{1}{4} - \frac{1}{4} = 0$$

The discriminant is zero, so the equation has one rational solution.

C $x^2 + 5 = 0$

SOLUTION

Identify a, b, and c: $a = 1$, $b = 0$, and $c = 5$.

$$b^2 - 4ac = 0^2 - 4 \bullet 1 \bullet 5 = 0 - 20 = -20$$

The discriminant, -20, is negative, so the equation has no real solutions. ■

Application: Determining Whether a Polynomial Is Factorable

The expression $ax^2 + bx + c$ is factorable if the solutions to the equation $ax^2 + bx + c = 0$ are rational. The expression $ax^2 + bx + c$ is factorable if the discriminant is either a perfect square or zero.

EXAMPLE 3

Determine whether the polynomial is factorable.

A $30x^2 - 31x - 44$

SOLUTION

Find the discriminant.

$$a = 30, b = -31, \text{ and } c = -44$$

$$\begin{aligned} b^2 - 4ac &= (-31)^2 - 4 \cdot 30 \cdot (-44) \\ &= 961 + 5280 \\ &= 6241 \end{aligned}$$

Because $6241 = 69^2$, it is a perfect square, so $30x^2 - 31x - 44$ is factorable.

B $27x^2 + 14x - 15$

SOLUTION

Find the discriminant.

$$a = 27, b = 14, \text{ and } c = -15$$

$$\begin{aligned} b^2 - 4ac &= 14^2 - 4 \cdot 27 \cdot (-15) \\ &= 196 + 1620 \\ &= 1816 \end{aligned}$$

Because 1816 is not a perfect square, $27x^2 + 14x - 15$ is not factorable. ■

Solving Quadratic Equations

To determine the best method for solving a quadratic equation, first examine the equation.

Methods for Solving Quadratic Equations

Method 1 **Take the square root of each side.** Use only with perfect square equations.

Method 2 **Factor and use the zero product property.** Use when one side of an equation is equal to 0, and the other side is easily factored.

Method 3 **Complete the square.** Use when an equation is of the form $x^2 + bx + c = 0$, where b is an even number and $x^2 + bx + c$ is not factorable.

Method 4 **Use the quadratic formula.** Use when other methods are too difficult or cannot be used.

Choosing a Method for Solving a Quadratic Equation

EXAMPLE 1

Determine the best method for solving the equation.

A $x^2 + 4x - 1 = 0$

SOLUTION

Complete the square or use the quadratic formula. The equation is of the form $x^2 + bx + c = 0$, where b is an even number and $x^2 + bx + c$ is not factorable.

▶ **Remember** Use the discriminant to determine whether a quadratic expression is factorable.

B $x^2 + 6x + 9 = 49$

SOLUTION

Take the square root of each side. Since you can the write the equation as $(x + 3)^2 = 49$, it is a perfect square equation.

C $x^2 + 5x - 6 = 3$

SOLUTION

Use the quadratic formula. You can write the equation as $x^2 + 5x - 9 = 0$, and the trinomial $x^2 + 5x - 9$ is not factorable. Since b is not an even number, completing the square would be cumbersome. ■

Solving Quadratic Equations

EXAMPLE 2

Use the best method to solve the equation.

A $x^2 = -9x$

SOLUTION

Use the zero product property.

$$x^2 = -9x$$

$x^2 + 9x = 0$ Add $9x$ to each side.

$x(x + 9) = 0$ Factor the left side.

$x = 0$ or $x + 9 = 0$ Zero Product Property

$x = -9$

The solution set is $\{0, -9\}$.

Think About It You cannot divide both sides of the equation by x because you would lose a solution. Division by zero is undefined, so be careful when dividing by any variable expression.

B $x^2 + 4x = 6$

SOLUTION

Complete the square.

$$x^2 + 4x = 6$$

$$x^2 + 4x + 2^2 = 6 + 4 \qquad \text{Add } \left(\frac{4}{2}\right)^2 = 2^2 = 4 \text{ to each side.}$$

$$(x + 2)^2 = 10 \qquad \text{Factor the left side.}$$

$$(x + 2) = \pm\sqrt{10} \qquad \text{Take the square root of each side.}$$

$$x = -2 \pm \sqrt{10} \qquad \text{Subtract 2 from each side.}$$

The solution set is $\left\{-2 + \sqrt{10}, -2 - \sqrt{10}\right\}$.

C $-x^2 - 6 = 0$

SOLUTION

Isolate the perfect square, and then take the square root of each side.

$$-x^2 - 6 = 0$$

$$-x^2 = 6 \qquad \text{Add 6 to each side.}$$

$$x^2 = -6 \qquad \text{Divide each side by } -1.$$

The square of a real number cannot be negative. The equation has no real solutions. This can be verified by finding the discriminant.

$$b^2 - 4ac = 0^2 - 4 \bullet (-1) \bullet (-6) = -24$$

D $3x^2 - x + 1 = 0$

SOLUTION

Use the quadratic formula with $a = 3$, $b = -1$, and $c = 1$.

$$x = \frac{-b \pm \sqrt{b^2 - 4ac}}{2a}$$

$$= \frac{-(-1) \pm \sqrt{(-1)^2 - 4 \bullet 3 \bullet 1}}{2 \bullet 3}$$

$$= \frac{1 \pm \sqrt{1 - 12}}{6}$$

$$= \frac{1 \pm \sqrt{-11}}{6}$$

The discriminant is -11, so there is no real solution. ■

Application: Geometry

EXAMPLE 3

The length of a rectangular window is 6 ft longer than its width w. Find the width if the area is 10 ft^2. Round your answer to the nearest hundredth.

SOLUTION

Use w for width and $w + 6$ for length.

$A = lw$	
$10 = (w + 6) \bullet w$	Area is length times width.
$10 = w^2 + 6w$	Distributive Property
$10 + 9 = w^2 + 6w + 9$	Complete the square.
$19 = (w + 3)^2$	Factor the perfect square.
$\pm\sqrt{19} = (w + 3)$	Take the square root of each side.
$-3 \pm \sqrt{19} = w$	Subtract 3 from each side.

The solutions are $w = -3 + \sqrt{19} \approx 1.36$ and $w = -3 - \sqrt{19} \approx -7.36$. Since width cannot be negative, the width of the rectangle to the nearest hundredth is 1.36 ft.

CHECK

$$
\begin{aligned}
10 &= w(w+6) \\
10 &\stackrel{?}{=} 1.36(1.36+6) \\
10 &\stackrel{?}{=} 1.36 \bullet 7.36 \\
10 &\approx 10.0096 \checkmark
\end{aligned}
$$

The answer is correct. ■

Formulas with Quadratics

Many formulas include squared variables. To solve for a squared variable in a formula, you can use the same techniques you use to solve quadratic equations with a single variable.

EXAMPLE 1

Solve the formula $F = \frac{GmM}{r^2}$ for r.

SOLUTION

$F = \frac{GmM}{r^2}$

$r^2F = GmM$ — Multiply each side by r^2.

$r^2 = \frac{GmM}{F}$ — Divide each side by F.

$r = \pm\sqrt{\frac{GmM}{F}}$ — Take the square root of each side.

$r = \pm\frac{\sqrt{GmM}}{\sqrt{F}} \cdot \frac{\sqrt{F}}{\sqrt{F}}$ — Rationalize the denominator.

$r = \pm\frac{\sqrt{GmMF}}{F}$ — Simplify.

The solutions are $r = \frac{\sqrt{GmMF}}{F}$ and $r = -\frac{\sqrt{GmMF}}{F}$. ■

▶ **Think About It** In the formula for Example 1, F is the force of gravity between two bodies with masses m and M having centers that are separated by a distance r. G is a proportionality constant.

EXAMPLE 2

Solve $d = -16t^2 + 64t$ for t.

SOLUTION

The equation has terms of t^2 and t. You can rewrite the equation in standard form $ax^2 + bx + c = 0$, using t instead of x as the variable.

$$d = -16t^2 + 64t$$

$$0 = -16t^2 + 64t - d \qquad \text{Subtract } d \text{ from each side.}$$

$$-16t^2 + 64t - d = 0 \qquad \text{Standard form}$$

You can now use the quadratic formula to solve $-16t^2 + 64t - d = 0$ for t.

$$x = \frac{-b \pm \sqrt{b^2 - 4ac}}{2a} \qquad \text{Quadratic formula}$$

$$t = \frac{-64 \pm \sqrt{64^2 - 4(-16)(-d)}}{2(-16)} \qquad \text{Let } x = t,\ a = -16,\ b = 64, \text{ and } c = -d$$

$$t = \frac{-64 \pm \sqrt{4096 - 64d}}{-32} \qquad \text{Simplify.}$$

$$t = \frac{-64 \pm \sqrt{64(64 - d)}}{-32} \qquad \text{Factor 64 out of both terms in the radicand.}$$

$$t = \frac{-64 \pm 8\sqrt{64 - d}}{-32} \qquad \text{Simplify.}$$

$$t = \frac{8 \pm \sqrt{64 - d}}{4} \qquad \text{Simplify.}$$

The solutions are $t = \frac{8 + \sqrt{64 - d}}{4}$ and $t = \frac{8 - \sqrt{64 - d}}{4}$. ■

▶ **Think About It** In the formula for Example 2, d is the distance (in feet) above the ground for an object t seconds after it is released with an upward velocity of 64 ft/s.

Applications: Area Problems

You can solve many area problems by using quadratic equations.

Application: Rectangles

The area of a rectangle is $A = lw$. When l and w are variables, the area is a quadratic.

EXAMPLE 1

A The length of a rectangle is 5 more than 3 times its width. Find the length and width of the rectangle with an area of 182 units^2.

SOLUTION

Write expressions for the length and width and use the formula for the area of a rectangle. Let w represent the width of the rectangle. Let l represent the length of the rectangle: $l = 3w + 5$.

$A = lw$	
$182 = (3w + 5)w$	Substitution Property
$182 = 3w^2 + 5w$	Distributive Property
$0 = 3w^2 + 5w - 182$	Subtract 182 from each side.

Find the value of the discriminant for $a = 3$, $b = 5$, and $c = -182$ to find the number of roots.

$$b^2 - 4ac = 5^2 - 4 \cdot 3 \cdot (-182) = 25 + 2184 = 2209$$

Since the discriminant is positive, there are two roots. Since the quadratic equation cannot be easily factored, use the quadratic formula to find the roots of the equation.

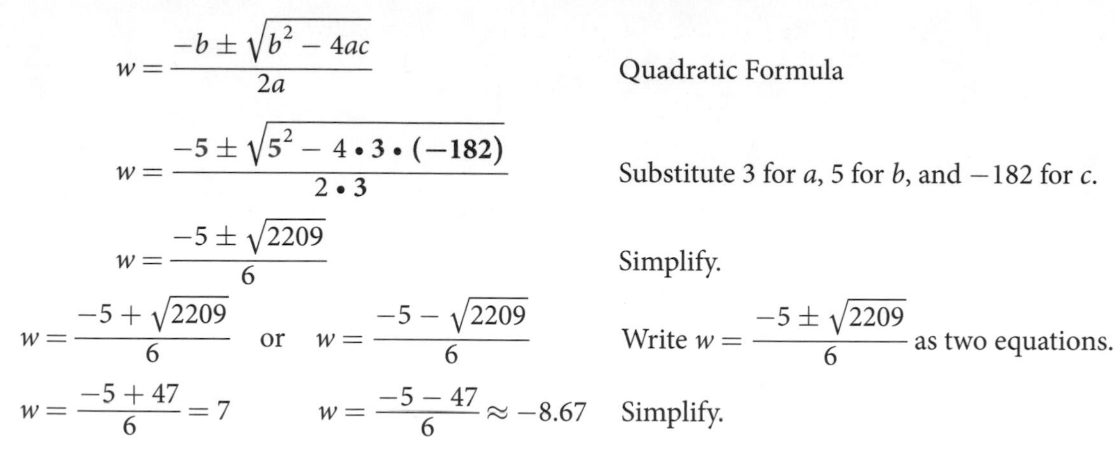

$$w = \frac{-b \pm \sqrt{b^2 - 4ac}}{2a}$$ Quadratic Formula

$$w = \frac{-5 \pm \sqrt{5^2 - 4 \cdot 3 \cdot (-182)}}{2 \cdot 3}$$ Substitute 3 for a, 5 for b, and -182 for c.

$$w = \frac{-5 \pm \sqrt{2209}}{6}$$ Simplify.

$$w = \frac{-5 + \sqrt{2209}}{6} \quad \text{or} \quad w = \frac{-5 - \sqrt{2209}}{6}$$ Write $w = \frac{-5 \pm \sqrt{2209}}{6}$ as two equations.

$$w = \frac{-5 + 47}{6} = 7 \qquad w = \frac{-5 - 47}{6} \approx -8.67$$ Simplify.

When $w = 7$, $3w + 5 = 3 \cdot 7 + 5 = 26$

Notice there are two answers, 7 and -8.67. Since width can only be positive, discard the negative answer. The width is 7 units and the length is 26 units.

▶ **Remember** Distance is always positive.

CHECK

$7 \cdot 26 = 182$ and 26 is 5 more than 3 times 7.

B The length of a rectangle is twice its width. If the width is tripled and the length is decreased by 5, the area is increased by 4. Find the width.

SOLUTION

For the original rectangle: Let w represent the width of the rectangle. Let l represent the length of the rectangle: $l = 2w$.

Arrange the information in a table.

	Original rectangle	New rectangle
Width	w	$3w$
Length	$2w$	$2w - 5$
Area	$2w \cdot w = 2w^2$	$3w(2w - 5) = 6w^2 - 15w$

$$\underbrace{\text{The new area}}_{6w^2 - 15w} \quad \underbrace{\text{is}}_{=} \quad \underbrace{\text{the area of the original rectangle}}_{2w^2} \quad \underbrace{\text{increased by 4.}}_{+4}$$

$$6w^2 - 15w = 2w^2 + 4$$

$4w^2 - 15w - 4 = 0$ Simplify so one side of the equation equals 0.

$(4w + 1)(w - 4) = 0$ Factor.

$w = -\frac{1}{4}$ or $w = 4$ Zero Product Property

Discard the negative solution because width can only be positive. The width of the rectangle is 4 units.

CHECK

Original area: $4 \cdot 8 = 32$, New area: $12 \cdot 3 = 36$, and $36 = 32 + 4$ ■

Application: Triangles and Circles

The area of a triangle is $A = \frac{1}{2}bh$. When b and h are variables, the area is a quadratic.

EXAMPLE 2

The height of a triangle is 3 times the length of its base. A new triangle is formed by lengthening the base by 1 and dividing the height by 3. The area is 60 less than the area of the original triangle. What are the length of the base and the height of the original triangle?

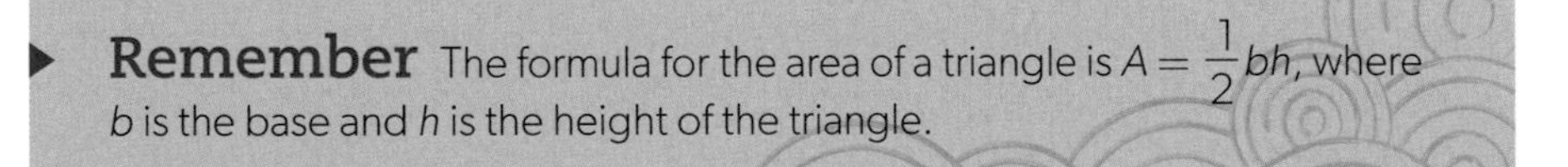

▶ **Remember** The formula for the area of a triangle is $A = \frac{1}{2}bh$, where b is the base and h is the height of the triangle.

SOLUTION

Let b represent the base of the original triangle. Let h represent the height of the original triangle: $h = 3b$.

Arrange the information in a table.

	Original triangle	New triangle
Base	b	$b + 1$
Height	$3b$	b
Area	$\frac{1}{2} \cdot b \cdot 3b = \frac{1}{2}\left(3b^2\right)$	$\frac{1}{2}(b + 1) \cdot b = \frac{1}{2}\left(b^2 + b\right)$

The new area is the area of the original triangle decreased by 60.

$$\underbrace{\frac{1}{2}\left(b^2 + b\right)}_{\text{The new area}} \underbrace{=}_{\text{is}} \underbrace{\frac{1}{2} \cdot 3b^2}_{\text{the area of the original triangle}} \underbrace{- 60}_{\text{decreased by 60}}$$

$$\frac{1}{2}(b^2 + b) = \frac{1}{2} \cdot 3b^2 - 60$$

$$b^2 + b = 3b^2 - 120$$ Multiply each side by 2 to eliminate the fractions.

$$-2b^2 + b + 120 = 0$$ Simplify so one side of the equation equals 0.

Use the quadratic formula to solve.

$$b = \frac{-b \pm \sqrt{b^2 - 4ac}}{2a}$$ Quadratic Formula

$$b = \frac{\mathbf{-1} \pm \sqrt{\mathbf{1}^2 - 4 \cdot \mathbf{(-2)} \cdot \mathbf{(120)}}}{2 \cdot \mathbf{(-2)}}$$ Substitute -2 for a, 1 for b, and 120 for c in the quadratic formula.

$$b = \frac{-1 \pm \sqrt{961}}{-4}$$ Simplify.

$$b = \frac{-1 + \sqrt{961}}{-4} \quad \text{or} \quad b = \frac{-1 - \sqrt{961}}{-4}$$ Write $b = \frac{-1 \pm \sqrt{961}}{-4}$ as two equations.

$$b = -7.5 \qquad b = 8$$ Simplify.

When $b = 8$, $h = 3b = 3 \cdot 8 = 24$.

Remember to discard the negative solution because the base of a triangle can only be positive. The original triangle has a base of 8 units and a height of 24 units. ■

> ▶ **Remember** Don't confuse the variable *b* in the area formula with the *b* in the quadratic formula.

The area of a circle is $A = \pi r^2$. When the radius or diameter is variable, the area is a quadratic.

EXAMPLE 3

The area of the shaded region is 56π in^2. Find the width of the shaded region.

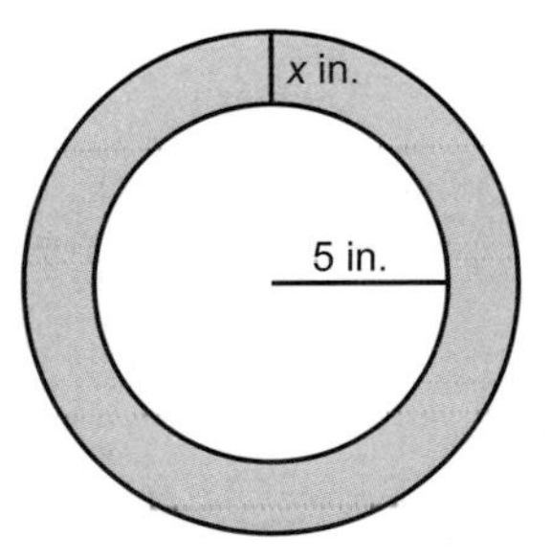

SOLUTION

The area of the shaded region is the difference between the area of the larger circle and the area of the unshaded region.

$56\pi = (5 + x)^2 \pi - 25\pi$	The width of the shaded area is x.
$56 = (5 + x)^2 - 25$	Divide each side by π.
$56 = 25 + 10x + x^2 - 25$	Square the binomial.
$56 = 10x + x^2$	Simplify the right side.
$0 = x^2 + 10x - 56$	Subtract 56 from each side.
$0 = (x + 14)(x - 4)$	Factor.
$x = -14$ or $x = 4$	Zero Product Property

Discard the negative solution because width is always positive. The shaded region has a width of 4 in. ■

Quadratic Functions

Topic List

- Graphing Quadratic Functions
- Properties of Quadratic Functions
- Functions and Transformations
- Quadratic Rates of Change
- Linear/Quadratic Systems
- Applications: Quadratic Functions

Antoni Gaudí (1852–1926) used parabolic arches in many of his architectural designs. Gaudí's parabolic arches are both beautiful and strong.

Graphing Quadratic Functions

A **quadratic function** is a second-degree polynomial function.

Standard Form of a Quadratic Function

The standard form of a quadratic function is $f(x) = ax^2 + bx + c$, where $a \neq 0$. The graph of a quadratic function is called a **parabola**.

One way to graph a quadratic function is to create a table of ordered pairs, plot the points, and then draw a smooth curve through those points. As you study the following examples, recall that y and $f(x)$ are used interchangeably.

Using a Table to Graph a Quadratic Function

EXAMPLE 1

Graph the function.

A $y = x^2$

SOLUTION

x	-2	-1	0	1	2
y	4	1	0	1	4

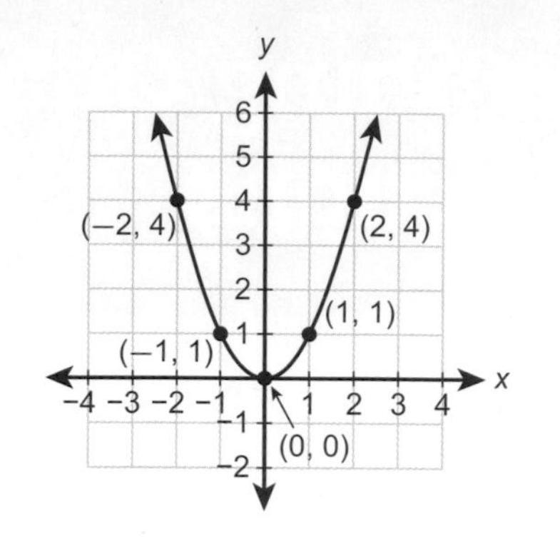

B $y = -2x^2 + 2x + 4$

SOLUTION

x	-2	-1	0	1	2
y	-8	0	4	4	0

The point $(-2, -8)$ is not shown.

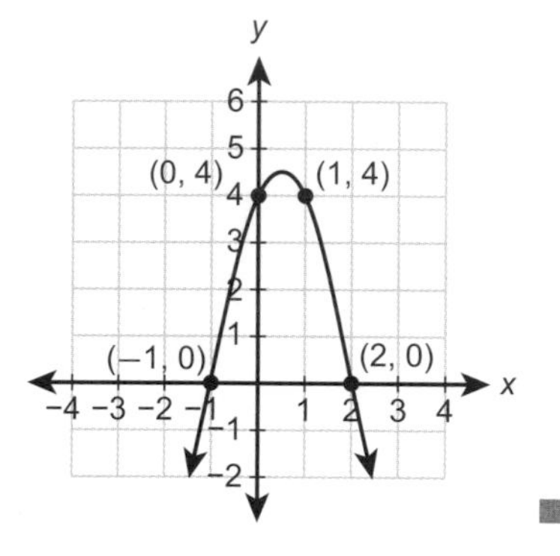

Graphing Quadratic Functions in Standard Form

All quadratic function graphs have in common the following characteristics, which can be used to create accurate graphs.

Properties of Quadratic Function Graphs

The graph of $f(x) = ax^2 + bx + c$ is a parabola with these characteristics:

- It opens up when $a > 0$; it opens down when $a < 0$.
- It has y-intercept c, so $(0, c)$ is a point on the graph.
- It has a vertex with x-coordinate $-\frac{b}{2a}$.
- It has an axis of symmetry with equation $x = -\frac{b}{2a}$.

  The axis of symmetry is the vertical line through the vertex. It separates the graph into two halves that are reflections (mirror images) of each other.

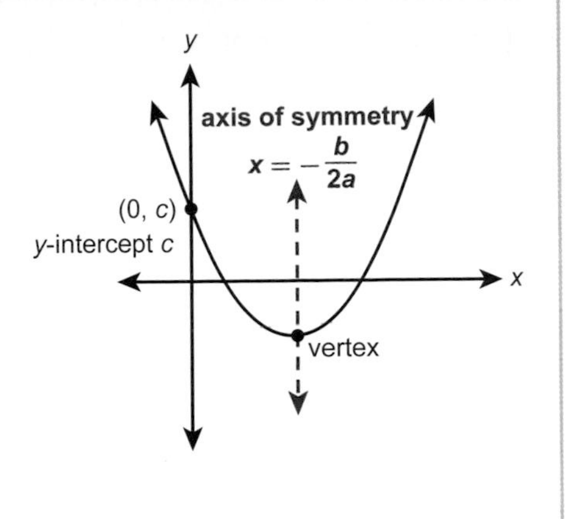

▶ **Think About It** The axis of symmetry is dashed because it is not part of the graph of the function.

EXAMPLE 2

Graph $y = 3x^2 - 12x + 6$.

SOLUTION

First identify the coefficients a, b, and c.

$$y = \underbrace{3x^2}_{a=3}\ \underbrace{-\ 12x}_{b=-12}\ \underbrace{+\ 6}_{c=6}$$

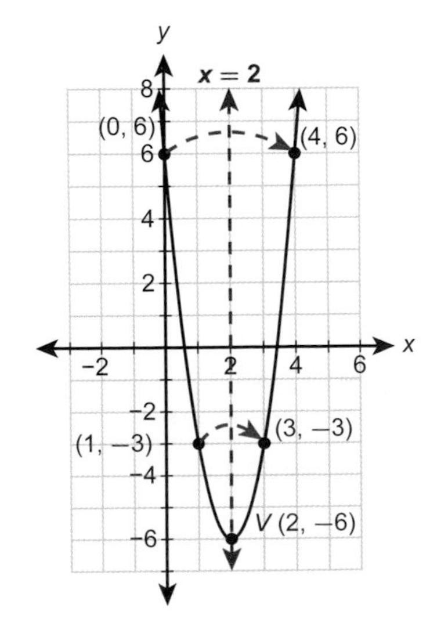

The leading coefficient a is positive, so the parabola opens up, not down.

The x-coordinate of the vertex is $-\frac{b}{2a} = -\frac{(-12)}{2 \cdot 3} = 2$.

To find the y-coordinate of the vertex, substitute 2 for x.

$$y = 3x^2 - 12x + 6 = 3 \cdot \mathbf{2}^2 - 12 \cdot \mathbf{2} + 6 = -6$$

The vertex, V, is $(2, -6)$, and the equation of the axis of symmetry is $x = 2$.

The y-intercept is $c = 6$, so $(0, 6)$ is a point on the graph. The reflection image of $(0, 6)$ over the axis of symmetry is $(4, 6)$, which is also on the graph.

Choose any value for x and substitute it to find one more point on the parabola. If $x = 1$, then $y = 3 \cdot 1^2 - 12 \cdot 1 + 6 = -3$. So $(1, -3)$ is on the graph, and its reflection image $(3, -3)$ is also on the graph.

Draw a smooth curve through all five points, including the vertex. ■

Determining the Number of Zeros of a Quadratic Function

Using properties of quadratic functions can help you determine how many times the graph of a given function crosses the x-axis.

Zeros of a Polynomial Function

The **zeros of a polynomial function $f(x)$** are the **roots** (solutions) of the equation $f(x) = 0$. The real zeros are the x-intercepts of the graph of $f(x)$.

Number of Real Zeros of a Quadratic Function

A quadratic function can have two, one, or no real zeros.

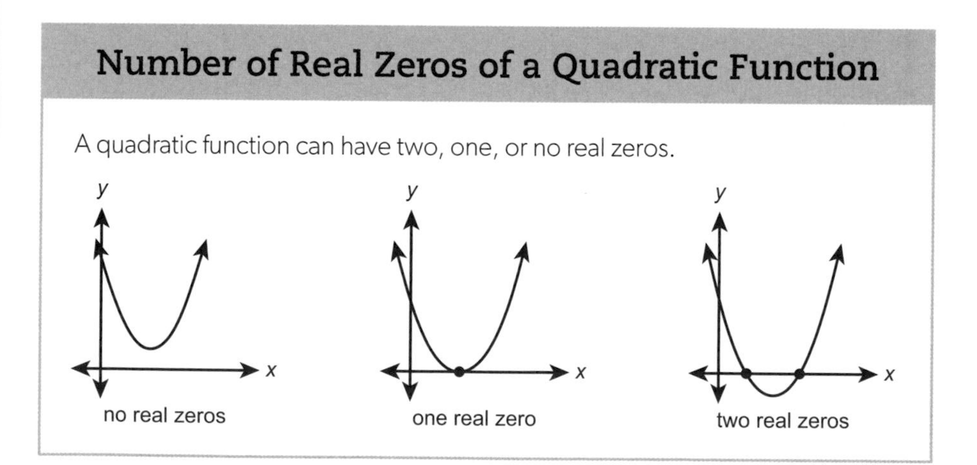

EXAMPLE 3

Determine the number of real zeros of the quadratic function.

A $y = x^2 + 6x + 9$

SOLUTION

$$a = 1, b = 6, \text{ and } c = 9$$

Since $a > 0$, the parabola opens up.

Use a and b to find the x-coordinate of the vertex, and then substitute to find the y-coordinate.

$$x = -\frac{b}{2a} = -\frac{\mathbf{6}}{\mathbf{2 \cdot 1}} = -3$$
$$y = x^2 + 6x + 9 = (\mathbf{-3})^2 + 6 \cdot (\mathbf{-3}) + 9 = 9 - 18 + 9 = 0$$

The vertex is $(-3, 0)$. The vertex is a zero of the function and because the parabola opens up, the vertex is also the lowest point on the graph. Therefore, it is the only real zero. Sketch the graph to verify.

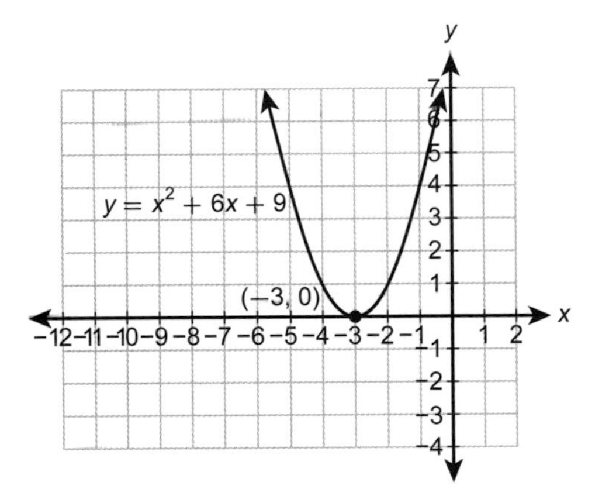

B $y = x^2 + 2$

SOLUTION

$$a = 1, b = 0, \text{ and } c = 2$$

Since $a > 0$, the parabola opens up.

Use a and b to find the x-coordinate of the vertex, and then substitute to find the y-coordinate.

$$x = -\frac{b}{2a} = -\frac{\mathbf{0}}{2 \bullet \mathbf{1}} = 0$$

$$y = x^2 + 2 = \mathbf{0}^2 + 2 = 2$$

The vertex is $(0, 2)$. Since the parabola opens up, the vertex is the lowest point on the graph. Therefore, the function has no real zeros. Sketch the graph to verify.

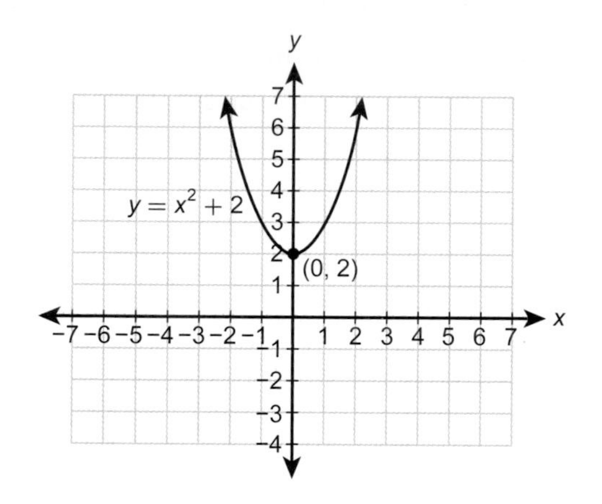

C $y = -x^2 + 4x - 1$

SOLUTION

$$a = -1, b = 4, \text{ and } c = -1$$

Since $a < 0$, the parabola opens down.

Use a and b to find the x-coordinate of the vertex, and then substitute to find the y-coordinate.

$$x = -\frac{b}{2a} = -\frac{\mathbf{4}}{2 \bullet (\mathbf{-1})} = 2$$

$$y = -x^2 + 4x - 1 = -\mathbf{2}^2 + 4 \bullet \mathbf{2} - 1 = -4 + 8 - 1 = 3$$

The vertex is $(2, 3)$. Since the parabola opens down, the vertex is the highest point. The graph must cross the x-axis at two points. Therefore, the function has two real zeros. Sketch the graph to verify.

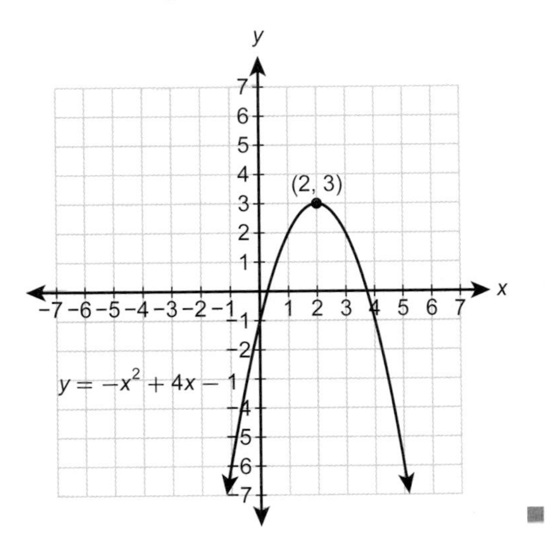

Finding Zeros of a Quadratic Function

The zeros of a quadratic function are the points where the graph of the function intersects the x-axis. So, to find the zeros algebraically, set $f(x) = 0$ and solve the resulting equation for x.

EXAMPLE 4

Find the zeros of the function.

A $f(x) = (x + 3)(2x - 1)$

SOLUTION

$0 = (x + 3)(2x - 1)$ Set $f(x)$ equal to 0 and factor.

$0 = x + 3$ or $0 = 2x - 1$

$-3 = x \quad 1 = 2x$

$\frac{1}{2} = x$

The zeros of the function are $x = -3$ and $x = \frac{1}{2}$.

B $f(x) = 2x^2 + 12x + 10$

SOLUTION

$0 = 2x^2 + 12x + 10$	Set $f(x)$ equal to 0.
$0 = x^2 + 6x + 5$	Divide each side by 2.
$0 = (x + 1)(x + 5)$	Factor.

$x + 1 = 0$ or $x + 5 = 0$

$x = -1 \qquad x = -5$

The zeros of the function are $x = -5$ and $x = -1$. ■

Graphing Quadratic Functions in Factored Form

Using the factored form of a quadratic function can help you graph the function.

▶ **Think About It** The x-intercepts of the graph of $f(x)$ are the roots of the equation $f(x) = 0$. By the zero product property, if $a(x - r_1)(x - r_2) = 0$, then $x - r_1 = 0$ or $x - r_2 = 0$. Solving these two equations for x gives the roots $x = r_1$ and $x = r_2$.

Factored Form of a Quadratic Function

The factored form of a quadratic function is $f(x) = a(x - r_1)(x - r_2)$.

The graph of $f(x) = a(x - r_1)(x - r_2)$ is a parabola with these characteristics:

- It opens up if $a > 0$; it opens down if $a < 0$.
- It has x-intercepts r_1 and r_2.
- It has an axis of symmetry with equation $x = \frac{r_1 + r_2}{2}$ (halfway between the x-intercepts).

EXAMPLE 5

Use the factored form to graph the function.

A $y = x^2 - 2x - 3$

SOLUTION

Factor the trinomial.

$$y = x^2 - 2x - 3 = (x + 1)(x - 3)$$

Since $a = 1$, the parabola opens up. Since $r_1 = -1$ and $r_2 = 3$, the x-intercepts are -1 and 3. Since $\frac{r_1 + r_2}{2} = \frac{-1 + 3}{2} = \frac{2}{2} = 1$, the equation of the axis of symmetry is $x = 1$. Since the axis of symmetry passes through the vertex, the x-coordinate of the vertex must be 1. Substitute 1 for x in the function to find the y-coordinate of the vertex.

$$y = x^2 - 2x - 3 = \mathbf{1}^2 - 2 \bullet \mathbf{1} - 3 = 1 - 2 - 3 = -4$$

The vertex, V, is $(1, -4)$.

Find two more points, such as $(0, -3)$ and its reflection, $(2, -3)$. Then sketch the curve through all the points.

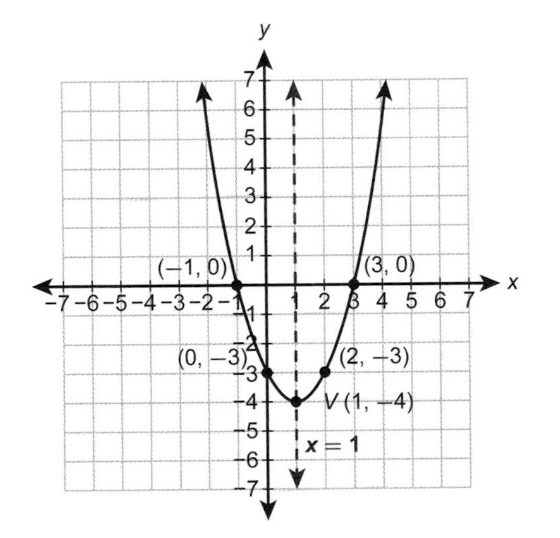

B $y = -0.4x^2 + 0.4x + 4.8$

SOLUTION

Factor out -0.4 and then factor the trinomial.

$$y = -0.4x^2 + 0.4x + 4.8 = -0.4\left(x^2 - x - 12\right) = -0.4(x - 4)(x + 3)$$

Since $a = -0.4$, the parabola opens down. Since $r_1 = 4$ and $r_2 = -3$, the x-intercepts are 4 and -3. Since $\frac{r_1 + r_2}{2} = \frac{4 + (-3)}{2} = \frac{1}{2} = 0.5$, the equation of the axis of symmetry is $x = 0.5$. Since the axis of symmetry passes through the vertex, the x-coordinate of the vertex must be 0.5. Substitute 0.5 for x in the function to find the y-coordinate of the vertex.

$$y = -0.4(x - 4)(x + 3) = -0.4(\mathbf{0.5} - 4)(\mathbf{0.5} + 3) = 4.9$$

The vertex, V, is $(0.5, 4.9)$.

Find two more points, such as $(2, 4)$ and its reflection, $(-1, 4)$. Then sketch the curve through all the points.

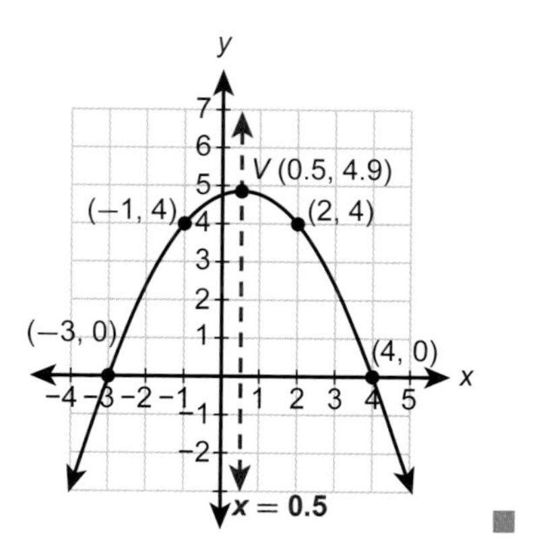

Properties of Quadratic Functions

Just as there are different forms for the equation of a linear function, there are different forms for the equation of a quadratic function.

Quadratic Functions in Vertex Form

Vertex Form of a Quadratic Function

The vertex form of a quadratic function is $f(x) = a(x - h)^2 + k$, where $a \neq 0$.

The vertex is (h, k). The equation of the axis of symmetry is $x = h$.

$f(x) = x^2$ is the parent function of the quadratic family. Every quadratic function $f(x) = a(x - h)^2 + k$ is a transformation of $f(x) = x^2$.

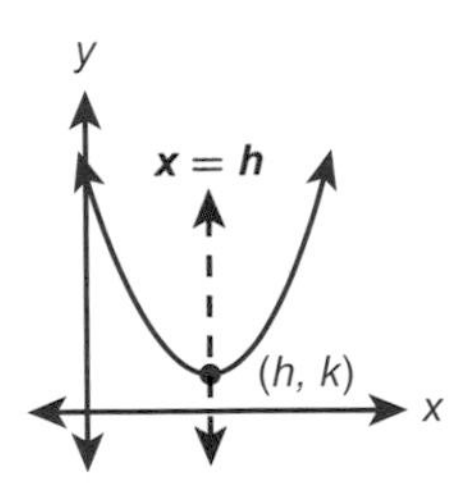

If $a > 0$, the graph opens up, extending infinitely up, left, and right. The minimum function value is k. There is no maximum function value.

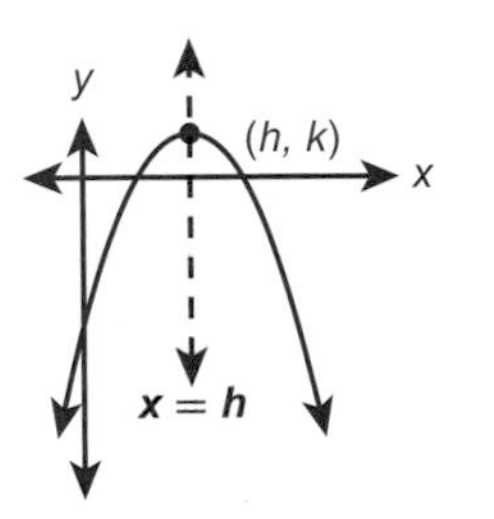

If $a < 0$, the graph opens down, extending infinitely down, left, and right. The maximum function value is k. There is no minimum function value.

EXAMPLE 1

Graph $f(x) = \frac{1}{2}(x - 4)^2 - 2$.

SOLUTION

Since $h = 4$ and $k = -2$, the vertex is $(4, -2)$ and the line of symmetry is $x = 4$. Find two other points on the graph.

x	$\frac{1}{2}(x-4)^2 - 2$	$f(x)$
5	$\frac{1}{2}(5-4)^2 - 2 = \frac{1}{2} \cdot 1 - 2$	$-1\frac{1}{2}$
6	$\frac{1}{2}(6-4)^2 - 2 = \frac{1}{2} \cdot 4 - 2$	0

Reflect the points $(5, -1.5)$ and $(6, 0)$ across the axis of symmetry to get two points on the other side: $(3, -1.5)$ and $(2, 0)$. Draw a smooth curve through all the points.

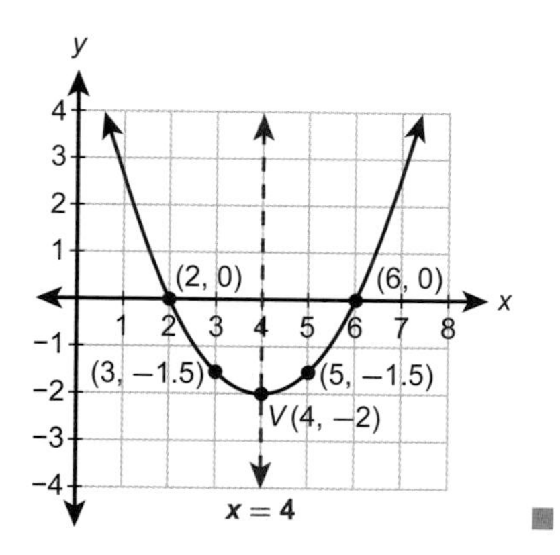

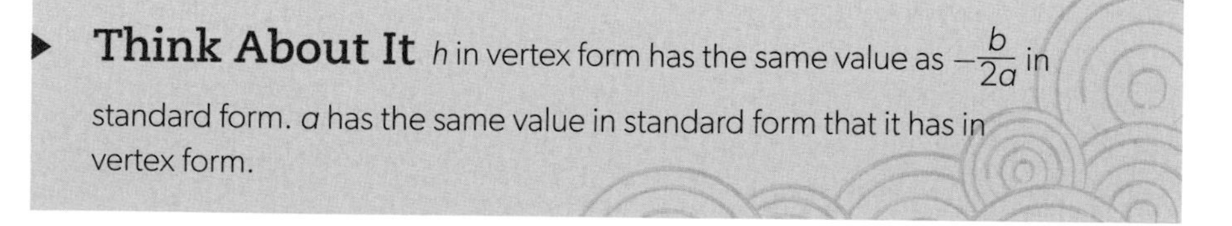

Think About It h in vertex form has the same value as $-\frac{b}{2a}$ in standard form. a has the same value in standard form that it has in vertex form.

Writing an Equation of a Quadratic Function, Given a Graph Showing the Vertex and Another Point

EXAMPLE 2

Write an equation for the quadratic function graphed.

A

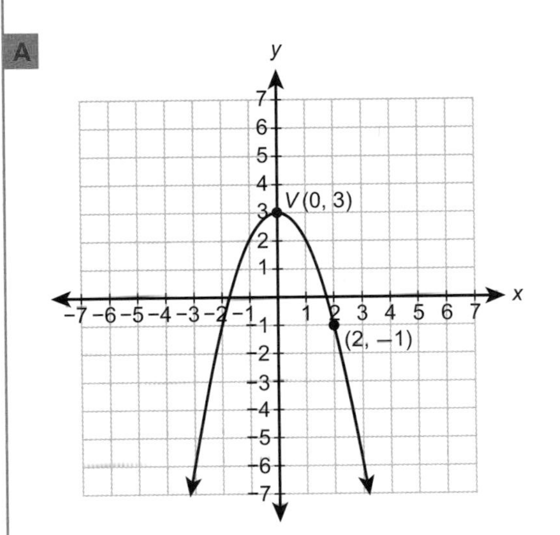

SOLUTION

The vertex $(h, k) = (0, 3)$, so $h = 0$ and $k = 3$.

$f(x) = a(x - h)^2 + k$	Vertex form
$f(x) = a(x - \mathbf{0})^2 + \mathbf{3}$	Substitute 0 for h and 3 for k.
$f(x) = ax^2 + 3$	Simplify.
$\mathbf{-1} = a \cdot \mathbf{2}^2 + 3$	Substitute 2 for x and -1 for y.
$-1 = 4a + 3$	Simplify.
$-4 = 4a$	Solve for a.
$-1 = a$	

The equation is $f(x) = -x^2 + 3$.

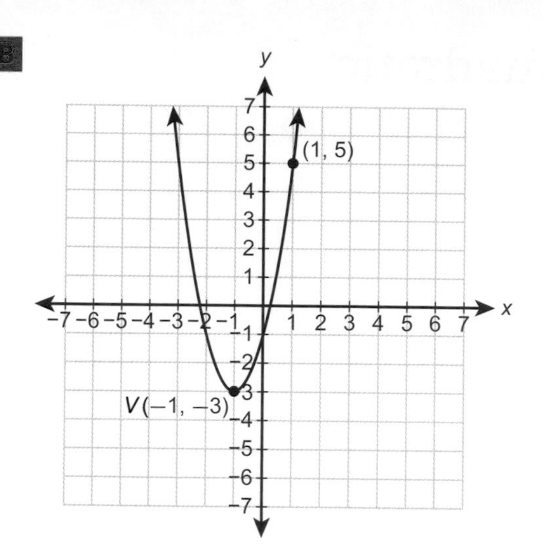

SOLUTION

The vertex $(h, k) = (-1, -3)$, so $h = -1$ and $k = -3$.

$f(x) = a(x - h)^2 + k$ Vertex form

$f(x) = a(x - \mathbf{(-1)})^2 \mathbf{- 3}$ Substitute -1 for h and -3 for k.

$f(x) = a(x + 1)^2 - 3$ Simplify.

$\mathbf{5} = a(\mathbf{1} + 1)^2 - 3$ Substitute 1 for x and 5 for y.

$5 = a \bullet 2^2 - 3$ Simplify.

$5 = 4a - 3$ Solve for a.

$8 = 4a$

$2 = a$

The equation is $f(x) = 2(x + 1)^2 - 3$. ■

Converting from Vertex Form to Standard Form

By using the FOIL method and collecting like terms, you can convert an equation given in vertex form into standard form.

EXAMPLE 3

Write $y = 3(x + 4)^2 - 8$ in standard form.

SOLUTION

$y = 3(x + 4)^2 - 8$	Original equation
$y = 3(x + 4)(x + 4) - 8$	Rewrite the exponent as multiplication.
$y = (3x^2 + 8x + 16) - 8$	Use the FOIL method to multiply the binomials.
$y = 3x^2 + 24x + 48 - 8$	Distribute the 3.
$y = 3x^2 + 24x + 40$	Simplify. ■

Converting from Standard Form to Vertex Form

Converting an equation from standard to vertex form is a bit tougher than converting the other way, but if you remember how to complete the square, you can get it done.

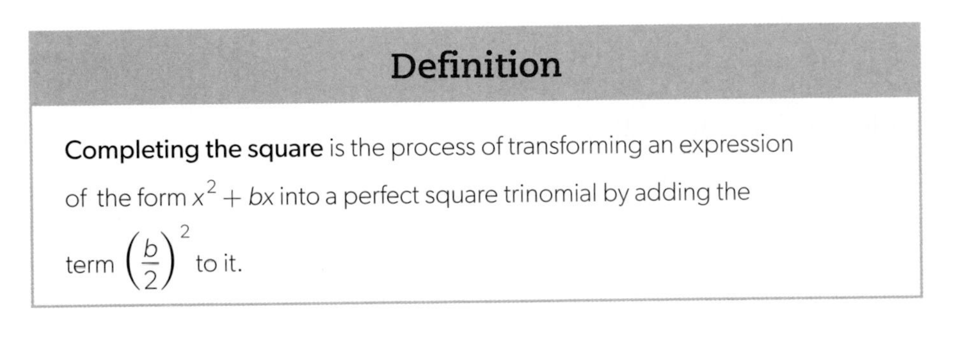

Definition

Completing the square is the process of transforming an expression of the form $x^2 + bx$ into a perfect square trinomial by adding the term $\left(\frac{b}{2}\right)^2$ to it.

EXAMPLE 4

Write the function in vertex form by completing the square.

> ▶ **Think About It** When you complete the square, always be sure either to add a form of zero to one side or to add the same quantity to both sides of the equation. Otherwise, the resulting equation won't be equivalent to the original equation.

A $f(x) = x^2 + 8x + 9$

SOLUTION

$$
\begin{aligned}
f(x) &= x^2 + 8x + 9 \\
f(x) &= \left(x^2 + 8x\right) + 9 \\
f(x) &= \left(x^2 + 8x + 16 - 16\right) + 9 \\
f(x) &= \left(x^2 + 8x + 16\right) - 16 + 9 \\
f(x) &= (x + 4)^2 - 7
\end{aligned}
$$

The function in vertex form is $f(x) = (x + 4)^2 - 7$.

B $y = -3x^2 + 12x + 5$

SOLUTION

$$
\begin{aligned}
y &= -3x^2 + 12x + 5 \\
y &= -3\left(x^2 - 4x\right) + 5 \\
y &= -3\left(x^2 - 4x + 4 - 4\right) + 5 \\
y &= -3\left(x^2 - 4x + 4\right) - 3(-4) + 5 \\
y &= -3(x - 2)^2 + 12 + 5 \\
y &= -3(x - 2)^2 + 17
\end{aligned}
$$

The function in vertex form is $y = -3(x - 2)^2 + 17$. ■

Graphs of Quadratic Functions

Quadratic Function Graph Family: $f(x) = a(x - h)^2 + k$, where $a \neq 0$

The graph of $f(x) = a(x - h)^2 + k$, $a \neq 0$, is a parabola with vertex (h, k) and axis of symmetry $x = h$. The parent graph is $f(x) = x^2$.

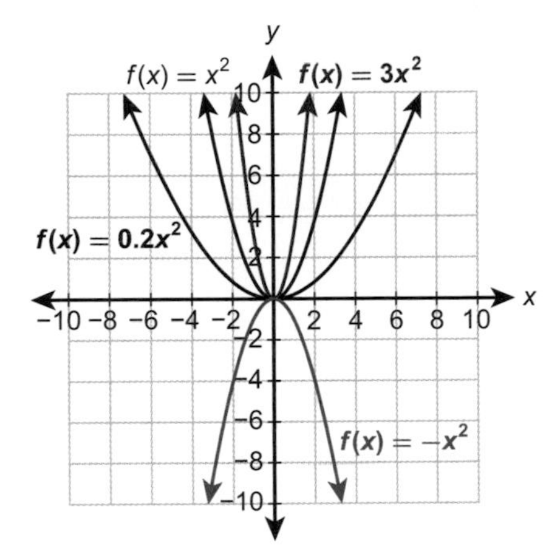

Changing a determines how wide or narrow the parabola is and whether it opens up or down.

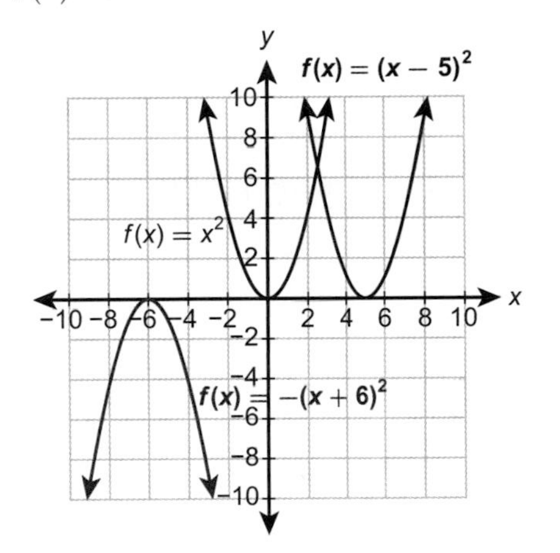

Changing h moves the vertex left or right.

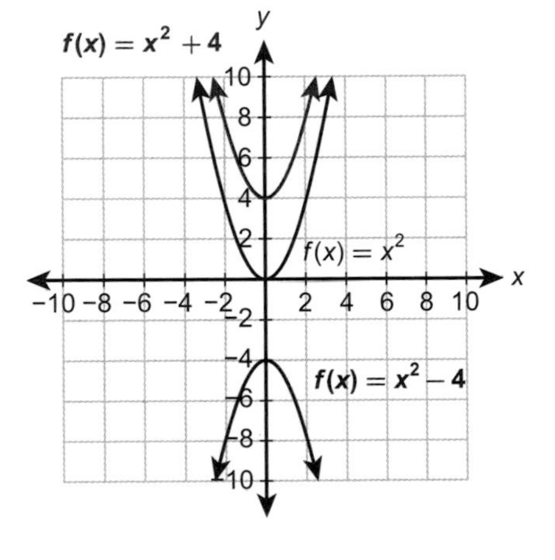

Changing k moves the vertex up or down.

Finding Zeros of a Quadratic Function

Quadratic functions represented as graphs and tables can be used to answer questions about real-world situations.

EXAMPLE 5

The graph is a quadratic function that represents the height of a ball, in feet, x seconds after being kicked vertically into the air.

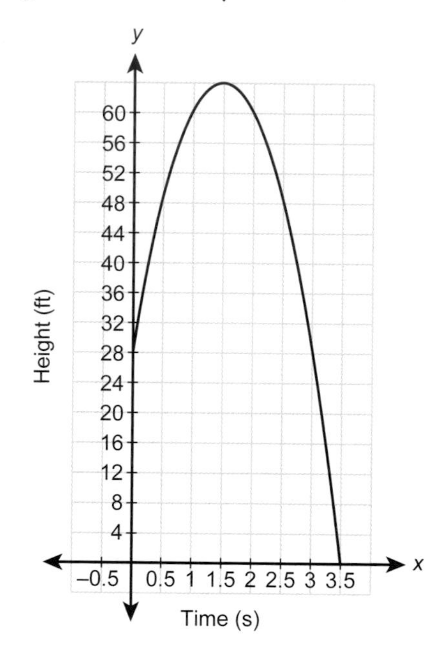

▶ **Think About It** The graph represents a real-world context, so the parabola only shows positive values for x and y.

A Where is the function increasing or decreasing?

SOLUTION

The graph is increasing from $x = 0$ to $x = 1.5$ because as x increases, so does y. The graph is decreasing from $x = 1.5$ to $x = 3.5$ because as x increases, y decreases.

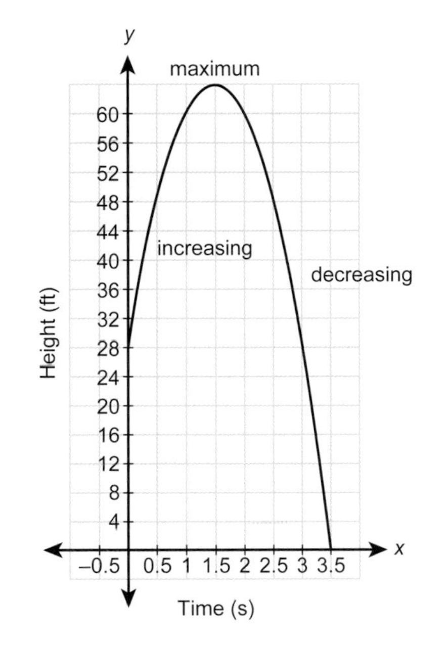

B What is the maximum value of the function, and what does it mean in the context of the situation?

SOLUTION

The maximum value occurs at $x = 1.5$ because that is the greatest value for y. The ball reaches its maximum height of 64 ft after 1.5 s. ■

EXAMPLE 6

The table shows a quadratic function, $f(x)$, that represents the cost for the production of x skateboards.

x	50	55	60	65	70	75	80	85	90	95	100
$f(x)$	500	225	200	125	100	125	200	325	500	725	1000

A Would a parabola that represents the values in the table point up or down?

SOLUTION

The parabola would point up because the y-values decrease until $x = 70$ and then increase after $x = 70$. The minimum value occurs at $x = 70$.

B At what value of the domain does the minimum cost occur?

SOLUTION

Use the bottom row of the table to identify the lowest cost and then identify the number of skateboards for that cost.

The lowest cost is $100, which occurs when 70 skateboards are sold. ■

Functions and Transformations

You can predict the effects of transforming a quadratic function $f(x)$ to another quadratic function $g(x)$.

Identifying Transformations

The parameter k determines the kind of transformation used to transform a function $f(x)$ to $g(x)$.

- When $k < 0$, the function $g(x) = f(x) + k$ is a vertical translation k units down from $f(x)$. When $k > 0$, $g(x) = f(x) + k$ is a vertical translation k units up from $f(x)$.
- When $k < 0$, the function $g(x) = f(x + k)$ is a horizontal translation k units to the right of $f(x)$. When $k > 0$, the function $g(x) = f(x + k)$ is a horizontal translation k units to the left of $f(x)$.
- When $k < -1$ or $k > 1$, the function $g(x) = k \bullet f(x)$ is a vertical stretch of $f(x)$ by a factor of k. When $-1 < k < 1$, the function $g(x) = k \bullet f(x)$ is a vertical compression of $f(x)$ by a factor of k.
- When $k < -1$ or $k > 1$, the function $g(x) = f(k \bullet x)$ is a horizontal compression of $f(x)$ by a factor of $\frac{1}{k}$. When $-1 < k < 1$, $g(x) = f(x \bullet k)$ is a horizontal stretch of $f(x)$ by a factor of $\frac{1}{k}$.

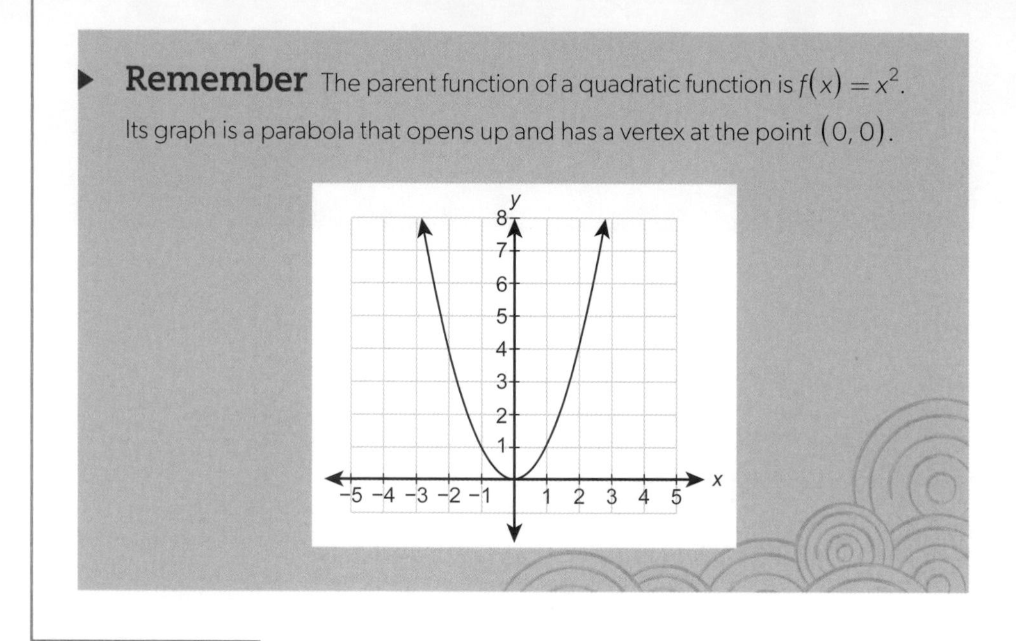

EXAMPLE 1

Describe the transformation from $f(x)$ to $g(x)$. Write the equation for $g(x)$.

A $f(x) = x^2 + 6$ and $g(x) = 2 \bullet f(x)$

SOLUTION

Step 1 Identify the general form that matches $g(x)$.

$g(x) = 2 \bullet f(x)$

$k \bullet f(x)$ General form

$k = 2$

▶ **Remember** When $k < -1$ or $k > 1$, the function $g(x) = k \bullet f(x)$ is a vertical stretch of $f(x)$ by a factor of k.

The function $g(x)$ is a vertical stretch of $f(x)$ by a factor of 2.

Step 2 Write the equation for $g(x)$.

$$g(x) = 2 \bullet f(x)$$
$$g(x) = 2 \bullet (x^2 + 6)$$
$$g(x) = 2x^2 + 12$$

Step 3 Graph $f(x)$ and $g(x)$.

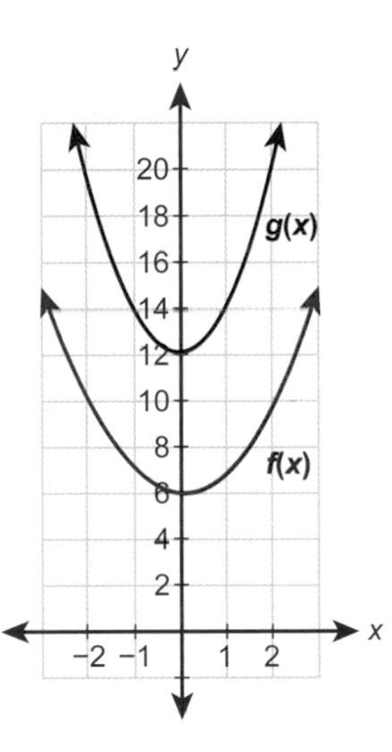

The function $g(x) = 2x^2 + 12$ is a vertical stretch by a factor of 2 and a vertical translation 6 units up from $f(x) = x^2 + 6$.

B $f(x) = x^2 + 4x - 5$ and $g(x) = f(x - 1)$

SOLUTION

Step 1 Identify the general form that matches $g(x)$.

$g(x) = f(x - 1)$

$f(x + k)$ General form

$k = -1$

▶ **Remember** When $k < 0$, the function $g(x) = f(x + k)$ is a horizontal translation k units to the right of $f(x)$.

The function $g(x)$ is a horizontal translation 1 unit to the right of $f(x)$.

Step 2 Write the equation for $g(x)$.

$$g(x) = f(x - 1)$$
$$g(x) = (x - 1)^2 + 4(x - 1) - 5$$
$$g(x) = x^2 - 2x + 1 + 4x - 4 - 5$$
$$g(x) = x^2 + 2x - 8$$

Since $g(x)$ affects the input, find the vertex to determine the horizontal translation. Writing $f(x)$ and $g(x)$ in vertex form gives both the vertex and y-intercept to make graphing easier.

$f(x) = x^2 + 4x - 5$	$g(x) = x^2 + 2x - 8$
$f(x) = (x + 2)^2 - 4 - 5$	$g(x) = (x + 1)^2 - 1 - 9$
$f(x) = (x + 2)^2 - 9$	$g(x) = (x + 1)^2 - 9$

Step 3 Graph $f(x)$ and $g(x)$.

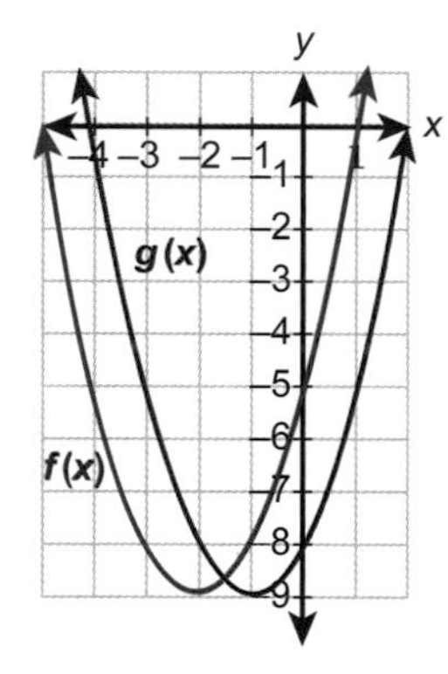

The function $g(x) = x^2 + 2x - 8$ is a horizontal translation 1 unit to the right of $f(x) = x^2 + 4x - 5$. ■

EXAMPLE 2

Describe the transformation of $f(x)$ to $g(x)$.

A $f(x) = 3x^2 + 7$ and $g(x) = 7 + f(x)$

SOLUTION

Step 1 Identify the general form that matches $g(x)$.

$g(x) = f(x) + 7$	Commutative Property
$f(x) + k$	General form
$k = 7$	

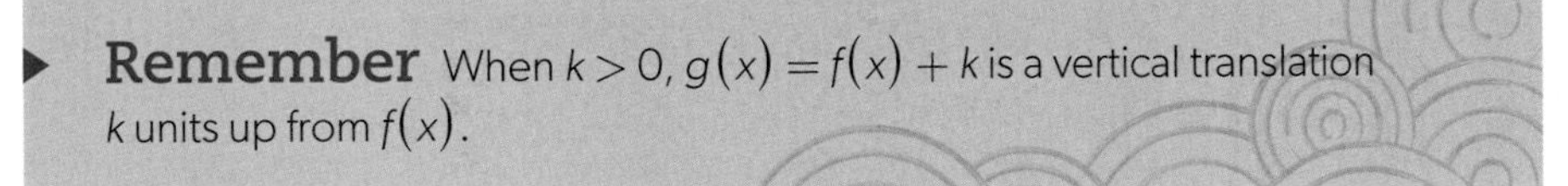

The function $g(x)$ is a vertical translation 7 units up from $f(x)$.

Step 2 Write the equation for $g(x)$.

$$g(x) = 7 + f(x)$$
$$g(x) = 7 + 3x^2 + 7$$
$$g(x) = 3x^2 + 14$$

Step 3 Graph $f(x)$ and $g(x)$.

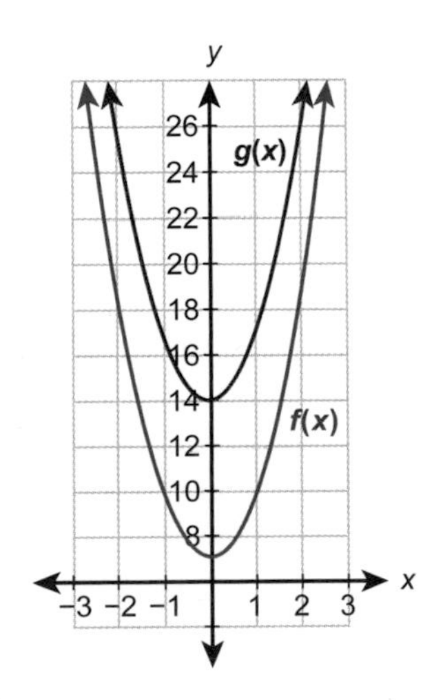

The function $g(x) = 3x^2 + 14$ is a vertical translation 7 units up from $f(x) = 3x^2 + 7$.

B $f(x) = x^2 + 10x$ and $g(x) = 4x^2 + 20x$

SOLUTION

Step 1 Identify the general form that matches $g(x)$.

$g(x) = 4x^2 + 20x$

$g(x) = (2x)^2 + 10(2x)$

$f(k \cdot x)$ General form

$k = 2$

> **Remember** When $k < -1$, or $k > 1$, the function $g(x) = f(k \cdot x)$ is a horizontal compression of $f(x)$ by a factor of $\frac{1}{k}$.

The function $g(x)$ is a horizontal compression of $f(x)$ by a factor of $\frac{1}{2}$.

Step 2 Since $g(x)$ affects the input, determine the vertex for each quadratic function to check for horizontal translation. An alternative to writing the function in vertex form is to find the x-coordinate of the vertex.

> **Remember** To find the x-coordinate of the vertex, use the formula $x = -\frac{b}{2a}$.

$f(x) = x^2 + 10x$ $g(x) = 4x^2 + 20x$

$x = -\frac{10}{2 \cdot 1} = -5$ $x = -\frac{20}{2 \cdot 4} = -2.5$

The function $g(x)$ is a horizontal compression, and it is also a horizontal translation 2.5 units to the right.

Step 3 Graph $f(x)$ and $g(x)$.

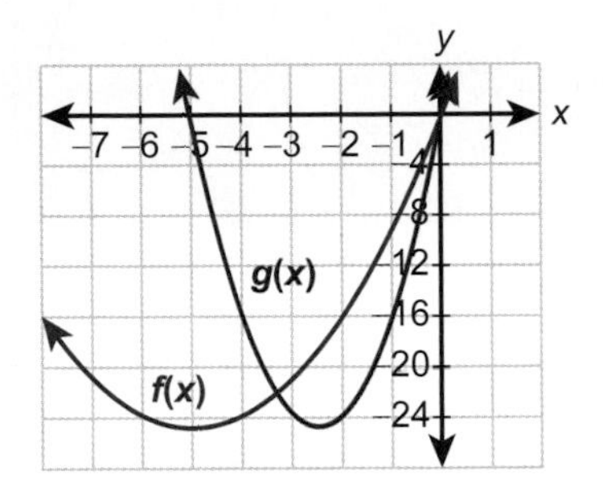

The function $g(x) = 4x^2 + 20x$ is a horizontal compression by a factor of $\frac{1}{2}$ and a horizontal translation to the right 2.5 units from $f(x) = x^2 + 10x$. ■

Quadratic Rates of Change

To calculate the average rate of change of a quadratic function, determine the slope of a line that passes through two points on the function.

Calculating Average Rate of Change

Average Rate of Change Formula

The average rate of change of the function $f(x)$ with respect to x from $x = a$ to $x = b$ is defined as follows:

$$\text{average rate of change} = \frac{f(b) - f(a)}{b - a}.$$

EXAMPLE 1

Complete the table to show the average rate of change for various pairs of points on the function $f(x) = x^2$. Explain what happens to the slope as the segments get farther from the vertex at $(0, 0)$.

From $x = a$	To $x = b$	Average rate of change from a to b
0	1	$\frac{f(1)-f(0)}{1-0} = \frac{1^2 - 0^2}{1} = \frac{1-0}{1} = 1$
1	2	$\frac{f(2)-f(1)}{2-1} = \frac{2^2 - 1^2}{1} = \frac{4-1}{1} = 3$
2	3	$\frac{f(3)-f(2)}{3-2} = \frac{3^2 - 2^2}{1} = \frac{9-4}{1} = 5$
3	4	$\frac{f(4)-f(3)}{4-3} = \frac{4^2 - 3^2}{1} = \frac{16-9}{1} = 7$

Look at a graph of the function with line segments showing the first three rates. You can see that each segment has a different slope. Also, the absolute value of the slope continues to increase as the segment gets farther from the vertex.

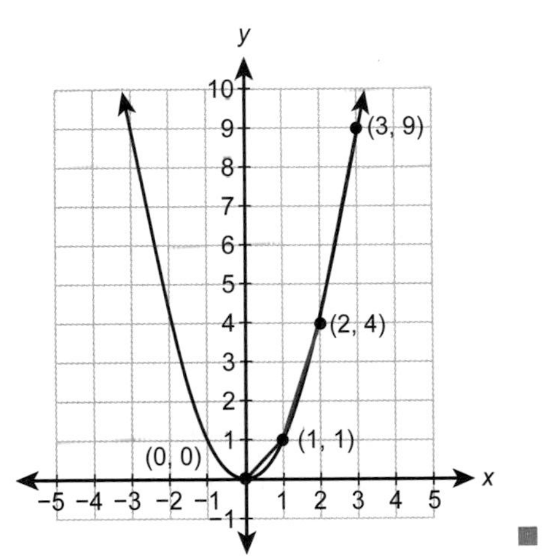

EXAMPLE 2

Use a table to show the values of the linear function, $f(x)$; the quadratic function, $g(x)$; and the exponential function, $h(x)$, for all integer values of x from 0 through 9. For each x, list the functions from least to greatest value.

$$f(x) = 5x \qquad g(x) = x^2 \qquad h(x) = 2^x$$

SOLUTION

x	$f(x)$	$g(x)$	$h(x)$	Least to greatest
0	0	0	1	$f(x), g(x), h(x)$
1	5	1	2	$g(x), h(x), f(x)$
2	10	4	4	$g(x), h(x), f(x)$
3	15	9	8	$h(x), g(x), f(x)$
4	20	16	16	$g(x), h(x), f(x)$
5	25	25	32	$f(x), g(x), h(x)$
6	30	36	64	$f(x), g(x), h(x)$
7	35	49	128	$f(x), g(x), h(x)$
8	40	64	256	$f(x), g(x), h(x)$
9	45	81	512	$f(x), g(x), h(x)$

Comparing the growth of linear, quadratic, and exponential functions that are increasing in value shows that over time, the value of any quadratic function will eventually exceed the value of any linear function. In addition, the value of any exponential function will eventually exceed the value of any quadratic function.

Finding the Average Rate of Change from a Function Equation

The average rate of change between two points on a quadratic function can be found from the function's equation. It is the slope of the line that passes through those points.

EXAMPLE 3

Find the average rate of change of $f(x) = -3x^2 + 5$ from $x = 2$ to $x = 6$.

SOLUTION

Use the formula for average rate of change for the quadratic function $f(x)$.

▸ **Think About It** The formula for average rate of change is similar to the slope formula.

$$\text{average rate of change} = \frac{f(b) - f(a)}{b - a}$$

Step 1 From $x = a$:

$a = 2$

$f(a) = -3(\mathbf{2})^2 + 5$ Substitute.

$= -3(4) + 5$

$= -12 + 5$

$= -7$

Step 2 To $x = b$:

$$b = 6$$

$$\begin{aligned} f(b) &= -3(\mathbf{6})^2 + 5 \qquad \text{Substitute.} \\ &= -3(36) + 5 \\ &= -108 + 5 \\ &= -103 \end{aligned}$$

Step 3 Substitute $a = 2, f(a) = -7, b = 6$, and $f(b) = -103$ into the formula for average rate of change.

$$\frac{f(b) - f(a)}{b - a} = \frac{-103 - (-7)}{6 - 2} = \frac{-96}{4} = -24$$

The average rate of change from $x = 2$ to $x = 6$ is -24. ■

Linear/Quadratic Systems

Linear and quadratic equations can share points that are solutions to both equations.

Definition

A **system of equations** is a group of two or more equations in the same variables.

A system of equations that consists of one linear and one quadratic equation can share two points, one point, or no points. The points of intersection for the linear and quadratic graphs represent ordered pairs that are solutions to both equations.

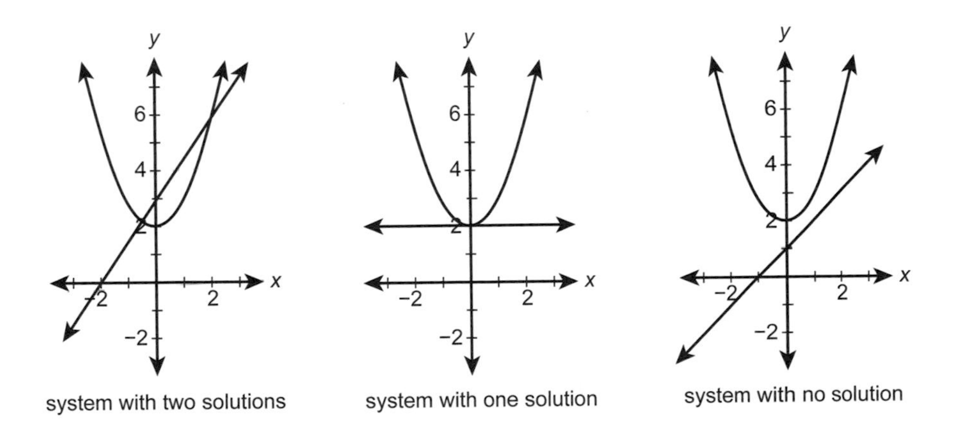

system with two solutions system with one solution system with no solution

The solutions to a linear/quadratic system of equations are ordered pairs. The ordered pairs can be determined by graphing the equations on the coordinate plane or by finding the solution using substitution.

Solving Systems by Graphing

EXAMPLE 1

Use a graph to find the solution to the linear/quadratic system.

$$y = x^2 + 1$$
$$y - x = 1$$

SOLUTION

Create a table of ordered pairs for each equation.

$$\mathbf{y = x^2 + 1}$$

x	−2	−1	0	1	2
y	5	2	1	2	5

$$\mathbf{y - x = 1}$$

x	−1	0	2	1	4
y	0	1	3	2	5

Graph each equation.

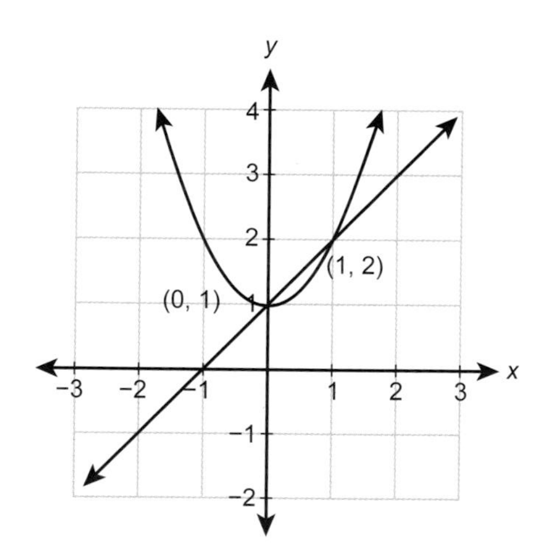

The linear and quadratic equations in the system share two points. The solution to the system consists of the ordered pairs $(0, 1)$ and $(1, 2)$. ■

Solving Systems by Substitution

EXAMPLE 2

Use substitution to find the solution to the linear/quadratic system.

$$y = x^2 - 2x + 2$$
$$y - 2x = -2$$

SOLUTION

Solve the linear equation for y.

$y - 2x = -2$

$y - 2x + 2x = -2 + 2x$ Add $2x$ to both sides.

$y = 2x - 2$ Simplify.

Substitute the expression for y into the quadratic equation.

$y = x^2 - 2x + 2$

$\mathbf{2x - 2} = x^2 - 2x + 2$ Substitute.

$2x - 2 - 2x = x^2 - 2x + 2 - 2x$ Subtract $2x$ from both sides.

$-2 = x^2 - 4x + 2$ Simplify.

$-2 + 2 = x^2 - 4x + 2 + 2$ Add 2 to both sides.

$0 = x^2 - 4x + 4$ Simplify.

$0 = (x - 2)(x - 2)$ Perfect square trinomial

Use the Zero Product Property.

$x - 2 = 0$

$x - 2 + 2 = 0 + 2$ Add 2 to both sides.

$x = 2$ Simplify.

Substitute the value $x = 2$ into the linear equation to find y.

$y - 2x = -2$

$y - 2(2) = -2$ Substitute.

$y - 4 = -2$ Simplify.

$y - 4 + 4 = -2 + 4$ Add 4 to both sides.

$y = 2$ Simplify.

The linear and quadratic equations in the system share one point. The solution to the system is the ordered pair $(2, 2)$. ■

EXAMPLE 3

Use substitution to find the solution to the linear/quadratic system.

$$y = x^2 + 3$$
$$y - x = -2$$

SOLUTION

Solve the linear equation for y.

$y - x = -2$

$y - x + x = -2 + x$ Add x to both sides.

$y = x - 2$ Simplify.

Substitute the value for y into the quadratic equation.

$y = x^2 + 3$

$\mathbf{x - 2} = x^2 + 3$ Substitute.

$x - 2 - x = x^2 + 3 - x$ Subtract x from both sides.

$-2 = x^2 - x + 3$ Simplify.

$-2 + 2 = x^2 - x + 3 + 2$ Add 2 to both sides.

$0 = x^2 - x + 5$ Simplify.

Use the quadratic formula.

$$a = 1, b = -1, \text{ and } c = 5$$

$$x = \frac{-b \pm \sqrt{b^2 - 4ac}}{2a}$$

$$x = \frac{-(-1) \pm \sqrt{(-1)^2 - 4(1)(5)}}{2(1)}$$ Substitute values for a, b, and c.

$$x = \frac{1 \pm \sqrt{1 - 20}}{2}$$ Simplify.

$$x = \frac{1 \pm \sqrt{-19}}{2}$$ Simplify.

The value under the radical is a negative number, so the value of x is not a real number. The system has no real solution. The two equations do not share any points. ■

Applications: Quadratic Functions

Quadratic functions can be used to model many real-world situations.

For some problems, you can create and solve a quadratic equation; for other problems, you can create and optimize a quadratic function.

Application: Furniture Dimensions

EXAMPLE 1

Television screens are described by their diagonal measurement and by their length-to-width ratio. Many widescreen televisions have a length-to-width ratio (usually called the aspect ratio) of 16 : 9. If Mr. Scott has a 40 in. widescreen television with an aspect ratio of 16 : 9, could he fit it in a piece of furniture with an opening that is 37 in. by 24 in.?

SOLUTION

Draw a rectangular television screen. The 40 in. diagonal divides it into two congruent right triangles. Since the ratio of the sides is 16 : 9, the sides can be represented by the multiples $16x$ and $9x$.

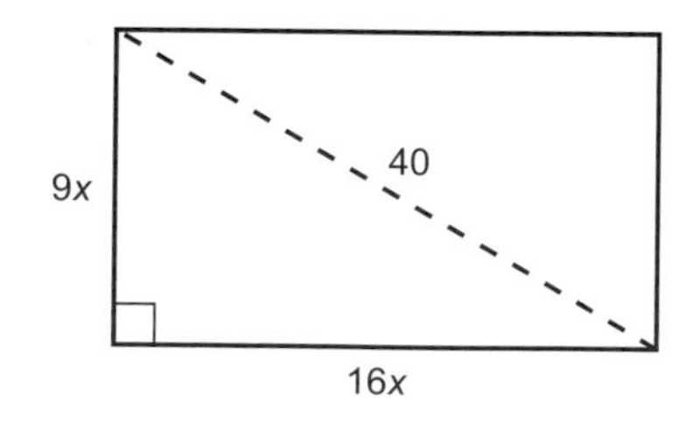

Use the Pythagorean theorem to set up a quadratic equation. Simplify the equation and solve for x.

$$
\begin{aligned}
a^2 + b^2 &= c^2 \\
(\mathbf{9x})^2 + (\mathbf{16x})^2 &= \mathbf{40}^2 \\
81x^2 + 256x^2 &= 1600^2 \\
337x^2 &= 1600^2 \\
x &= \pm\sqrt{\frac{1600}{337}} \approx \pm 2.18
\end{aligned}
$$

Because negative length is not helpful in this situation, -2.18 is an extraneous solution. The television's dimensions are as follows:

$$
\begin{aligned}
16x &\approx 16 \bullet \mathbf{2.18} = 34.88 \\
9x &\approx 9 \bullet \mathbf{2.18} = 19.62
\end{aligned}
$$

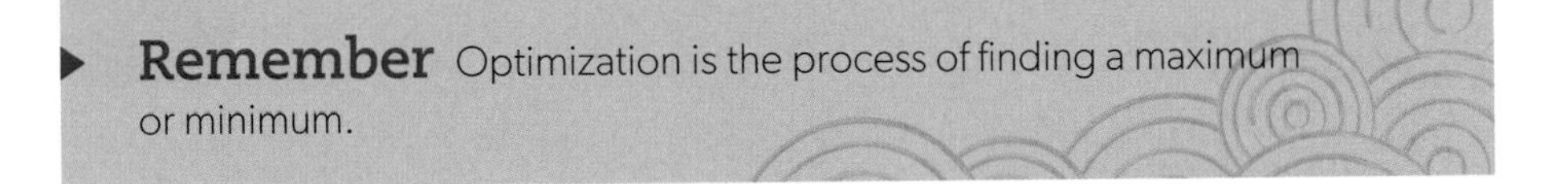

▶ **Remember** Optimization is the process of finding a maximum or minimum.

The dimensions of the 40 in. widescreen television are approximately 35 in. by 20 in. Mr. Scott's furniture can accommodate a 40 in. widescreen as long as the frame around the screen is no more than 1 in. wide on each side. ■

Application: Projectile Motion

Height of Projectile

The height, h, of a projectile after t seconds is given by the function

$$h(t) = \frac{1}{2}gt^2 + v_0 t + h_0$$

where v_0 is the initial vertical velocity, h_0 is the initial height, and g is the downward acceleration due to gravity (on the earth, $g \approx -32 \text{ ft/s}^2 \approx -9.8 \text{ m/s}^2$).

▸ **Remember** A projectile can be either a falling object or an object first projected into the air before it falls.

EXAMPLE 2

Kyle throws a baseball straight up from a height of 4 ft with an initial speed of 30 ft/s.

A Write an equation to model the height, y, of the ball after t seconds.

SOLUTION

Use the values $g = -32$, $v_0 = 30$, and $h_0 = 4$ to write a function for the height of Kyle's baseball.

$$h(t) = -\frac{1}{2} \cdot \mathbf{32}t^2 + \mathbf{30}t + \mathbf{4} = -16t^2 + 30t + 4$$

B Make a graph of the baseball's height as a function of time.

SOLUTION

Make a graph using any tool, such as a table of values, software, or a calculator.

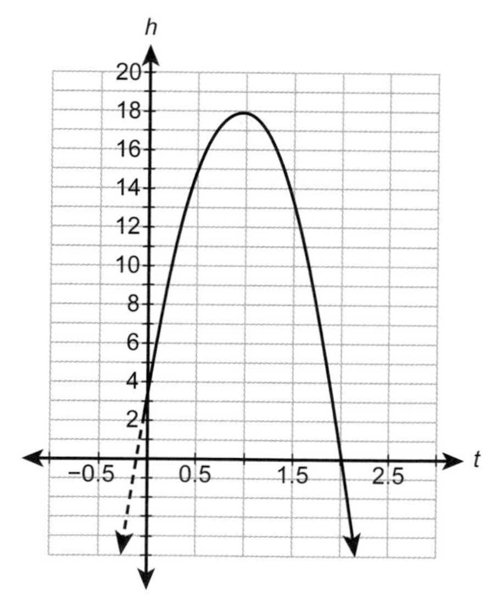

Think About It Keep in mind that the horizontal axis represents time, not horizontal distance. In fact, in this graph, Kyle's ball only moves up and down, not forward.

C What is the maximum height of the baseball?

SOLUTION

The maximum height (the maximum value of the function) corresponds to the h-value of the vertex. You can find the vertex by using your knowledge of the properties of quadratic functions.

$$t = -\frac{b}{2a} = -\frac{30}{2 \cdot (-16)} = \frac{15}{16} = 0.9375$$

The h coordinate of the vertex is $h(0.9375) \approx 18.1$. Therefore, the ball reaches a maximum height of about 18.1 ft.

D If Kyle doesn't catch the ball, when will the ball hit the ground?

Think About It You could also use factoring or the quadratic formula to solve this problem.

SOLUTION

The ground is height $h = 0$, so the ball is on the ground when $0 = -16t^2 + 30t + 4$.

Use the graph as a guide. The graph shows two roots. The leftmost root is extraneous, since negative time has no meaning in this problem. The positive root seems to be at $t = 2$.

$$\begin{aligned} h(2) &= -16 \cdot 2^2 + 30 \cdot 2 + 4 \\ &= -64 + 60 + 4 \\ &= 0 \end{aligned}$$

The ball hits the ground 2 s after Kyle throws it. ■

Application: Optimizing Area

EXAMPLE 3

Selena bought 12 m of fencing to make a rectangular pen for her rabbit. She will use the wall of her shed as 1 side of the pen and the fencing for the other 3 sides. What dimensions maximize the pen's area?

SOLUTION

Sketch and label a diagram of the pen. Let x represent the length of the 2 sides perpendicular to the shed. Of the 12 m of fencing, $12 - 2x$ remain for the third side. The dimensions of the pen are x and $12 - 2x$. Use the area formula for a rectangle to set up a quadratic function, and simplify.

shed wall

x

$12 - 2x$

x

$$\text{area} = \text{length} \cdot \text{width}$$

$$A = \mathbf{x} \cdot (\mathbf{12 - 2x})$$
$$A = -2x^2 + 12x$$

▶ **Remember** You could also find the coordinates of the vertex by completing the square.

Because the leading coefficient is negative, the graph of A would be a parabola that opens down; the coordinates of the vertex give the dimensions that yield the maximum area. The x-value of the vertex is

$$x = -\frac{b}{2a} = -\frac{\mathbf{12}}{2 \cdot (\mathbf{-2})} = 3.$$

Therefore, the pen will have maximum area when its dimensions are $x = 3$ and $12 - 2x = 6$, which gives an area of 18 m^2. ■

Univariate Data

Topic List

- Measures of Center
- Frequency Distributions
- Variability
- Selecting Measures of Center
- Outliers

The average height of a city's buildings can tell you something about the buildings in the city, but one or two remarkably tall buildings could throw off the average. Statistical values and graphs can help you make sense of data.

Measures of Center

Statistics is the branch of mathematics concerned with collecting, analyzing, describing, and interpreting data.

Finding Measures of Central Tendency

Numbers used to describe a data set are also called statistics. Some commonly used statistics are mean, median, and mode, which are measures of center, or measures of central tendency.

Definitions

The **mean** of a data set is the statistical average. For a data set with values $x_1, x_2, \ldots, x_n$, the mean is

$$\overline{x} = \frac{\sum_{i=1}^{n} x_i}{n} = \frac{x_1 + x_2 + \ldots + x_n}{n}.$$

The **median** is the middle value when the values are ordered. If the data set has an even number of values, the median is the mean of the two middle values.

The **mode** is the value that occurs most frequently.

▶ **Think About It** The symbol $\overline{x}$ is read "*x*-bar." It is used to denote the mean of a sample of data. The mean of an entire population is denoted by the Greek letter mu: μ.

A **stem-and-leaf plot** is a useful way to organize and display a data set. It shows the individual data values in increasing order, so it can be used to find the measures of central tendency. In a stem-and-leaf plot, each data value is separated into two parts: The leftmost digit is the **stem**, and the other digit(s) form the **leaf**.

EXAMPLE 1

Make a stem-and-leaf plot of the data values. Then find the mean, median, and mode.

120, 78, 99, 72, 101, 118, 78, 90, 97, 112

SOLUTION

For the stem-and-leaf plot, draw a vertical line segment. Write the stems in increasing order in a column to the left of the line segment. Write the leaves for each stem in increasing order in a row to the right of the segment. Notice that 8 is included as a stem, even though there are no leaves for it; also notice that each leaf is made up of only one digit.

Stem	Leaves
7	2 8 8
8	
9	0 7 9
10	1
11	2 8
12	0

Key: 7 | 2 = 72

$$\text{mean: } \overline{x} = \frac{\sum_{i=1}^{n} x_i}{n} = \frac{72 + 78 + 78 + 90 + 97 + 99 + 101 + 112 + 118 + 120}{10}$$

$$= \frac{965}{10} = 96.5$$

median: Look at the stem-and-leaf plot. There are 10 values, so the middle of the set is the average of the fifth and sixth values.

$$\text{median} = \frac{97 + 99}{2} = \frac{196}{2} = 98$$

mode: In the data set, 78 occurs twice, more than any other value, so the mode is 78. ■

Finding a Value That Will Result in a Given Mean

You can calculate the score you need on the next test to get the average you desire.

EXAMPLE 2

Sharlene earned scores of 90, 84, and 87 on the first three algebra tests. What score must Sharlene earn on the fourth test to have an average of 90?

SOLUTION

Substitute the given values into the rule for finding $\overline{x}$.

$$\overline{x} = \frac{\sum_{i=1}^{4} x_i}{4} = \frac{90 + 84 + 87 + x_4}{4} = 90$$

Solve for x_4.

$$\frac{90 + 84 + 87 + x_4}{4} = 90$$

$$90 + 84 + 87 + x_4 = 4 \bullet 90$$
$$261 + x_4 = 360$$
$$x_4 = 99$$

Sharlene must earn a 99 on the fourth test to have an average of 90. ■

Comparing Measures of Center

You can compare two or more sets of real-world data using measures of center.

EXAMPLE 3

The lists below give the donations, in dollars, that two different charities received in 1 day. Compare the means of the two data sets.

Plant-a-Tree Society: 40, 20, 16, 20, 17, 12, 15

Franklin Park Expansion: 25, 12, 9, 15, 35, 20, 6, 30

SOLUTION

Substitute the given values into the rule for finding $\overline{x}$.

Plant-a-Tree Society:

$$\begin{aligned}\overline{x} &= \frac{\sum_{i=1}^{7} x_i}{7} \\ &= \frac{40 + 20 + 16 + 20 + 17 + 12 + 15}{7} \\ &= \frac{140}{7} \\ &= 20\end{aligned}$$

Franklin Park Expansion:

$$\begin{aligned}\overline{x} &= \frac{\sum_{i=1}^{8} x_i}{8} \\ &= \frac{25 + 12 + 9 + 15 + 35 + 20 + 6 + 30}{8} \\ &= \frac{152}{8} \\ &= 19\end{aligned}$$

▶ **Think About It** The Franklin Park Expansion received more donations than the Plant-a-Tree Society did, but the average donation to the Plant-a-Tree Society was greater than the average donation to the Franklin Park Expansion.

The mean donation to the Plant-a-Tree Society was \$20. The mean donation to the Franklin Park Expansion was \$19. The donations to the Plant-a-Tree Society had a greater mean than the donations to the Franklin Park Expansion. ■

Frequency Distributions

A frequency distribution is often a useful way to organize and display a data set.

Definitions

A **frequency distribution** is a table or graph that describes the number of times a value or interval of values occurs in a data set. When the distribution is shown as a table, it is called a **frequency table**. One type of graph that shows a distribution is called a **histogram**.

Making a Frequency Table and a Histogram

In a frequency table or histogram, the interval sizes should be equal, and the intervals must not overlap—that is, each data value must occur in exactly one interval. Intervals are also called **classes**.

EXAMPLE 1

Make a frequency table for the following set of test scores. Then use the table to make a histogram.

62, 88, 95, 97, 81, 78, 65, 91, 85, 84, 98, 89, 85,
89, 72, 77, 80, 93, 97, 70, 58, 66, 94, 82, 75

SOLUTION

Step 1 Determine the number of classes you will use. As a general rule, use 5 to 15 classes. For these test scores, use 10 classes.

Step 2 Set up classes of equal width. The lowest and highest data values are 58 and 98. Convenient limits that include 58 and 98 are 50 and 100. Find the difference.

$$100 - 50 = 50$$

Divide by the number of classes.

$$50 \div 10 = 5$$

Finally, set up the classes, beginning at 50 and ending close to 100.

50–54, 55–59, 60–64, . . . , 95–99

(Note that the first numbers of consecutive classes differ by 5: 50, 55, 60, and so on.)

Step 3 Make the frequency table. The frequency for each class is the number of times the data values in that class occur.

Class	Frequency
50–54	0
55–59	1
60–64	1
65–69	2
70–74	2
75–79	3
80–84	4
85–89	5
90–94	3
95–99	4

Step 4 Make the histogram. Use a bar to represent the frequency of each class. The greatest frequency in the table is 5, so use a scale on the Frequency axis that goes slightly higher than 5, such as 0 to 6. There should be no spaces between bars (unless a class has a frequency of 0).

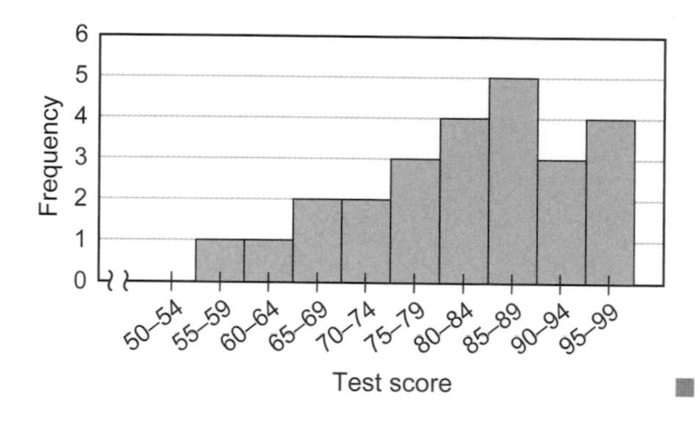

▶ **Think About It** How many classes should you use for your histograms? There is no one right answer. In Example 1, 10 classes worked pretty well. In general, you want to use just enough classes so you can see what is happening with the data.

Examining Uniform, Bell-Shaped, and Skewed Distributions

The values in many data sets are distributed symmetrically. Two common symmetric distributions are the **uniform distribution** and the **bell-shaped distribution**. In a perfectly uniform distribution, all intervals have the same frequency. In a distribution that is nearly uniform or nearly bell-shaped, the mean and median are nearly equal.

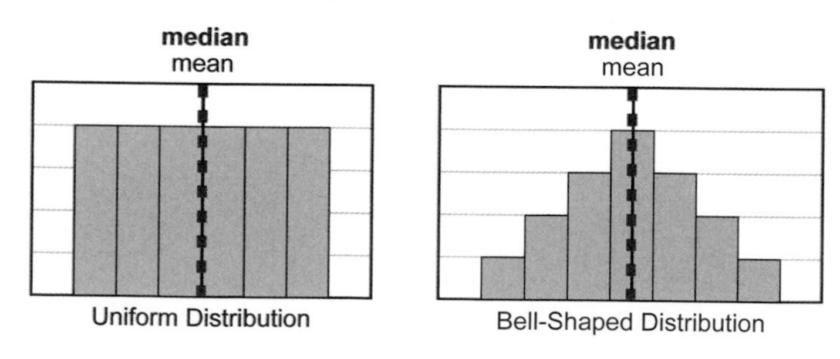

▶ **Think About It** Real-world data sets are not likely to be perfectly uniform or bell-shaped. However, many real-world data sets are approximately uniform or bell-shaped.

In a **skewed distribution**, one side has lower frequencies than the other side. If the distribution is skewed to the right, the mean will be greater than the median. If the distribution is skewed to the left, the mean will be less than the median.

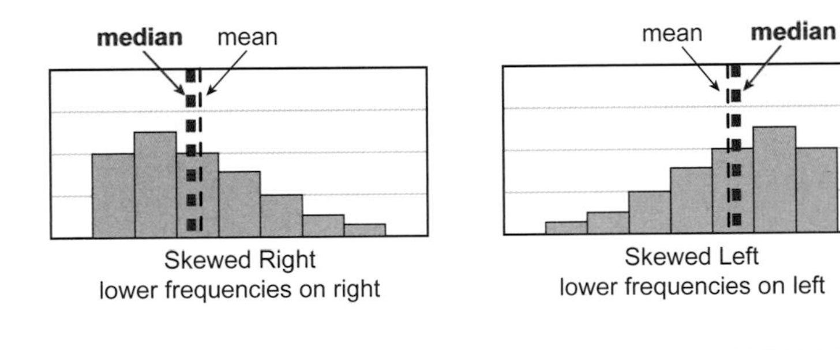

▶ **Think About It** *Skewed to the right* means the mean is greater than (i.e., to the right of) the median.

Skewed to the left means the mean is less than (i.e., to the left of) the median.

Interpreting a Frequency Table and a Histogram

EXAMPLE 2

Describe the type of distribution. Identify the relationship of the mean and the median.

A

Class	Frequency
1–15	3
16–30	2
31–45	11
46–60	17
61–75	17

SOLUTION

There are fewer data values in the classes with the lower values. This distribution is skewed left. A histogram would have lower bars on the left side than on the right side. The mean of the data set is less than the median.

B

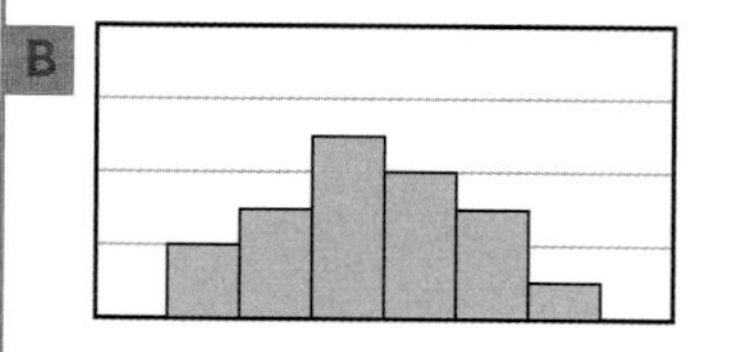

SOLUTION

The histogram is nearly bell-shaped, so the mean and median are nearly equal. ■

EXAMPLE 3

The histogram shows the distance in meters jumped by the competitors in a track meet.

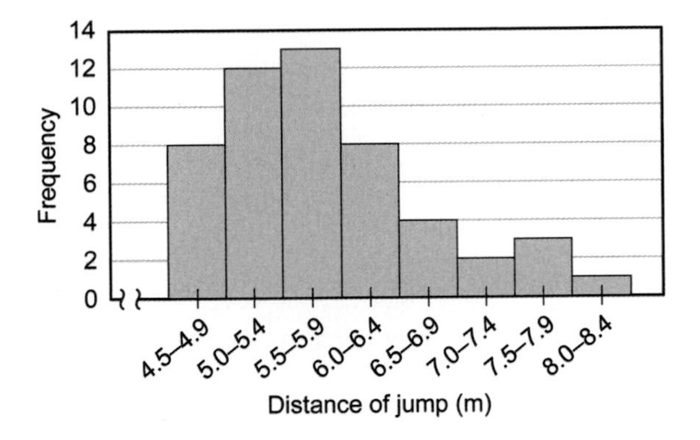

A Where are the data clumped together or spread out?

SOLUTION

Most of the data are clumped together in the classes on the left side of the distribution. So most of the competitors jumped less than a distance of 6.4 m.

B Is the distribution more closely uniform, bell, skew, or none? Why?

SOLUTION

This distribution is skewed right because there are fewer data values on the right than on the left.

C What is the relationship of the mean and the median?

SOLUTION

The average distance jumped in the track meet will be more than the median distance jumped.

D Isaiah jumped 6.4 m in the meet. About what percent of people jumped farther than Isaiah?

SOLUTION

The heights of the bars greater than 6.4 appear to be one-fourth of the height of the bars less than 6.4, so about 25% of the competitors jumped farther than Isaiah. ■

Creating a Line Plot

In the NCAA Women's Soccer tournament, the final game determines the champion. The table shows the number of goals scored in each championship game since the tournament began in 1982.

A **line plot** can help you see the shape of the data.

Year	Goals
1982	1
1983	4
1984	2
1985	2
1986	2
1987	1
1988	5
1989	2
1990	6
1991	4
1992	10
1993	6
1994	5
1995	1
1996	1
1997	2
1998	1
1999	2
2000	3
2001	1
2002	3
2003	6
2004	2
2005	4
2006	3
2007	2
2008	3
2009	1
2010	1

NCAA 2016

How to Create a Line Plot

Step 1 Find the minimum and maximum values in the data set.

Step 2 Draw a number line that includes the minimum and maximum values and has an appropriate tick interval.

Step 3 Draw a dot for every data point. Move up by uniform increments.

Step 4 Count the total number of data items and the total number of dots. They must be the same.

For the soccer final data, the line plot looks like this.

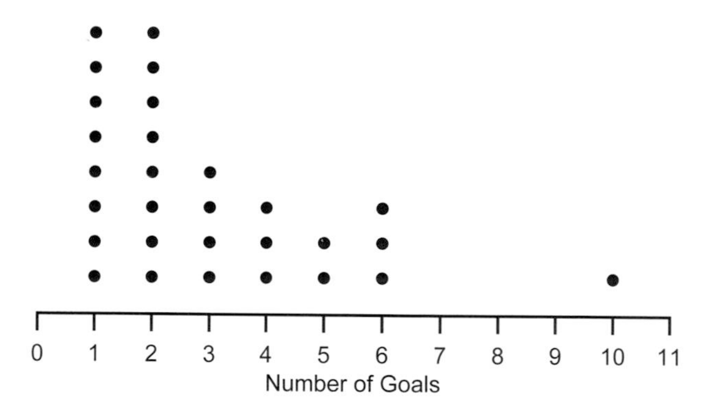

Interpreting a Line Plot

You can tell quite a bit from a line plot. For instance,

- Would a total of only 2 goals be unusual? Not at all. In most games, either 1 or 2 goals were scored.
- In how many games were more than 4 goals scored? There were 6 games in which more than 4 goals were scored (that's about 21% of the time).
- Would a total of 7 goals be a lot for a final? Yes, it would. Only once was more than 6 goals scored. So any value more than 6 would be pretty rare.

Variability

Measures of variability describe how data are spread out.

Think About It Measures of variability are also called measures of spread and measures of dispersion.

A simple measure of variability is range. Other statistics used to describe variability are quartiles, variance, and standard deviation.

Defining Measures of Variability

Certain statistics measure the spread of a data set.

Definitions

The **range** of a data set is the difference between its greatest value (**maximum**) and its least value (**minimum**).

The **second quartile**, Q_2, is the median of the entire data set. It separates the ordered data set into a lower subset and an upper subset.

The **first quartile**, Q_1, is the median of the lower subset.

The **third quartile**, Q_3, is the median of the upper subset.

The three quartiles separate the ordered data set into four parts, each part having the same number of values.

The minimum, the maximum, and the three quartiles are called the **five-number summary**.

Making a Box-and-Whisker Plot

A **box-and-whisker plot** shows how data are spread out. The **box** extends from Q_1 to Q_3. The median is on the vertical line in the box. The **whiskers** extend from the first quartile to the minimum and from the third quartile to the maximum.

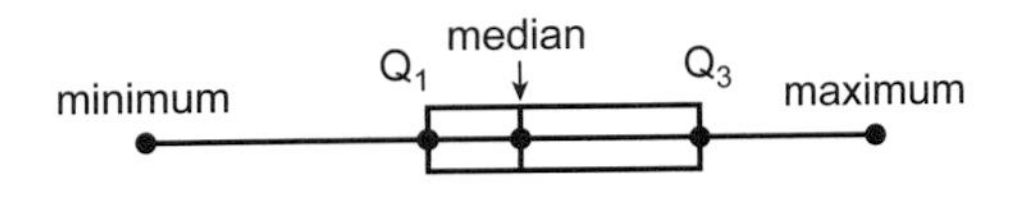

EXAMPLE 1

Colin, an employee at Game Zone, recorded the number of computer games he sold each week for the past 9 wk: 15, 20, 21, 9, 3, 16, 9, 14, 17.

A Identify the five-number summary.

SOLUTION

Make a stem-and-leaf plot of the data, then use it to identify Q_2, the median of the entire data set. Then identify Q_1 and Q_3.

0	3 9 | 9
1	4 (5) 6 7 |
2	0 1

Key: 1 | 4 = 14

The five-number summary is minimum = 3, first quartile = 9, second quartile (median) = 15, third quartile = $(20 - 17) \div 2 = 18.5$, maximum = 21.

▶ **Think About It** In a stem-and-leaf plot, circle the median and use a short segment to indicate the first and third quartiles.

B Find the range.

SOLUTION

$$\text{range} = \text{maximum} - \text{minimum} = 21 - 3 = 18$$

C Draw a box-and-whisker plot.

SOLUTION

For the box-and-whisker plot, draw five dots above or below a number line to correspond to the numbers in the five-number summary. Draw a box from Q_1 to Q_3. Inside the box, draw a short vertical line segment $(|)$ through the dot at Q_2. Finally, draw the whiskers—horizontal line segments from the minimum to Q_1 and from Q_3 to the maximum.

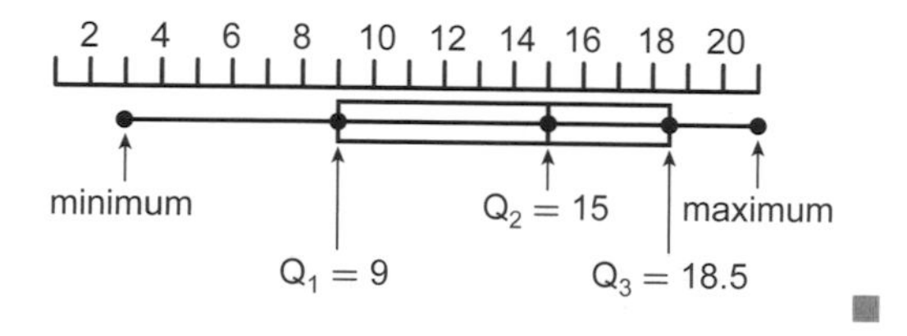

Notice that the left whisker is longer than the right whisker, and the left portion of the box is longer than the right portion. These features show that the lower subset of the data is more spread out than the upper subset.

Computing Variance and Standard Deviation

Two other measures of variability are variance and standard deviation.

Definitions

For a data set with values $x_1, x_2, \ldots, x_n$, the **variance** is

$$s^2 = \frac{\sum_{i=1}^{n}(x_i - \overline{x})^2}{n-1}.$$

Each difference $x_i - \overline{x}$ is called a **deviation**.

Standard deviation is the square root of the variance.

$$s = \sqrt{s^2}$$

EXAMPLE 2

Compute the variance and standard deviation of the data set.

10, 14, 35, 11, 4, 26, 20, 32

▶ **Think About It** Each difference $x_i - \overline{x}$ is called a deviation, so the numerator of the variance formula is the sum of the squared deviations.

SOLUTION

Step 1 Compute the mean.

$$\overline{x} = \frac{10 + 14 + 35 + 11 + 4 + 26 + 20 + 32}{8} = \frac{152}{8} = 19$$

Step 2 Find all the deviations $x_i - \overline{x}$. In this case, $\overline{x} = 19$, so find all the differences $x_i - 19$. Then find all the squares of the deviations $(x_i - \overline{x})^2$. Calculate the sum of those squares. Organize your values in a table.

x_i	$x_i - \overline{x}$	$(x_i - \overline{x})^2$
10	−9	81
14	−5	25
35	16	256
11	−8	64
4	−15	225
26	7	49
20	1	1
32	13	169
		Sum: 870

Step 3 Divide the sum by $n - 1$. In this case, $n = 8$, so divide by 7.

$$s^2 = \frac{\sum_{i=1}^{n} (x_i - \overline{x})^2}{n - 1} = \frac{870}{7} \approx 124.3$$

The variance is about 124.3.

Step 4 To find the standard deviation, find the square root of the variance.

$$s = \sqrt{s^2} = \sqrt{\frac{870}{7}} \approx 11.1$$

The standard deviation is about 11.1. ■

Comparing Standard Deviations Without Computing

Standard deviation is a measure of how far the data values are from the mean. The less spread out the data values, the closer they are to the mean, and the lower the standard deviation.

▶ **Think About It** If there is no spread, all the data values are the same, and the standard deviation is 0.

EXAMPLE 3

Without computing, determine which data set has the greatest standard deviation and which has the least standard deviation.

A **Set A:** 1, 5, 9, 10, 15
Set B: 19, 20, 22, 24, 26
Set C: 96, 99, 99, 100, 102

SOLUTION

The numbers in Set A are the most spread out, so Set A has the greatest standard deviation. The numbers in Set C are the least spread out, so Set C has the least standard deviation.

B 20 22 24 26 28 30 32 34 36 38 40

Set A

Set B

Set C

SOLUTION

The box-and-whisker plot for Set A is the least spread out, so Set A has the least standard deviation. Set B has more spread than Set A, but still has less than Set C. Set C has the greatest standard deviation. ■

Comparing Data Sets by Using Standard Deviations and Box Plots

EXAMPLE 4

Compare Sets A and C from Example 3A by using standard deviations and box plots

SOLUTION

Set A: $\overline{x} = \dfrac{1 + 5 + 9 + 10 + 15}{5} = \dfrac{40}{5} = 8$

x_i	$x_i - \overline{x}$	$(x_i - x)^2$
1	−7	49
5	−3	9
9	1	1
10	2	4
15	7	49
		Sum: 112

$$s^2 = \frac{112}{5-1} = 28$$

$$s = \sqrt{28} \approx 5.29$$

Set C: $\overline{x} = \dfrac{96 + 99 + 99 + 100 + 102}{5} = \dfrac{496}{5} = 99.2$

x_i	$x_i - \overline{x}$	$(x_i - x)^2$
96	−3.2	10.24
99	−0.2	0.04
99	−0.2	0.04
100	0.8	0.64
102	2.8	7.84
		Sum: 18.8

$$s^2 = \frac{18}{5-1} = 4.7$$

$$s = \sqrt{4.7} \approx 2.17$$

The standard deviations and box plots indicate that Set A is more spread out than Set C is. ■

Selecting Measures of Center

To determine the best measure of center for a data set, look at the shape of the data distribution.

Choosing an Appropriate Measure

EXAMPLE 1

The sales prices of the cars that Mario sold last month, rounded to the nearest hundreds of dollars, are shown.

11,400	31,600	23,600	22,000	11,100	23,400	69,700	17,900
12,100	17,500	15,200	17,800	81,000	28,500	10,400	

Which measure or measures of central tendency best reflect the data?

SOLUTION

Create a histogram to see the data distribution.

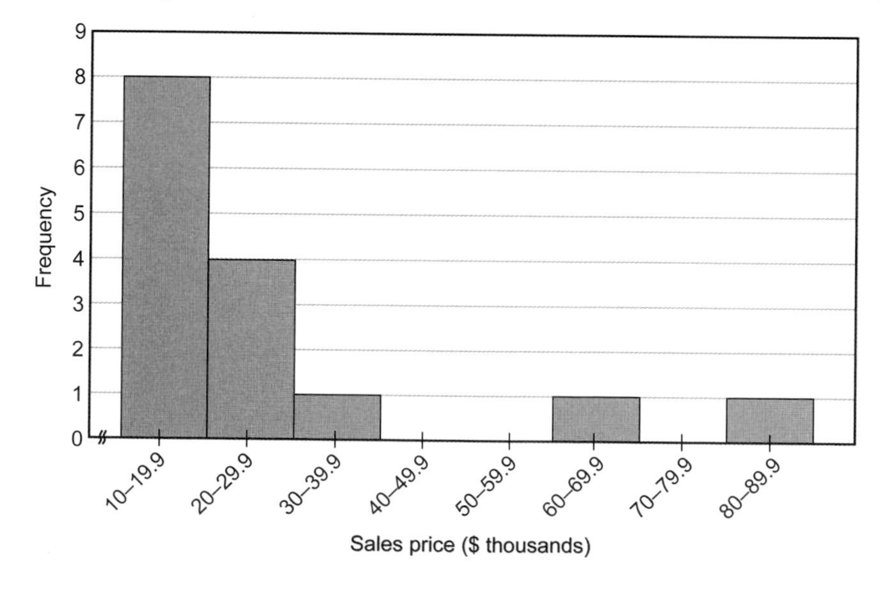

▶ **Think About It** In Example 1, the mean is about $26,213 and the median is $17,900. Only 4 of the 15 prices are greater than the mean.

Because the data are skewed right, the mean is pulled to the right, away from the center of the distribution. The mean is not an honest reflection of the sale prices. There is no mode. The median would best reflect the data. ■

EXAMPLE 2

The numbers of traffic tickets written by each police officer in a city a day are shown.

21 11 14 16 10 18 5 16 19 20 17 5 6 10 13

Which measure or measures of central tendency best reflect the data?

▶ **Think About It** In Example 2, the mean is 13.4 and the median is 14.

SOLUTION

Create a histogram to see the data distribution.

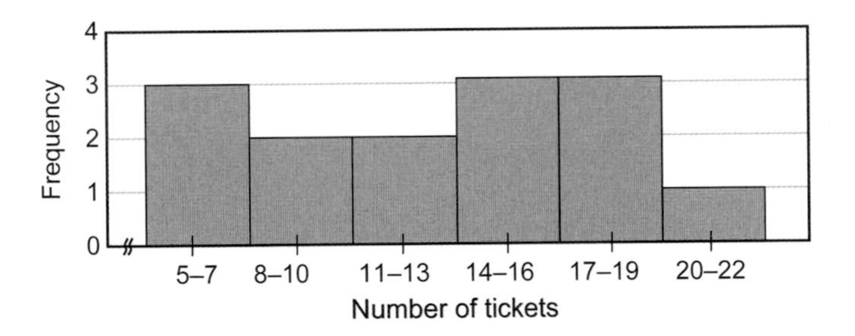

The distribution is fairly uniform, so the mean and median are approximately equal. There are three modes, 5, 10, and 16, which are not helpful since they are spread throughout the distribution. Both the mean and the median reflect the data well. ■

Outliers

You can use formulas to determine whether a data set has any points that can be considered far from the other data points.

Determining Whether a Data Set Has Outliers

Definition

The **interquartile range (IQR)** is the difference between the third and first quartiles.

$$\text{IQR} = Q_3 - Q_1$$

▶ **Remember** In a box-and-whisker plot, the IQR is the length of the box.

An **outlier** is a value far away from most other values in a data set. A value is commonly considered an outlier if its distance from either the first or third quartile is more than one and a half times the IQR.

The borders between outliers and values that are not outliers are called **fences**.

Fences and Outliers

In a data set, an outlier is any number less than the lower fence or greater than the upper fence.

$$\text{lower fence} = Q_1 - 1.5 \bullet \text{IQR}$$
$$\text{upper fence} = Q_3 + 1.5 \bullet \text{IQR}$$

EXAMPLE 1

The race times of 15 contestants, rounded to the nearest minute, are shown. Determine whether the data set has any outliers.

45 40 36 52 49 53 56 74 36 40 42 35 60 47 47

SOLUTION

Order the data and find the quartiles.

35 36 36 **40** 40 42 45 47 **47** 49 52 **53** 56 60 74

40	47	53
↑	↑	↑
Q_1	median	Q_3

Find the IQR.

$$\begin{aligned} IQR &= Q_3 - Q_1 \\ &= 53 - 40 \\ &= 13 \end{aligned}$$

Find the lower fence.

$$\begin{aligned} Q_1 - 1.5 \bullet IQR &= 40 - 1.5 \bullet 13 \\ &= 40 - 19.5 \\ &= 20.5 \end{aligned}$$

Find the upper fence.

$$\begin{aligned} Q_3 + 1.5 \bullet IQR &= 53 + 1.5 \bullet 13 \\ &= 53 + 19.5 \\ &= 72.5 \end{aligned}$$

There are no data values less than 20.5, but there is a data value greater than 72.5. The time of 74 min is an outlier. ■

Drawing Modified Box Plots

A **modified box-and-whisker plot** shows outliers with dots. The whiskers then extend to the least and greatest values that are not outliers.

EXAMPLE 2

Draw a modified box-and-whisker plot for the data set in Example 1.

SOLUTION

The five-number summary is minimum = 35, first quartile = 40, median = 47, third quartile = 53, and maximum = 74. Because 74 is an outlier, draw a dot at 74 and extend the right whisker to the next greatest value: 60. ■

30 35 40 45 50 55 60 65 70 75 80

▶ **Think About It** If a data set has two outliers, the modified box-and-whisker plot will have two dots.

Bivariate Data

Topic List

- Interpreting Two-Way Tables
- Scatter Plots
- Association
- Correlation
- Fitting a Line to Data
- Least Squares Regression
- More Regression
- Residuals

Is there a relationship between rainfall amounts and crop yield? Scientists have seen patterns relating growing season rainfall and the quantity of a crop harvest. These patterns can be described with linear equations that farmers can use to make plans.

Interpreting Two-Way Tables

Information about a sample group can be shown in a Venn diagram or a two-way table.

▶ **Remember** A Venn diagram is a diagram that shows all possible relations between groups.

Definition

A **two-way table** shows data from one sample group as it relates to two different categories.

Using a Venn Diagram to Create a Two-Way Table

Venn diagrams are often converted to two-way tables to evaluate the probability of events.

▶ **Remember** Qualitative data are the results of measurements. On the other hand, categorical data aren't the results of measurements; they are the results of grouping into a finite number of categories. Examples of categories include gender, type of animal, hair color, and so on.

EXAMPLE 1

Construct a two-way table using the information shown in the Venn diagram.

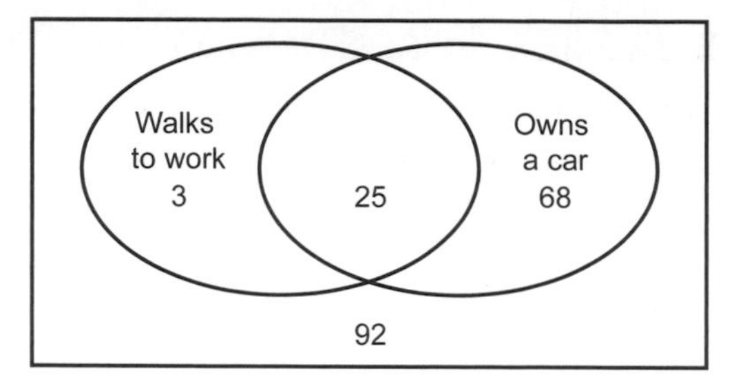

SOLUTION

The categories shown in the Venn diagram are how a person gets to work and ownership of a car.

The Venn diagram shows that 3 of the people who walk to work do not own a car, 25 people who walk to work own a car, 68 people who own a car do not walk to work, and 92 people do not own a car and do not walk to work.

The two-way table for the Venn diagram is shown in the table.

	Owns a car	Does not own a car
Walks to work	25	3
Does not walk to work	68	92

Two-way tables often include totals for each category and a grand total for the entire sample. For example, the previous two-way table with totals is shown.

	Owns a car	Does not own a car	Total
Walks to work	25	3	28
Does not walk to work	68	92	160
Total	93	95	188

Knowing the total information for categories is helpful when translating information from a descriptive form into a two-way table.

Creating a Two-Way Table from Data

EXAMPLE 2

There are 200 students in a school. One hundred twenty of the students are in Spanish class. Fifty students are in music class and 22 of them also are in Spanish. Use this information to construct a two-way table.

SOLUTION

The categories described are students in Spanish and students in music. The first step is to create the two-way table.

	In Spanish	Not in Spanish	Total
In music			
Not in music			
Total			

Based on the description, there are 200 students total. There are 120 students total who take Spanish. There are 50 students total who are in music. There are 22 students in music who are also in Spanish. Place this information in the two-way table.

	In Spanish	Not in Spanish	Total
In music	22		50
Not in music			
Total	120		200

The two-way table can now be used to find the number of students in music but not in Spanish, the number of students in Spanish but not in music, the total number of students not in music, and the total number of students not in Spanish.

	In Spanish	Not in Spanish	Total
In music	22	$50 - 22 = 28$	50
Not in music	$120 - 22 = 98$		$200 - 50 = 150$
Total	120	$200 - 120 = 80$	200

The final step is to calculate the number of students who are not in Spanish and not in music. The two-way table shows that information.

	In Spanish	Not in Spanish	Total
In music	22	28	50
Not in music	98	$80 - 28 = 52$	150
Total	120	80	200

Displaying Relative Frequencies in a Two-Way Table

Two-way tables can also be used to show relative frequency.

Definition

Relative frequency is the ratio of the value of a subtotal to the value of the total.

In Example 1, the relative frequency of people who own a car and walk to work to the total number of people is $\frac{25}{188} \approx 0.13$.

EXAMPLE 3

Use the information in Example 2 to find the relative frequency of each subcategory to the total number of students.

SOLUTION

The table shows 22 students in music class and also in Spanish class. It also shows that there are 200 students total.

	In Spanish	Not in Spanish	Total
In music	22	28	50
Not in music	98	52	150
Total	120	80	200

The relative frequency of students in music and in Spanish to the total number of students is $\frac{22}{200} = 0.11$.

The relative frequency of students in music but not in Spanish to the total number of students is $\frac{28}{200} \approx 0.14$.

The relative frequency of students not in music but in Spanish to the total number of students is $\frac{98}{200} = 0.49$.

The relative frequency of students not in music and not in Spanish to the total number of students is $\frac{52}{200} \approx 0.26$.

The two-way table that displays relative frequency information is shown.

	In Spanish	Not in Spanish
In music	0.11	0.14
Not in music	0.49	0.26

■

Displaying Marginal Frequencies in a Two-Way Table

Two-way tables can also display marginal frequency.

Definition

Marginal frequency is the ratio of the total for a particular column or row to the overall total in a two-way table.

EXAMPLE 4

Use the information in Example 2 to find the marginal frequency of each column or row to the total number of students.

SOLUTION

The table shows that the total number of students in the column representing students in Spanish class is 120. It also shows that there are 200 students in total.

	In Spanish	Not in Spanish	Total
In music	22	28	50
Not in music	98	52	150
Total	120	80	200

The marginal frequency of students in Spanish is $\frac{120}{200} = 0.60$.

The marginal frequency of students not in Spanish is $\frac{80}{200} = 0.40$.

The marginal frequency of students in music is $\frac{50}{200} = 0.25$.

The marginal frequency of students not in music is $\frac{150}{200} = 0.75$.

The two-way table that displays both relative and marginal frequency information is shown.

	In Spanish	Not in Spanish	Total
In music	0.11	0.14	0.25
Not in music	0.49	0.26	0.75
Total	0.60	0.40	1.00

Each entry in this two-way table represents a probability for this sample. For instance, the probability that a student randomly selected from this sample is in Spanish is $0.60 = 60\%$. The probability of selecting a student from this sample who is not in music or in Spanish is $0.26 = 26\%$. ■

Comparing Categorical Data

How many servings of milk and soft drinks children and teenagers drink can change over time. Because there are two dimensions (type of drink and age range), a two-way table can help present the data.

Milk and Soft Drink Consumption
(number of 8 oz servings/day) by Age (years)

	1–3	4–8	9–13	14–18
Milk	1.4	1.0	0.9	0.7
Soft drinks	0.6	1.0	1.5	2.7

You can make quantitative comparisons (differences and ratios) based on the two-way table data.

What is the ratio of milk to soft drinks for the average 1- to 3-year-old?

$$\frac{1.4}{0.6} = \frac{14}{6} = \frac{7}{3}$$

What about for the average 9- to 13-year-old?

$$\frac{0.9}{1.5} = \frac{9}{15} = \frac{3}{5}$$

What percent of a 14- to 18-year-old's milk and soda consumption is milk?

$$\frac{0.7}{0.7 + 2.7} = \frac{0.7}{3.4} \approx 0.21 = 21\%$$

Scatter Plots

A scatter plot reveals patterns in a set of bivariate data.

Bivariate Data

Definition

Bivariate data are data containing two variables. Bivariate data are sometimes called paired data.

Two kinds of taxes that states use are sales tax and income tax. Many states have both, while others have one but not the other.

Tax Rates for High-Population States (2010)

State	Highest income tax rate (%)	Sales tax rate (%)
CA	10.3	8.25
TX	0	6.25
IN	3.4	7
MA	5.3	6.25
IL	5	6.25
PA	3.07	6
OH	5.925	5.5
MD	5.5	6
GA	6	4
VA	5.75	5
FL	0	6

Tax Foundation 2015 a, b

The table represents a set of bivariate data in which two variables are represented by a set of 11 ordered pairs. These ordered pairs show sales tax rates and highest income tax rates (in 2010) for a sample of populous states (more than 5 million residents).

For example, Georgia is represented by the ordered pair (6, 4), which means that in 2010, the highest income tax rate in that state was 6% while the sales tax rate was 4%.

Displaying Bivariate Data

Definition

A **scatter plot** is a graph that displays a set of bivariate data.

Look at this scatter plot that represents the data set in the table.

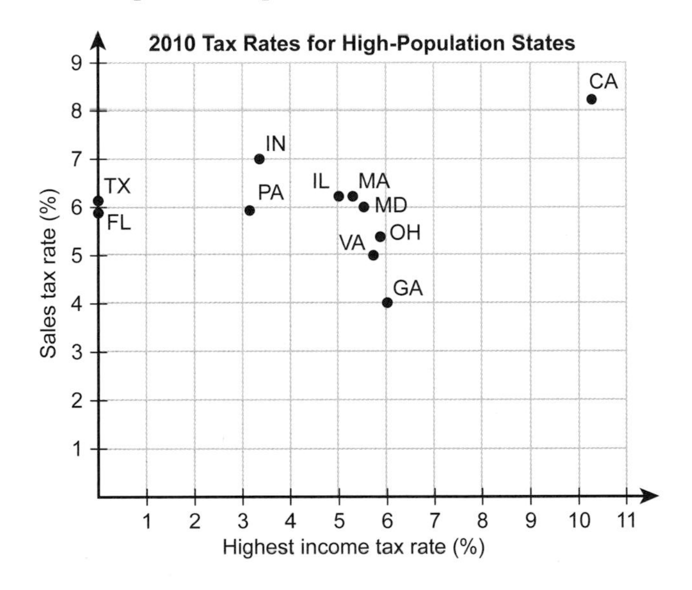

The scatter plot makes it easier to identify patterns that the table alone can't reveal. For example, the scatter plot shows that Texas and Florida have close to the same sales tax rate, but no income tax (as of the tax year 2010). It also shows that California is an outlier, with greater sales tax and highest income tax rates than any other state in the sample for 2010.

In the scatter plot, there is a grouping of six states (Illinois, Massachusetts, Maryland, Ohio, Virginia, and Georgia) where sales tax rates and highest income tax rates are similar. This grouping, which is revealed clearly in the scatter plot, is an example of a cluster.

▸ **Think About It** In clusters, data points have many neighbors. In contrast, outliers are data points that have few or no neighbors.

Creating a Scatter Plot

The table shows sales tax rates and highest income tax rates (in 2010) for a sample of low-population states (fewer than 1 million residents).

Sales tax rates range from 0% to 9.9%, while highest income tax rates range from 0% to 7%. Therefore, it makes sense to have a range of 0 to 8 for the vertical axis, and 0 to 11 for the horizontal axis.

Tax Rates for Low-Population States (2010)

State	Highest income tax rate (%)	Sales tax rate (%)
SD	0	4
VT	9.5	6
ND	5.54	5
AK	0	0
WY	0	4
DE	5.5	0
MT	6.9	0
RI	9.9	7
NH	5	0
ME	8.5	5

Tax Foundation 2015 a, b

Association

The points on a scatter plot often display noticeable patterns.

Direction of Association

The price of gasoline is subject to many fluctuations due to factors ranging from the time of year to political developments around the world.

The scatter plot shows the average price for a gallon of gasoline in nine states in mid-May 2010 and mid-May 2011.

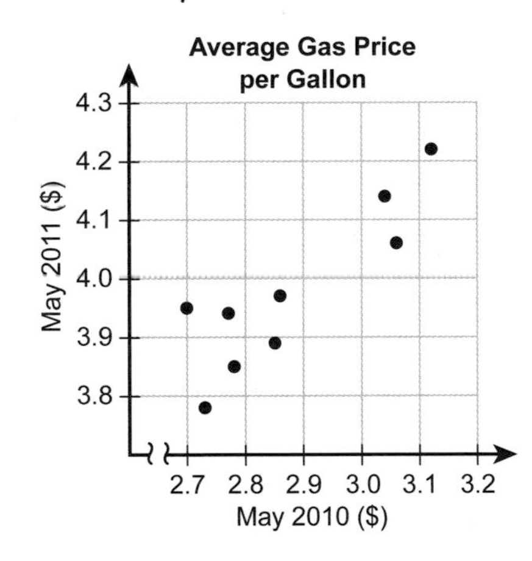

Looking at the scatter plot, you can see a trend between these two variables: The greater the average price of gas in mid-May 2010, the greater the average price of gas in mid-May 2011. This example shows a **positive association**, where the points in a scatter plot increase from left to right.

▶ **Think About It** If the points in a scatter plot go up to the right, then there is a positive association between the variables.

This scatter plot shows average gas price per gallon and average number of miles driven per day. It also shows another trend: As average gas prices increase, the average number of miles driven per day decreases. This scatter plot is an example of a **negative association**, where points in a scatter plot decrease from left to right.

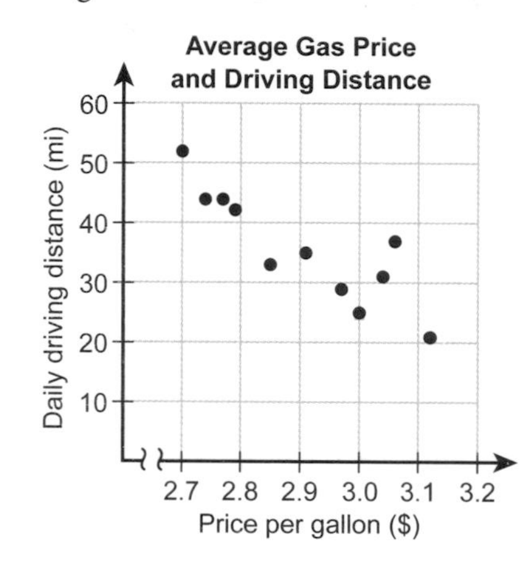

▶ **Think About It** If the points in a scatter plot go down to the right, then there is a negative association between the variables.

Strength of Association

Some scatter plots show a stronger association between two variables than others. In general, the more closely the data points fit a straight line pattern, the stronger the association between the two variables.

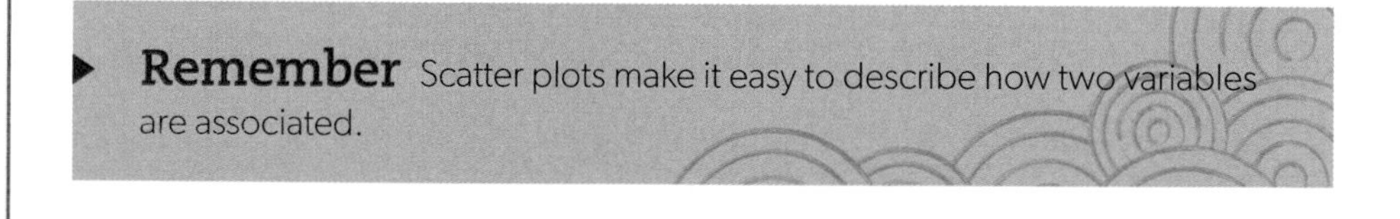

▶ **Remember** Scatter plots make it easy to describe how two variables are associated.

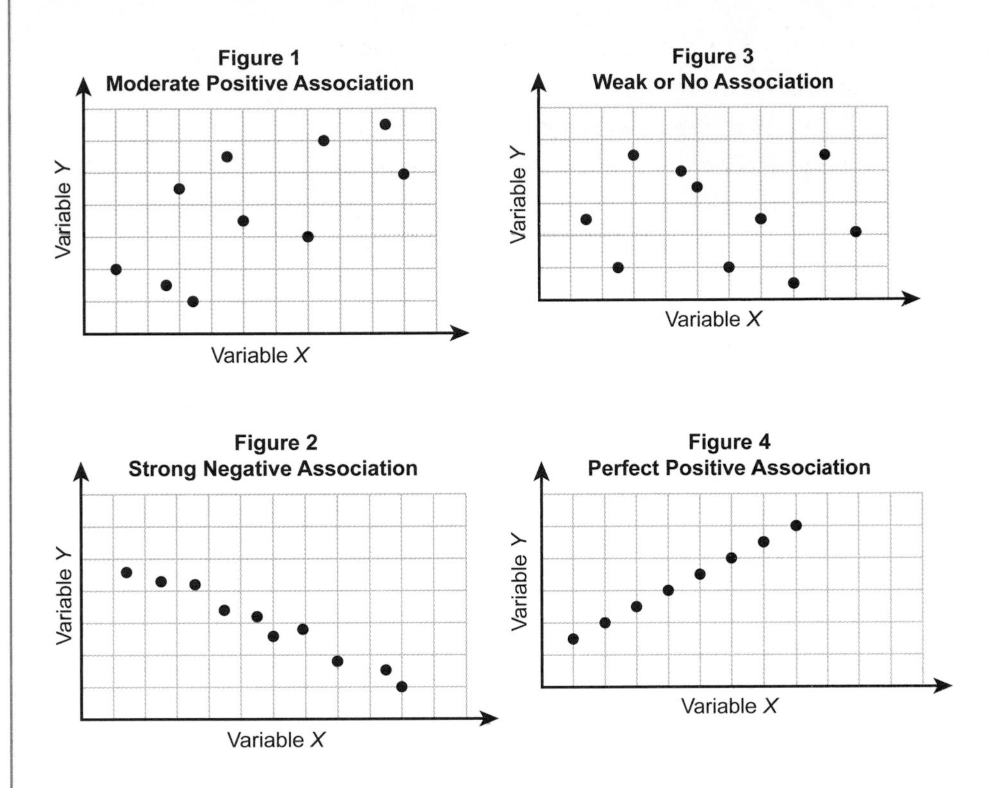

Determining the **strength of association** is often a matter of judgment. For example, the variables in Figure 1 are positively associated but do not show as strong of an association as do the variables in Figure 2. For this reason, Figure 1 shows a moderate positive association, and Figure 2 shows a strong negative association.

Because there is no apparent pattern in Figure 3, the variables have no association. Because all of the data points in Figure 4 fall on the same line, there is a perfect positive association between the variables.

Correlation

You can use a single number to describe the relationship between the variables in a scatter plot.

Describing an Association

To completely describe the **association**, or relationship, between two variables, give both the direction of the association and its strength.

Definitions

If two variables have a **positive association**, then the data values from one set increase as the data values from the other set increase.

If two variables have a **negative association**, then the data values from one set decrease as the data values from the other set increase.

If two variables have **no association**, then the points appear randomly scattered when the data sets are graphed on a scatter plot.

▶ **Think About It** In a positive association, points tend to move up from left to right. In a negative association, points tend to move down from left to right.

Generally speaking, the stronger an association, the more closely the points fit a pattern. The strength of an association can be described as **strong**, **moderate**, or **weak**.

EXAMPLE 1

Determine the direction and strength of the association between the variables. If there is no association, write *no association*.

A

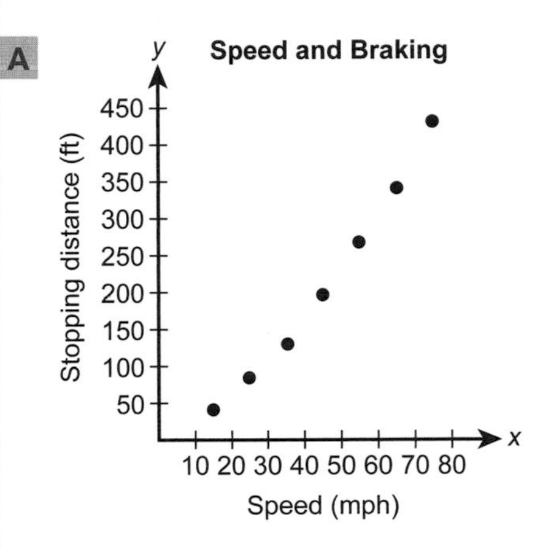

SOLUTION

As the speeds increase, the stopping distances increase, so the direction is positive. The points are very close to forming a straight line, which is a strong positive association.

B

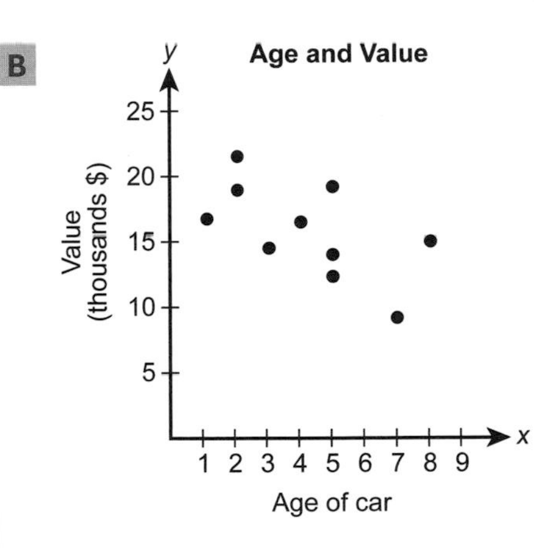

SOLUTION

As the ages increase, the values generally decrease, so the direction is negative. The points loosely follow along a line, which is a moderate negative association.

C

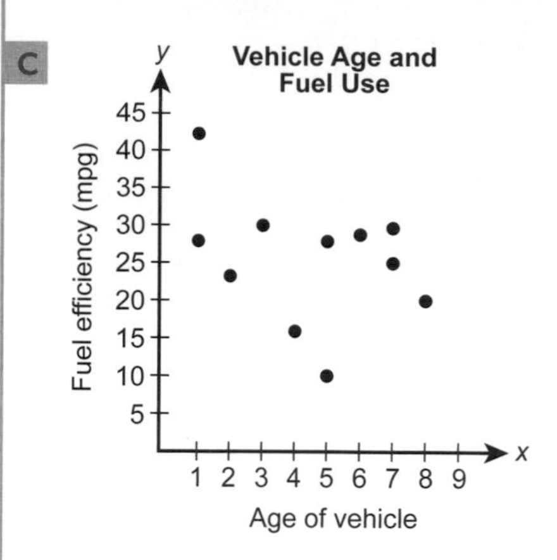

SOLUTION

There is a lot of scatter among the points. But the younger vehicles tend to have higher fuel efficiencies, which is a weak negative association.

D

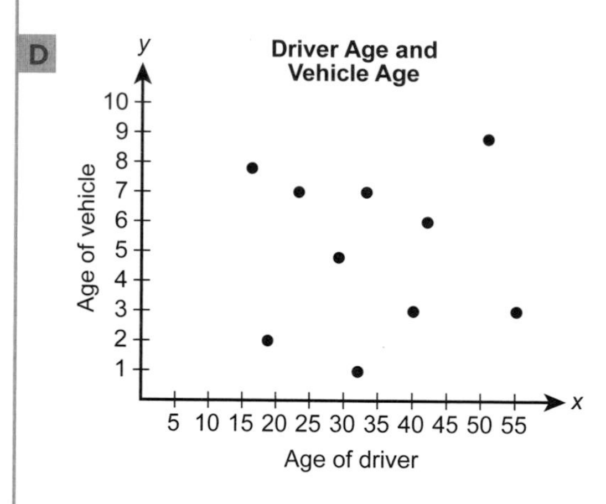

SOLUTION

There is no pattern at all among the points. So there is no association between the age of the driver and the age of the vehicle. ■

Estimating the Correlation Coefficient

Correlation is another word for *association.*

Definition

The **correlation coefficient** r is a number used to describe the association between two variables. Values of r range from -1 to 1.

perfect negative correlation — no correlation — perfect positive correlation

-1 — strong negative — moderate negative — weak negative — 0 — weak positive — moderate positive — strong positive — 1

▶ **Think About It** The sign of r indicates the direction of the correlation. The absolute value of r indicates the strength of the correlation.

EXAMPLE 2

Estimate the correlation coefficient between the variables.

A

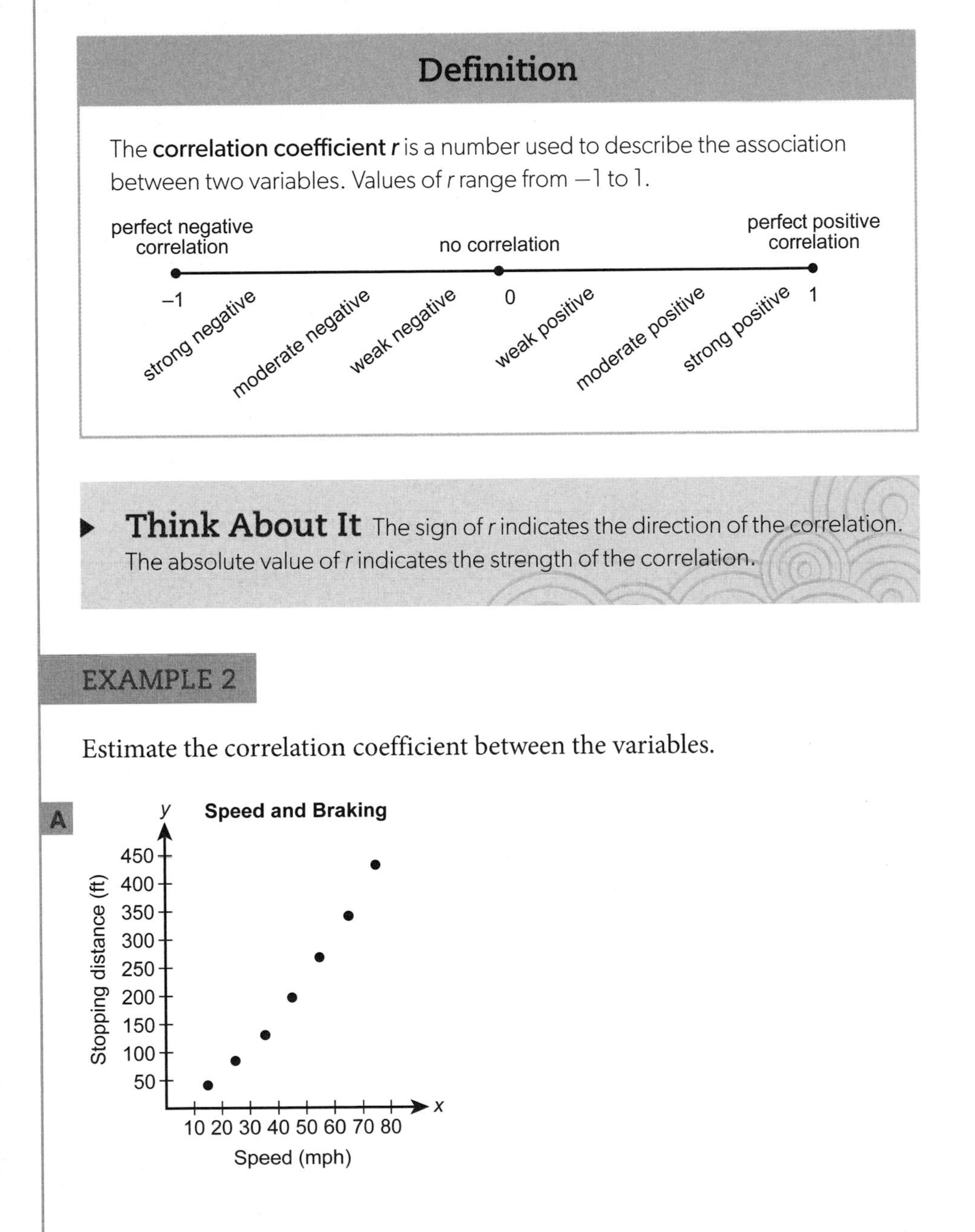

SOLUTION

This is a very strong positive correlation, so a good estimate for r is about 0.98.

B

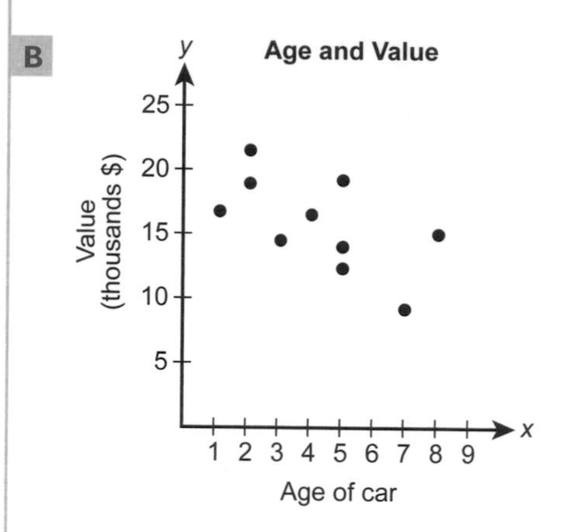

SOLUTION

This is a moderate negative correlation, so a good estimate for r is about -0.65. ■

Finding *r*

You can find a correlation coefficient by using a graphing calculator. On a graphing calculator (TI-84 is the recommended model), first make sure your diagnostics are on by pressing **2nd CATALOG**, scrolling to **DiagnosticOn**, and pressing **ENTER**.

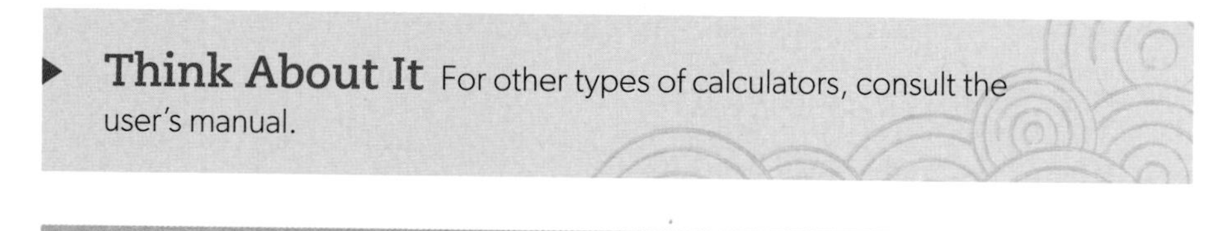

▶ **Think About It** For other types of calculators, consult the user's manual.

How to Find *r* on a TI-84 Calculator

Step 1 Press **STAT**, and then select **1: Edit**.

Step 2 Enter the *x*-coordinates in L1 and the corresponding *y*-coordinates in L2.

Step 3 Press **STAT**, arrow over to **CALC**, select **4: LinReg(ax+b)**, and press **ENTER**. The value of *r* is on the last line.

EXAMPLE 3

The table shows fuel efficiency ratings for the top 10 most fuel-efficient vehicles (excluding electric and plug-in hybrid electric vehicles) in 2013. Find and interpret *r*.

City mpg	51	53	47	47	45	42	41	43	44	40
Highway mpg	48	46	47	47	45	48	44	40	40	39

www.fueleconomy.gov 2013

SOLUTION

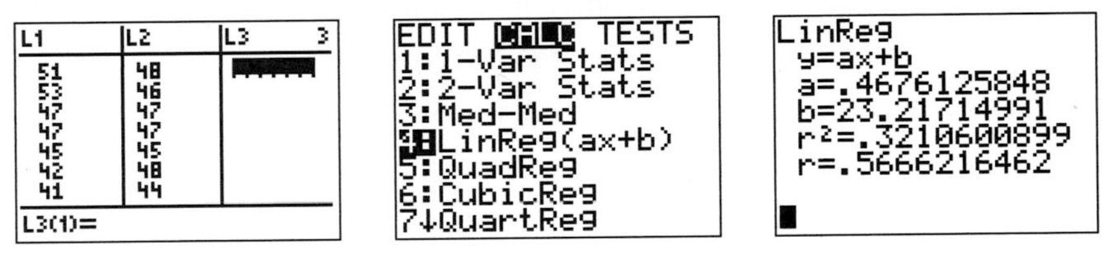

The value of *r* is about 0.57. There is a moderate positive correlation between the city miles per gallon and the highway miles per gallon of the 10 vehicles. ■

You can also use a spreadsheet to find *r*. In most spreadsheet programs, enter "=" and then type **CORREL**. Then enter the arrays, or lists of data (**A2:A11** and **B2:B11** in this example), and press **OK**. Other spreadsheet programs will have similar commands.

A13 fx =CORREL(A2:A11,B2:B11)

	A	B	C
1	City mpg	Highway mpg	
2	51	48	
3	53	46	
4	47	47	
5	47	47	
6	45	45	
7	42	48	
8	41	44	
9	43	40	
10	44	40	
11	40	39	
12			
13	0.56662		
14			

Correlation and Causation

A strong correlation between two variables does not necessarily indicate a cause-and-effect relationship between the variables.

Definition

There is a **causation** relationship between two variables when a change in one variable causes a change in the other variable.

Although it is easy to see when two variables have a strong correlation, causation is much more difficult to prove. Causation can be shown only if there are no other variables that could have influenced the relationship.

For example, an ice-cream vendor may see increased sales when the outside temperatures increase. However, the increase in temperature does not necessarily cause the increase in sales. Any number of other variables may influence the relationship, such as the availability of coupons, a sale by the vendor, the day of the week, or increased customer traffic due to a special event. Every possible variable would have to be ruled out to show that the increase in temperature causes the increase in ice-cream sales.

On the other hand, suppose a pharmaceutical company tests a new medication on several patients who have high blood pressure. The study demonstrates a strong correlation between patients who took the medication and a reduction in blood pressure. If the study was conducted properly so that every other possible variable was eliminated, then the conclusion can be reached that the medication causes a reduction in blood pressure.

Fitting a Line to Data

A line can be used to summarize a linear trend in a scatter plot.

Drawing a Regression Line

When it appears that the points in a scatter plot reasonably fit a straight line pattern, then a **regression line** can be drawn through the points to summarize the pattern.

The scatter plot shows the 2010 median weekly earnings of U.S. citizens with various levels of education, as reported by the Bureau of Labor Statistics. Since the points appear to follow a straight line pattern, a linear model has been drawn through the points, summarizing the pattern.

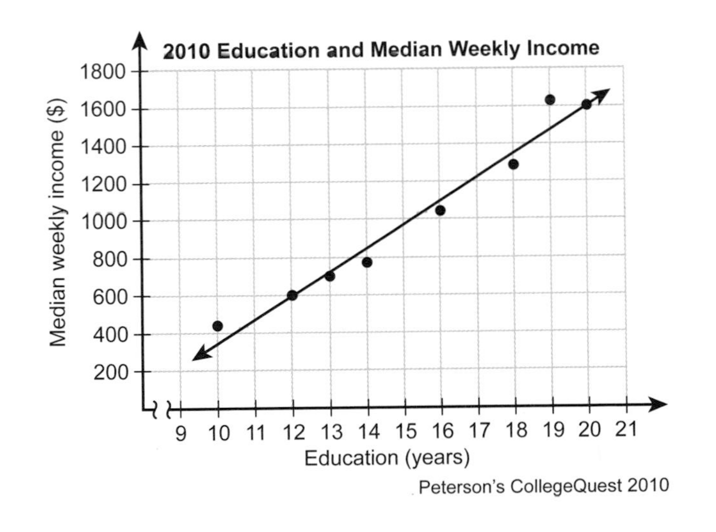

▶ **Think About It** According to the linear model drawn, what is the approximate median weekly income for a person with 17 years of education?

Using a line to represent data in this way can be useful for estimating values of the **response variable** based on values of the **explanatory variable.** Using the linear model, the response variable (median weekly income) can be estimated based on values of the explanatory variable (years of education).

Finding the Equation of a Linear Model

Once a linear model has been drawn, you can find the equation of the line using algebra. Values of the explanatory variable can then be substituted into the equation to make predictions.

How to Find the Equation of a Linear Model

When a linear model has been drawn to summarize data in a scatter plot, the following steps can be used to find its equation.

Step 1 Choose two points that appear to be closest to the line drawn.

Step 2 Determine the equation of the line through the two points using algebra.

Find the equation of the linear model for the scatter plot. You can choose the points $(12, 600)$ and $(20, 1600)$, since they appear to be closest to the line.

The slope of the line is $m = \frac{1600 - 600}{20 - 12} = \frac{1000}{8} = 125.$

$y - y_1 = m(x - x_1)$	Point Slope Formula
$y - 1600 = 125(x - 20)$	Substitute slope and one point on the line.
$y - 125x = -900$	Equation in $y = ax + b$ form

Use the notation $\hat{y}$ (read "y hat") in the equation of the linear model as a reminder that $\hat{y}$ is a predicted value of y, based on a certain value of x. The equation of the linear model would be written as $\hat{y} = 125x - 900$.

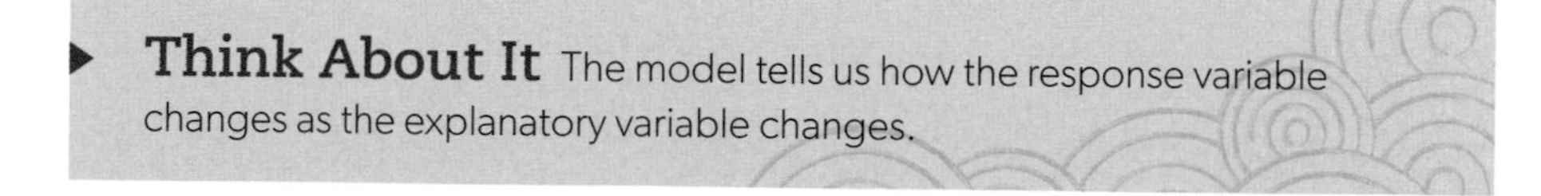

Making Predictions

The equation of the linear model can be used to estimate, or predict, values of the response variable based on values of the explanatory variable. Suppose you want to estimate the median weekly income for a person with 17 years of education.

For a person with 17 years of education, the value of the explanatory variable is $x = 17$. The predicted value is $\hat{y} = 125(17) - 900 = 1225$. A person with 17 years of education would have a predicted median weekly income of about $1225.

▶ **Think About It** The model can only predict for a certain range of values of the explanatory variable. For example, why doesn't the predicted median weekly income for someone with 6 years of education make sense?

Specifying and Interpreting the Intercept

The y-intercept of a linear regression model can be interpreted in the context of the data set. In general, the y-intercept of a linear model gives the initial value of the function.

For example, suppose a small business owner collected data regarding how much money was spent on advertising each month and the corresponding amount of monthly sales. These data are shown in the scatter plot.

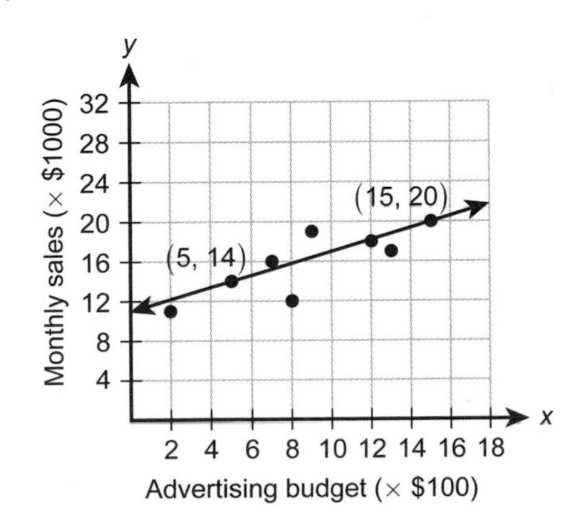

Think About It Use the points on the regression line to find the line's equation.

The regression model $y = 0.6x + 11$ represents the amount of monthly sales (in thousands) the business owner can expect when x dollars (in hundreds) are spent on advertising.

The y-intercept of the regression model is $(0, 11)$. These coordinates tell the business owner that, according to the model, if $0 is spent on advertising during a given month, she can expect the sales for the month to be about $11,000.

Least Squares Regression

The least squares regression equation is called the line of best fit.

Least Squares Regression Line

Drawing a linear model to fit a scatter plot does not always give consistent results. In fact, it is possible that two slightly different linear models could be drawn on the same scatter plot yielding vastly different predictions for the same value. A method for finding a linear model that does not depend on guessing is called least squares regression.

The **least squares regression line** is the line that makes the sum of the squares of the vertical distances from each data point to the line as small as possible.

For this scatter plot with six data points, the goal would be to find the line that minimizes *S*—the sum of the squared distances to the line. Once this is achieved, a least squares regression line has been found and represents what statisticians call the **line of best fit**.

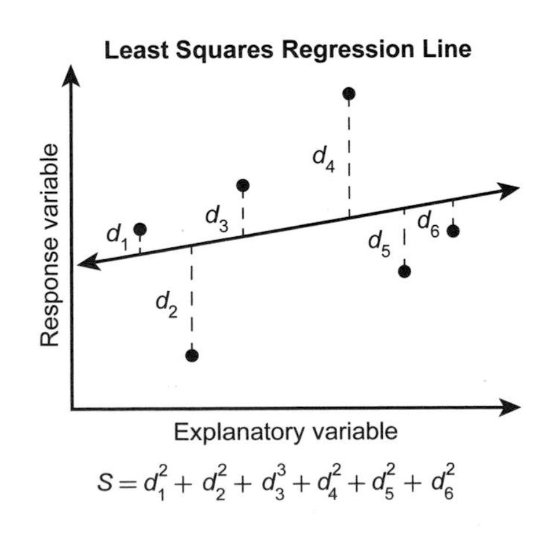

Finding the Least Squares Regression Equation

Without the aid of technology, finding the equation of the least squares regression equation for a data set can be time consuming. Fortunately, most graphing calculators and spreadsheets allow you to calculate the least squares regression equation once the paired data have been entered. Here is an example.

As digital music became more popular after 2000, sales of music CDs in the United States declined. The table represents annual CD sales (in million \$) from 2000 to 2009.

Year	2000	2001	2002	2003	2004	2005	2006	2007	2008	2009
CD sales (million \$)	942.5	881.9	803.3	746	767	705.4	619.7	511.1	368.4	292.9

To find the equation of the least squares regression line using technology, data from each variable should be entered as lists into a spreadsheet or graphing calculator. Here is what typical input/output will look like when using a graphing calculator.

Input: Input data into two lists.

L1	L2	L3
2000	942.5	
2001	881.9	
2002	803.3	
2003	746	
2004	767	
2005	705.4	
2006	619.7	
2007	511.1	
2008	368.4	
2009	292.9	

Output: Calculate the linear regression equation.

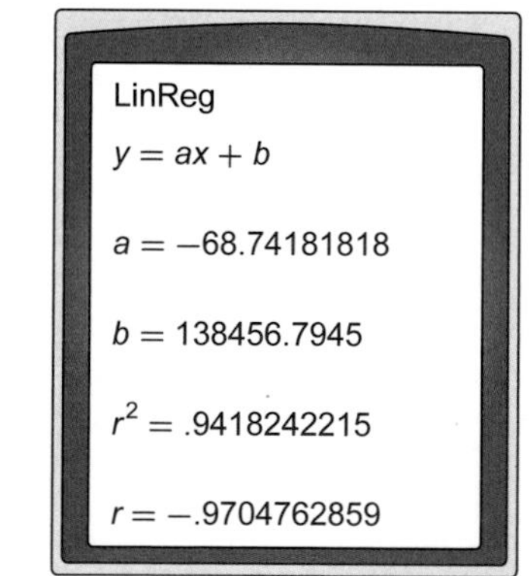

Using the values of a and b from the output, the least squares regression equation for these data is $\hat{y} = -68.7x + 138{,}457$ (rounded). The correlation coefficient $r = -0.97$ (rounded) indicates a strong negative association between the variables, which is verified by the scatter plot.

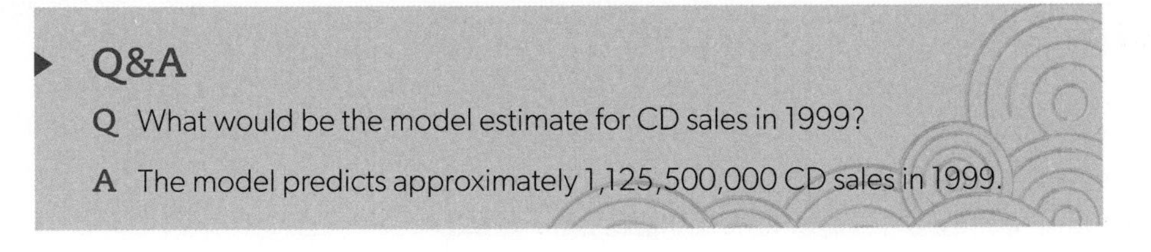

Q&A

Q What would be the model estimate for CD sales in 1999?

A The model predicts approximately 1,125,500,000 CD sales in 1999.

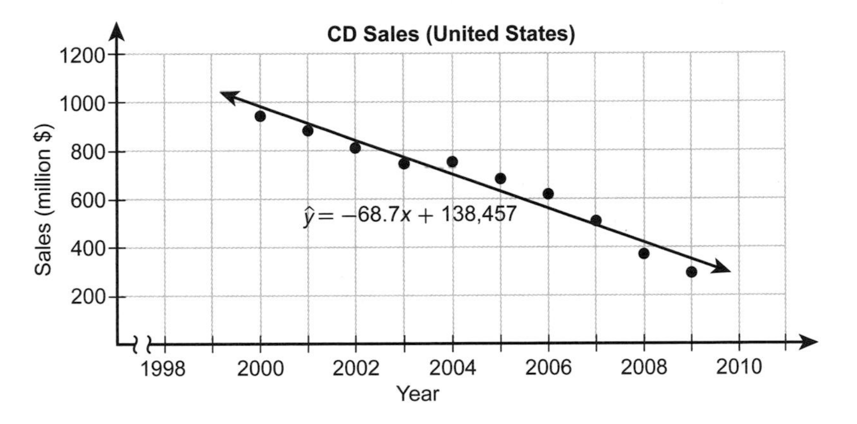

Finding the Coefficient of Determination

The **coefficient of determination** is the square of the correlation coefficient, and is written r^2. When r^2 is written as a percent, it represents the percent of variance (or change) of the response variable that is due to changes in the explanatory variable. In general, **variance** is a measure of variability of a data set relative to its mean.

> **Remember** The correlation coefficient describes the strength and direction of association of two data sets. The coefficient of determination describes the percent of variation in *y* associated with changes in *x*.

For the CD Sales (United States) scatter plot, the coefficient of determination is $r^2 = 0.94$ (rounded). So about 94% of the variance in CD sales is associated with changes in the year. The other 6% of variability is due to other factors.

More Regression

Not all patterns are straight-line patterns.

The points in the scatter plot of the number of registered buses in the United States from 1950 to 2010 tend to fall along a line. But the points in the scatter plot of the average number of registered automobiles per licensed driver in the United States from 1950 to 2010 tend to fall along a parabola.

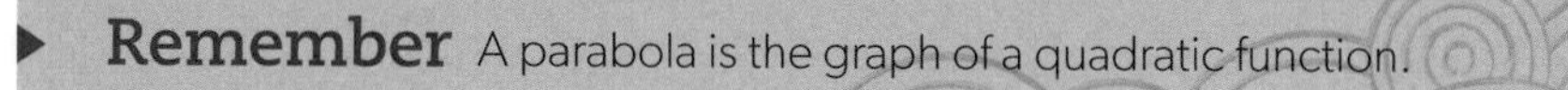
Remember A parabola is the graph of a quadratic function.

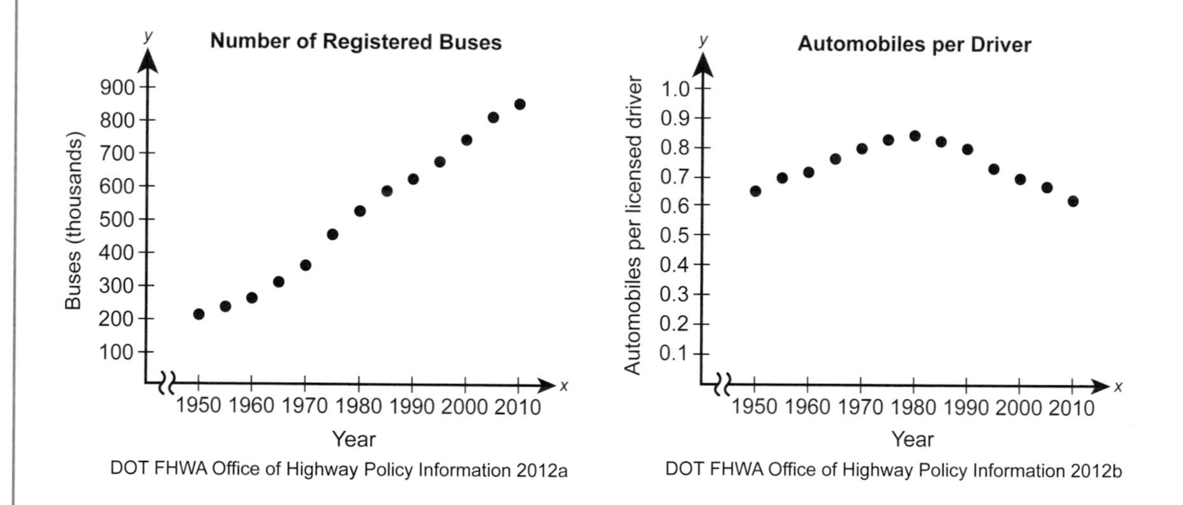

DOT FHWA Office of Highway Policy Information 2012a

DOT FHWA Office of Highway Policy Information 2012b

Finding a Quadratic Regression Equation

You can use a calculator to find a quadratic regression equation. On a graphing calculator, choose **5: QuadReg** from the **CALC** menu. Notice that the input values are entered as the number of years since 1900.

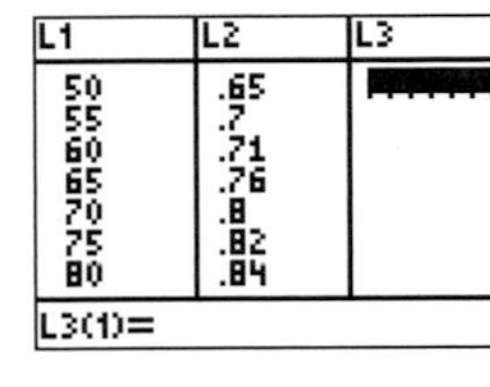

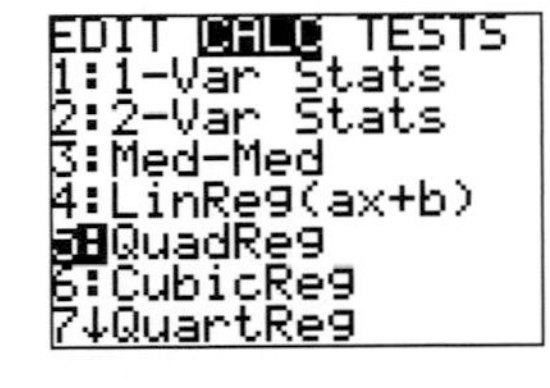

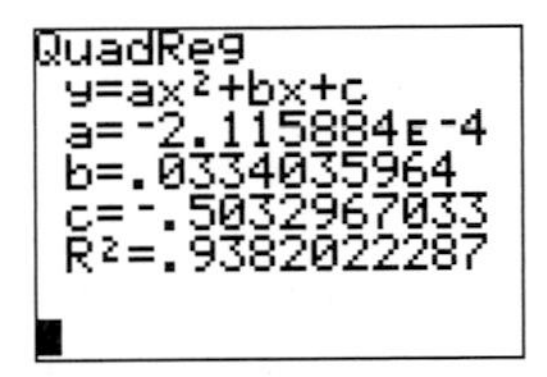

Substitute the values for a, b, and c into the equation $y = ax^2 + bx + c$, which is the standard form of a quadratic equation. When rounded to four significant digits, the quadratic regression equation is approximately $y = 0.0002x^2 + 0.0334x - 0.5033$.

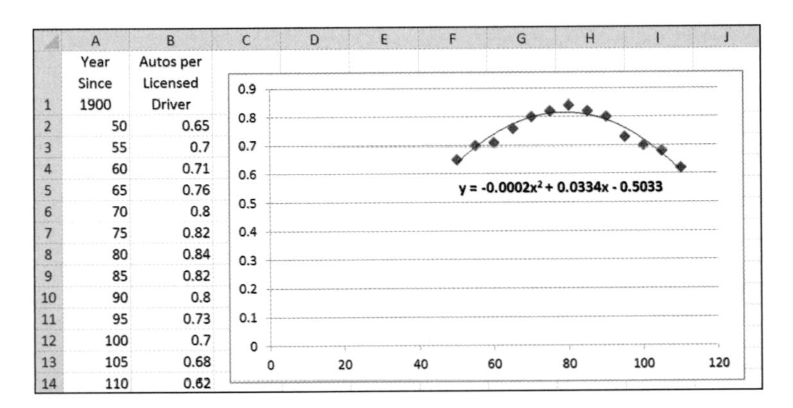

	A	B
1	Year Since 1900	Autos per Licensed Driver
2	50	0.65
3	55	0.7
4	60	0.71
5	65	0.76
6	70	0.8
7	75	0.82
8	80	0.84
9	85	0.82
10	90	0.8
11	95	0.73
12	100	0.7
13	105	0.68
14	110	0.62

To find the quadratic regression equation in a certain spreadsheet program, create a scatter plot, select a polynomial regression type after choosing to add a trend line, and pick 2 for the order because x is raised to a power of 2 in a quadratic equation.

Using a Quadratic Regression Equation

EXAMPLE 1

Use the equation of the quadratic regression curve to estimate the number of automobiles per licensed driver in 1987.

SOLUTION

Because the input variable is the number of years since 1900, substitute 87 for x and solve for y.

$$y = -0.0002x^2 + 0.0334x - 0.5033$$

$$y = -0.0002 \bullet \mathbf{87}^2 + 0.0334 \bullet \mathbf{87} - 0.5033$$

$$y = -1.514 + 2.906 - 0.5033 = 0.8889$$

In 1987, there was an average of about 0.9 automobiles per licensed driver. ■

▸ **Remember** The order of operations tells you to evaluate exponents before multiplying.

Finding an Exponential Regression Equation

Some data pairs fit well to an exponential model. In an exponential function, the outputs increase or decrease at an increasingly greater rate.

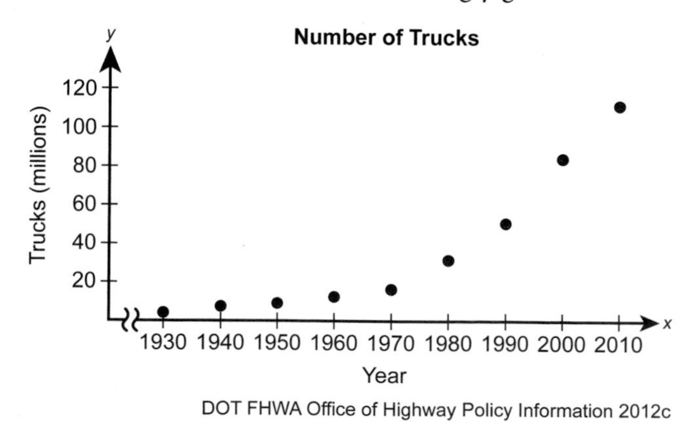

DOT FHWA Office of Highway Policy Information 2012c

This graph shows the number of registered trucks in the United States from 1930 to 2010. Notice how the increases between decades tend to get larger over time.

To find an exponential regression equation on a graphing calculator, scroll down to choose **0: ExpReg** from the **CALC** menu. Again, the input values have been entered as the number of years since 1900.

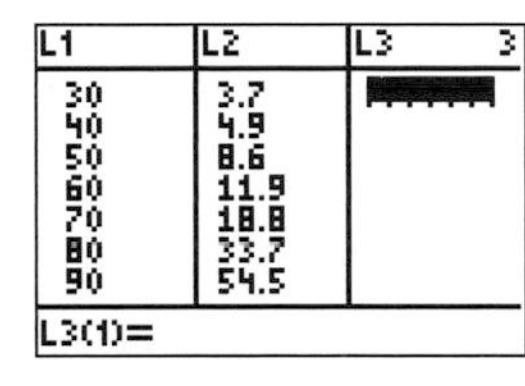

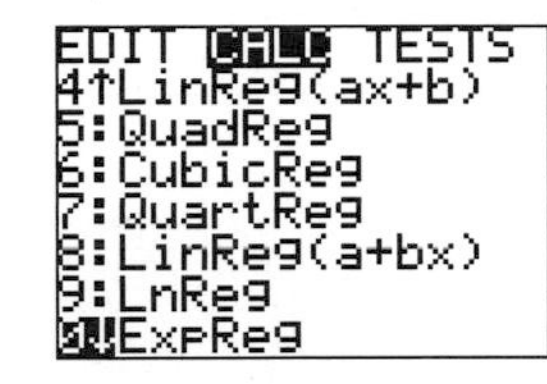

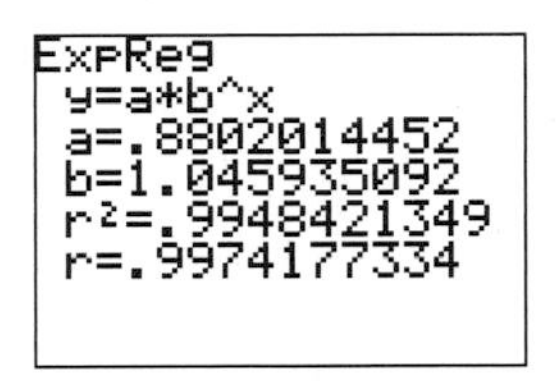

Substitute the values for a and b into the equation $y = a \bullet b^x$, which is one form of an exponential equation. When the values are rounded, the exponential regression equation is approximately $y = 0.8802 \bullet 1.0459^x$.

The exponential regression equation for these same data on a certain spreadsheet is $y = 0.8802 \bullet e^{0.0449x}$. The letter e represents a special number whose value is approximately 2.71828. You can use this value to make the equation from the spreadsheet look like the equation from the calculator.

$$e^{0.0449x} \approx \mathbf{2.71828^{0.0449x}} \approx \mathbf{1.0459^x}$$

▶ **Think About It** Some calculators have a key labeled e^x.

Using an Exponential Regression Equation

EXAMPLE 2

Use the equation of the exponential regression curve to predict the number of registered trucks that will be in the United States in 2020.

SOLUTION

Because the input variable is the number of years since 1900, substitute 120 for x and solve for y.

$$y = 0.8802 \cdot 1.0459^{x}$$

$$y = 0.8802 \cdot 1.0459^{120}$$

$$y \approx 0.8802 \cdot 218.1823221 \approx 192.04408$$

In 2020, there will be about 192 million registered trucks in the United States. ■

▶ **Think About It** The prediction is based on the assumption that current trends will continue, which they may not.

Determining the Best Regression Model

The points in the scatter plot of the number of registered trucks in the United States tend to fall along the right side of a parabola that opens upward. Therefore, you may wonder if a quadratic model would fit the data better than the exponential model.

To determine which type of regression best fits a data set, use the coefficient of determination, which may appear as either r^2 or R^2. The closer the coefficient is to 1, the better the fit.

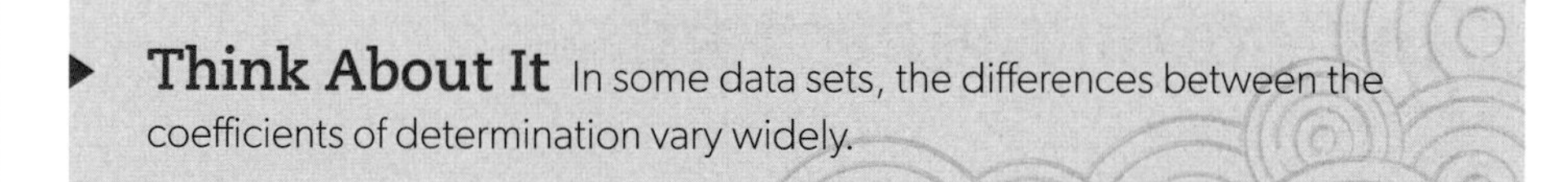

▶ **Think About It** In some data sets, the differences between the coefficients of determination vary widely.

Here are the approximate coefficients of determination for the data about the number of registered trucks in the United States.

linear regression: 0.852
quadratic regression: 0.993
exponential regression: 0.995

Both a quadratic model and an exponential model fit the data set very well. However, the exponential model has a slightly better fit because $0.995 > 0.993$.

The graph of the quadratic regression is shown in solid red, while the graph of the exponential regression is shown in dashed green.

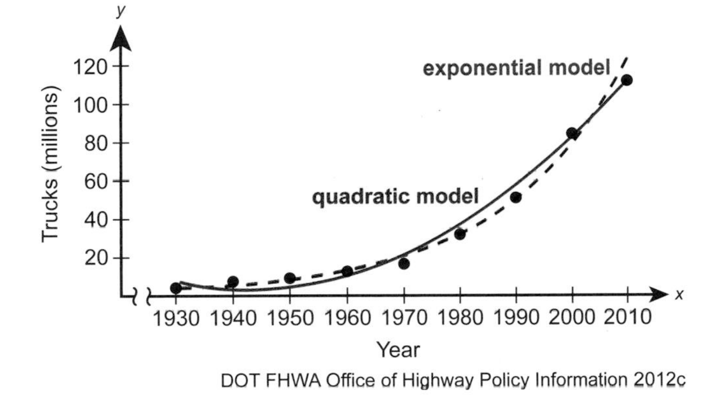

Residuals

Residuals show how well a model summarizes data.

Finding Residuals

The points on a scatter plot usually do not fall exactly on the regression line, which creates an error between observed and predicted values. This error, called a **residual**, is the vertical distance between a point on the scatter plot and the point on the linear model directly above or below the point.

Definition

A **residual** is the difference between an observed value and the predicted value from the model.

$$\text{residual} = \text{observed} - \text{predicted}$$

or

$$e = y - \hat{y}$$

In the scatter plot, when $x = 5$, the observed value is $y = 10$, the predicted value according to the regression line is $\hat{y} = 6$, and the residual is $e = 4$. When a point is below the regression line, the residual is negative. For example, when $x = 2$, the residual is $e = -4$.

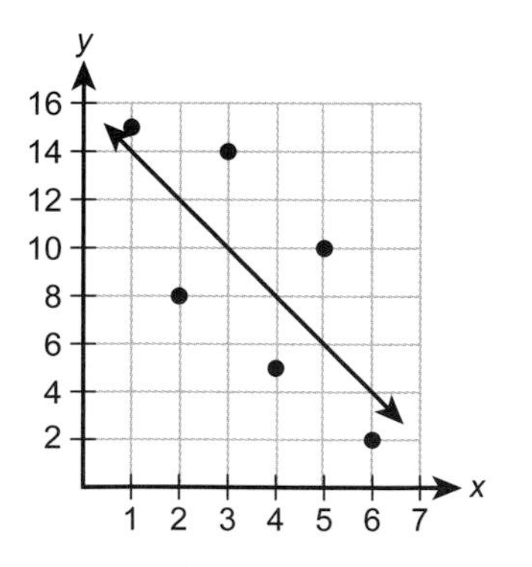

A **residual plot** is a graph that shows the residual for each value of the explanatory variable. The scatter plot shows a residual plot for the data.

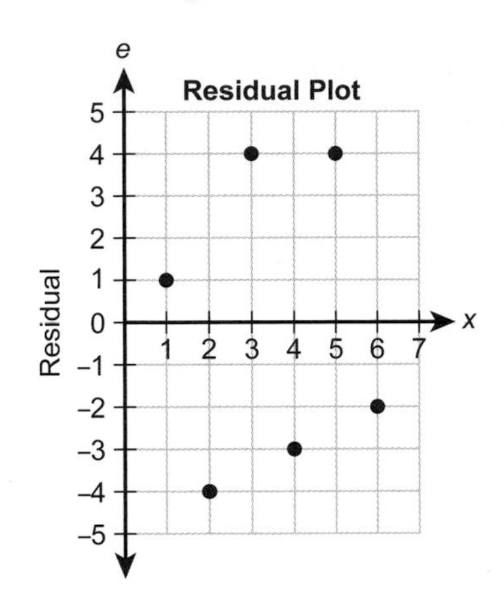

Interpreting Residual Plots

If the points in a residual plot show a pattern, then a straight line may not be an appropriate way to summarize the data. However, if the points have a random pattern that is scattered above and below the horizontal axis, then a line is probably an appropriate model.

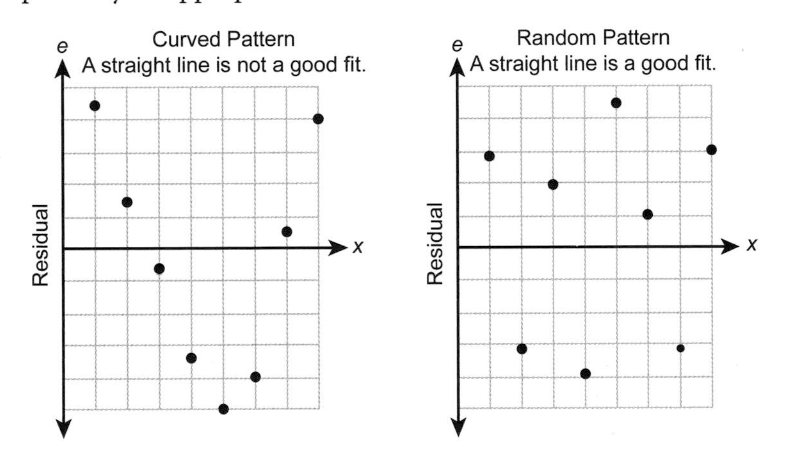

For example, looking at the scatter plot showing the amount of public debt in the United States from 2000 to 2010, it appears that a straight line might be a good way to summarize the data.

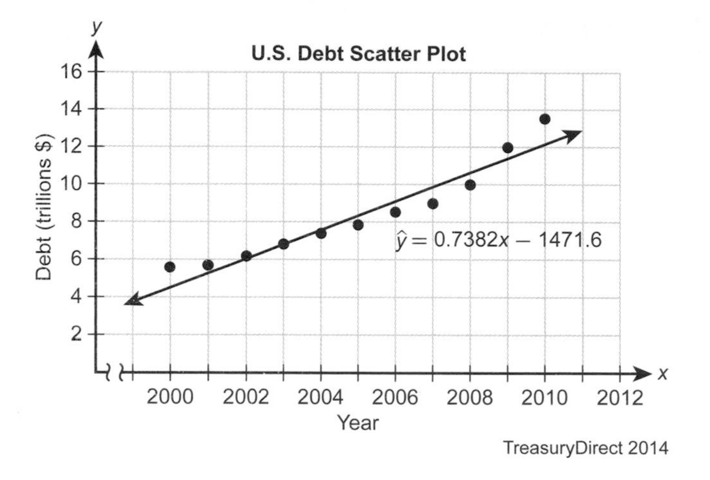

The residual plot shown below, however, tells a different story. The curved pattern indicates that a straight line is not the best fit for these data.

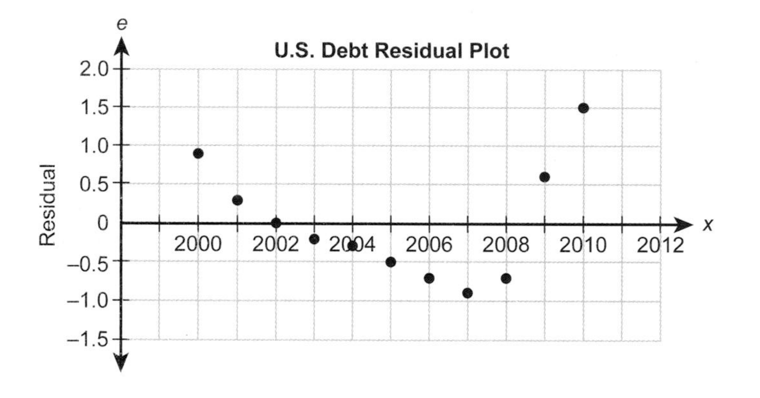

When a linear model is not the best fit, quadratic models, exponential models, and others can be used.

Pronunciation Guide

Pronunciation Guide

The tables provide sample words to explain the sounds associated with specific letters and letter combinations used in the respellings in this book. For example, *a* represents the short “a” sound in *cat*, while *ay* represents the long “a” sound in *day*.

Letter combinations are used to approximate certain more complex sounds. For example, in the respelling of *trapezoid*—TRA-puh-zoyd—the letters *uh* represent the vowel sound you hear in *shut* and *other*.

VOWELS

a	short a: apple, cat
ay	long a: cane, day
e, eh	short e: hen, bed
ee	long e: feed, team
i, ih	short i: lip, active
iy	long i: try, might
ah	short o: hot, father
oh	long o: home, throw
uh	short u: shut, other
yoo	long u: union, cute

LETTER COMBINATIONS

ch	chin, ancient
sh	show, mission
zh	vision, azure
th	thin, health
th	then, heather
ur	bird, further, word
us	bus, crust
or	court, formal
ehr	error, care
oo	cool, true, rule
ow	now, out
ou	look, pull, would
oy	coin, toy
aw	saw, maul, fall
ng	song, finger
air	Aristotle, barrister
ahr	cart, martyr

CONSONANTS

b	butter, baby
d	dog, cradle
f	fun, phone
g	grade, angle
h	hat, ahead
j	judge, gorge
k	kite, car, black
l	lily, mile
m	mom, camel
n	next, candid
p	price, copper
r	rubber, free
s	small, circle, hassle
t	ton, pottery
v	vase, vivid
w	wall, away
y	yellow, kayak
z	zebra, haze

Glossary

absolute value function a function whose rule contains an absolute value expression

accuracy how close a measure is to its true value

acute angles angles that measure less than 90°

addition counting principle if there are m ways of doing one thing and n ways of doing another thing, then there are $m + n$ ways of doing one thing or the other

adjacent angles angles that share a common side, have the same vertex, and do not share any interior common points

adjacent side of acute angle in a right triangle the side next to the given angle in a right triangle but is not the hypotenuse

alternate exterior angles angles outside the two lines that are not the transversal and are on diagonal opposite sides of the transversal

altitude of a pyramid a perpendicular line segment that joins the vertex to the plane of the base; An altitude may lie inside, on, or outside a pyramid.

altitude of a triangle a perpendicular segment from a vertex of the triangle to a line containing the base opposite the vertex

amplitude of a sinusoidal function one-half the distance between the maximum value and the minimum value; the height of a sinusoidal function above the midline

analytic geometry the study of geometry using the tools of algebra; also called coordinate geometry

angle a figure formed by two rays, called sides, that share the same endpoint

angle bisector a line or line segment or ray that divides an angle into two congruent angles

angle of depression of an object the downward angle that the object makes with the horizontal

angle of elevation of an object the upward angle that the object makes with the horizontal

annulus the region between two concentric circles

arc the set of points on a circle between two points on the circle

arc length a part of the circumference of a circle; It can be found by writing the part as a fraction over 360° and multiplying by the circumference.

arccosine (arccos) function $y = \arccos x$ if and only if $\cos y = x$ where $-1 \leq x \leq 1$ and $0 \leq y \leq \pi$

arcsine (arcsin) function $y = \arcsin x$ if and only if $\sin y = x$ where $-1 \leq x \leq 1$ and $-\frac{\pi}{2} \leq y \leq \frac{\pi}{2}$

area the number of square units contained in the interior of a figure

argument a set of statements, called premises, which are needed to reach a conclusion; Both the premise and the conclusion are considered to be part of the argument.

arithmetic sequence a sequence in which the difference between consecutive terms in a sequence is a constant

association the relationship between two variables

asymptote a line that a graph of a given function approaches without touching

average rate of change in a quantity the ratio of the change in a quantity to the change in time

axis of a cylinder the line connecting the centers of the bases

axis of a double-napped cone the line about which a generating line revolves to produce a double-napped cone

axis of symmetry a line drawn through a figure so that one side is a reflection of the image on the opposite side; also called a line of symmetry

base a number raised to an exponent; For example, in 5^2, 5 is the base.

base edges of pyramid edges that form the base of a pyramid; A base edge is formed when a lateral face and the base meet.

bell-shaped distribution a type of symmetric distribution of data sets that is nearly bell-shaped, where the mean and median are nearly equal

bi– prefix that means "two"

biased sample a sample that is not representative of its population

binomial a polynomial with two terms

bivariate data data that show the relationship between paired variables

boundary line a line that divides the coordinate plane into two half-planes

bounded closed interval an interval that includes both endpoints

bounded half-open interval an interval that includes one and only one endpoint

bounded interval the set of all real numbers between two numbers, called endpoints; The endpoints may or may not be included.

bounded open interval an interval that does not include either endpoint

box-and-whisker plot a diagram that shows the distribution or spread of data with the minimum, the maximum, and the three quartiles of the data; The box extends from Q_1 to Q_3. The median is on the vertical line in the box. The whiskers extend from the first quartile to the minimum and from the third quartile to the maximum.

ceiling function another name for the least integer function

center of a circle the point inside a circle that is an equal distance from every point on the circle

center of a polygon the point inside a polygon that is equidistant from each vertex

center of a sphere the point inside a sphere from which all points on the surface of the sphere are an equal distance

center of dilation the point where the lines connecting each point on the pre-image with its corresponding point on the image intersect

central angle of a circle an angle that has its vertex at the center of a circle and its sides as radii of the circle

central angle of a polygon an angle formed by line segments drawn from the center to two consecutive vertices

central limit theorem when several random samples of size n are taken from a population and n is sufficiently large, then the means of the samples will have a distribution that is approximately normal

centroid the point where all three medians of a triangle intersect

chord a segment that connects any two points on a circle

circle the set of all points in a plane that are a fixed distance r (the radius) from a given point (the center)

circle (as a conic section) a conic section formed when a plane intersects only one nappe, perpendicular to the axis

circle graph a graph that uses sectors of a circle to display and compare data that can be broken down into separate categories

circumcenter the point where the perpendicular bisectors on each side of a triangle intersect

circumscribed circle for a given triangle, the circle that contains each vertex of the triangle; The circumcenter of the triangle is the center of the circumscribed circle.

classes equal-sized groups used to separate and categorize data; also called intervals

closed half-plane a half-plane in a nonstrict inequality where the boundary line is a solid line

closed set a set such that, under an operation, the result of the operation on any two elements of the set is also an element of the set

coefficient the nonvariable factor of a term

coefficient of determination the square of the correlation coefficient; written r^2

coincident system a system with infinitely many solutions

collinear points that lie on the same line

common difference the difference between a term and the previous term; the constant difference d in an arithmetic sequence such that $d = a_n - a_{n-1}$

common factor a factor shared by two or more numbers

common logarithm a logarithm with base 10; Common logarithms, such as $\log_{10} x$, are usually written without the base, as $\log x$.

common logarithmic function with base 10 $f(x) = \log x$ when x is a positive real number; The domain is $x > 0$ and the vertical asymptote is $x = 0$.

common ratio of a geometric sequence the ratio of a term to the previous term; the constant r in a geometric sequence such that $r = \frac{a_n}{a_{n-1}}$

complementary angles angles whose measures sum to 90°

completing the square the process of transforming an expression of the form $x^2 + bx$ into a perfect square trinomial by adding the term $\left(\frac{b}{2}\right)^2$ to it

complex conjugates two complex numbers of the form $a + bi$ and $a - bi$

complex numbers numbers of the form $a + bi$ where a is the real part and b is the imaginary part and a and b are real numbers; denoted $\mathbb{C}$

complex plane the plane on which every complex number can be graphed; The horizontal axis is the real axis and the vertical axis is the imaginary axis.

compound event an event that consists of two or more simple events

compound inequality a pair of inequalities joined by the word *and* or the word *or*; a type of compound statement

computer algebra system (CAS) a computer program that performs algebraic manipulations such as simplifying algebraic expressions and solving equations

conclusion of a conditional statement the part of a conditional statement that includes the words following *then*

conclusion of an argument the end part of an argument that follows the premises

conditional probability the probability of an event given that another event has already happened; The conditional probability that event B occurs after event A has already occurred can be represented as $P(B \mid A)$, which is read as "the probability of B given A."

conditional statement a statement that has two parts; The first part begins with the word *if* and the second part begins with the word *then*.

cone a solid with a circular base, a vertex, and a curved surface

confidence interval an interval estimate that is likely to contain a population parameter being estimated

confidence level the percent chance that a population parameter falls inside the confidence interval

congruent line segments line segments that have equal length

congruent polygons polygons that are the same size and shape

conic section a two-dimensional graph that can be formed by the intersection of a plane with a double-napped cone

conjecture a statement that is thought to be true but is yet to be proven

conjugate binomials two binomials with the same terms but opposite signs; for example, $(a + b)$ and $(a - b)$

conjugate pair a pair of expressions of the form $a + bi$ and $a - bi$

conjunction a compound statement that uses the word *and*

consistent dependent system of equations a system with infinitely many solutions

consistent independent system of equations a system with exactly one solution

consistent system of equations a system with exactly one solution or infinitely many solutions

constant a term that has no variables

constant function a function is constant within an interval if the value of $f(x)$ remains the same

constraint a necessary condition in a problem, often written in the form of an inequality

continuous function a function with a connected graph

continuous random variable a variable whose outcomes are both random and continuous

contraction a dilation for which the absolute value of the scale factor is between 0 and 1

contradiction (equation) an equation that is true for no values of the variable; A contradiction has no solutions, represented by the null set: $\{ \}$ or $\varnothing$.

contradiction (statement) a statement that is logically at odds with a previous statement that was assumed to be true

converse a conditional statement that switches the hypothesis and the conclusion of the original conditional statement

conversion factor a fraction that is used to convert measures and rates and that has a numerator and denominator of the same quantity written in different units

coordinate the number on a number line that gives the location of a point

coordinate plane a plane in which the coordinates of any point are the point's distances from two intersecting perpendicular lines called axes (the x-axis and y-axis)

coplanar points that lie on the same plane

corollary a proposition that follows directly from a postulate or theorem and can be easily proven

correlation coefficient written as r, describes the strength and direction of the association between two variables; Values for r range from 1 (perfect positive correlation) to 0 (no correlation) to -1 (perfect negative correlation).

corresponding angles of figures the angles that lie in the same position or match up when a transversal intersects two lines

corresponding sides of figures the sides that lie in the same position or match up when a transversal intersects two lines

cosine function $\cos x = a$ is a trigonometric function of x when x is a radian measure of the angle that intercepts the unit circle at (a, b)

cosine of an angle the ratio of the length of the leg that is adjacent to that angle to the length of the hypotenuse; abbreviated cos

coterminal angles angles in standard position that have the same terminal side but have different amounts of rotation; Their angles differ by a multiple of 360°, or 2π radians.

counterexample an example that shows that a statement is false

critical z-scores z-scores for the upper limit and lower limit of the confidence interval

cylinder a solid with two parallel, congruent, circular bases joined by a curved surface

decreasing function a function is decreasing within an interval if the value of $f(x)$ decreases as the value of x increases

deductive reasoning a type of reasoning that uses previously proven or accepted properties to reach conclusions

degenerate conic section a conic section formed when a plane intersects the vertex of the double-napped cone

degree of a monomial the sum of the exponents of the variable factors

degree of a polynomial the degree of the monomial with the greatest degree

density the ratio of the mass of an object to its volume; density = mass ÷ volume

dependent events events in which knowing one outcome has an effect on the probability of the other event(s)

dependent variable the output variable of a function

descriptive statistics statistics that are used to numerically summarize or represent a set of data

deviation in a data set, the difference between a data value x_i and the mean $\overline{x}$ of the data set; $x_i - \overline{x}$

diagonals line segments with endpoints on nonconsecutive vertices

diameter a line segment that connects two points on a circle and contains the center of the circle; also the length of any diameter of a given circle

dilation a transformation that changes the size but not the shape of a figure, either by enlarging it or shrinking it

dimensional analysis the process of multiplying by conversion factors and dividing out common units

directed line segment a segment between two points A and B with a specified direction from A to B or from B to A and a standard distance between the two points

directrix one of two references in the definition of a parabola; The distance from any point on the parabola to the directrix (a line) is equal to the distance from that same point to the parabola's focus (a point).

discrete function a function with a graph that is disconnected

discriminant the radicand $b^2 - 4ac$ in the quadratic formula

disjunction a compound statement that uses the word *or*

dividend the number being divided by the divisor

divisor the number that divides the dividend

domain the set of all allowable inputs for a relation or function

double-napped cone cone formed by the generating line that intersects and revolves around another line called the axis; The axis is stationary and the two lines cannot be perpendicular.

element a member of a set

ellipse a conic section formed when a plane intersects only one nappe, not parallel to the generating line

end behavior how a function behaves when the domain values increase or decrease without bound

endpoints of an interval the minimum and maximum real numbers on a bounded interval

endpoints of an intercepted arc the points where the sides of an inscribed angle meet the circle

equal complex numbers complex numbers with real parts that are equal and with imaginary parts that are equal; $a + bi = c + di$ if and only if $a = c$ and $b = d$

equation a number sentence that indicates that two expressions have the same value

equiangular polygon a polygon with all angles congruent

equilateral triangle a triangle that has three congruent sides

equivalent equations equations with the same solution or solutions

equivalent fractions fractions that have the same value

equivalent inequalities inequalities with the same solutions

even function a function in which $f(-x) = f(x)$; The graph of an even function is symmetric about the y-axis.

event any particular subset of a sample space

expanded form of a sum a representation of a sum as every term added or subtracted to create the sum

expansion a dilation for which the absolute value of the scale factor is greater than 1

experiment any process that results in one or more results

explanatory variable the variable graphed along the horizontal axis in a scatter plot; the independent variable in a statistical analysis

exponent in a power, a number used to indicate the number of factors of the base that should be multiplied; For example, in 5^2, 2 is the exponent.

exponential equation an equation with variable expressions as exponents

exponential function an equation of the form $f(x) = b^x + k$ where $b > 0$ and $b \neq 1$

expression a number, a variable, or a combination of numbers, variables, and operations

exterior angle of a triangle an angle formed by one side of the triangle and another side of the triangle when it is extended

extremes the exterior variables of a proportion

factor one of two or more quantities that are multiplied together

factor of a number a number that divides into the given number without a remainder

factorial of a positive integer *n* the product of all the positive integers less than or equal to n; written $n!$

family of functions a group of functions with the same fundamental characteristics

feasible region the set of all ordered pairs that satisfy the constraints of an optimization problem and are possible solutions to the problem

Fermi estimate an estimate of a very large number using the Fermi process; This process involves being able to estimate quantities and then round the estimates to the nearest number that is a product of a counting number less than 10 and a power of 10.

finite set a set that has a number of elements that can be described with a whole number

first quartile, Q_1 the median of the lower subset of a data set

five-number summary the minimum, the maximum, and the three quartiles of a data set

floor function another name for the greatest integer function

flowchart proof a graphical representation of the logical flow of a proof; In a flowchart proof, statements and conclusions are connected with arrows.

focus for a parabola one of two references in the definition of a parabola; The distance from any point on the parabola to the focus (a point) is equal to the distance from that same point to the parabola's directrix (a line).

FOIL a mnemonic used for a method to perform the distributive property when multiplying binomials; first-outer-inner-last

frequency distribution a table or graph that describes the number of times a value or interval of values occurs in a data set

frequency of a sinusoidal function the number of periods per unit; A function's frequency is the reciprocal of its period.

frequency table a table that describes the number of times a value or interval of values occurs in a data set

function a relation in which each member of the domain is assigned to exactly one member of the range

function composition a mapping in which each element of the range of one function is the domain of another function; If f and g are functions of x, the composition of the f with g is denoted by fg and is defined as $f(g)$. The domain of $f(g(x))$ is the set of the domain values of g with range values that are in the domain of f.

function notation a function equation written so that the dependent variable is replaced with $f(x)$; for example, $f(x) = 2x + 4$

generating line of a double-napped cone the line that revolves about another line, called the axis, to produce a double-napped cone

geometric sequence a sequence in which the ratio between consecutive terms is a constant

geometric series a series that results from adding the terms of a geometric sequence

graph of an inequality a display of all possible solutions of the inequality

greatest integer function a function that assigns the greatest integer less than or equal to each real number in an interval; denoted by $f(x) = \lfloor x \rfloor$ or $f(x) = \text{int}(x)$; also called the floor function

half-life the length of time it takes for one-half of a radioactive substance to decay

half-plane a plane that has been divided in half by a boundary line

height the length of the altitude

histogram a bar graph that displays the frequency of data values that occur within certain intervals; The height of each bar gives the frequency in the respective interval.

horizontal asymptote the line $y = b$ for the graph of the function f if $f(x)$ approaches b as x approaches ∞ or $-\infty$

horizontal line test a test to determine whether a function f is invertible; If a horizontal line intersects a function more than once, then the function is not invertible. If every horizontal line intersects a function only once, then the function is invertible.

hyperbola a conic section formed when a plane intersects both nappes

hypotenuse the side opposite the right angle of a right triangle

hypothesis the part of a conditional statement that includes the words following *if*

identity an equation that is true for all values of the variable; It has infinitely many solutions and is often represented as $\{x \mid x \in \mathbb{R}\}$.

image a figure after transformation

imaginary axis the vertical axis of a complex plane along which the imaginary part of a complex number is graphed

imaginary number any number that can be written in the form ai where a is any real number and i is the imaginary unit

imaginary unit i where $i^2 = -1$ and $i = \sqrt{-1}$

improper fraction a fraction in which the numerator is greater than or equal to the denominator

incenter of a triangle the point where the angle bisectors drawn through each vertex intersect

included angle of a triangle an angle formed by two sides of a triangle

included side of a triangle a side of a triangle that lies between two specific angles

inconsistent system of equations a system with no solutions

increasing function a function is increasing within an interval if the value of $f(x)$ increases as the value of x increases

independent events two events in which knowing one outcome has no effect on the probability of the other event

independent variable the input variable of a function

index in sigma notation the variable i in sigma notation $\sum_{a=0}^{3} a_n$; the variable that takes on all integer values from the lower limit to the upper limit of the summation

index of a radical n in a radical expression $\sqrt[n]{b}$; The index is always greater than 1.

inductive reasoning a type of reasoning that starts with observation and moves from a specific observation to a general conclusion

inequality a statement formed by placing one of the inequality symbols $<$, $>$, $\leq$, $\geq$, or $\neq$ between two expressions

inferential statistics statistics used to draw conclusions or make predictions by taking the information gained from the sample and generalizing it to the population it came from

infinite set a set with a boundless number of elements

initial side of angle the ray from which the rotation of an angle starts

inscribed angle an angle that has its vertex on a circle and its sides as chords of the circle

inscribed circle for a given triangle, a circle in the interior of the triangle that touches each side of the triangle at a single point; The incenter is the center of the inscribed circle.

integers all the natural numbers, their opposites, and zero; denoted $\mathbb{Z} = \{\ldots, -2, -1, 0, 1, 2, \ldots\}$

intercepted arc the arc opposite an inscribed angle

interior angles of a triangle the three angles inside the triangle

interquartile range (IQR) the difference between the third and first quartiles of a data set; $\text{IQR} = Q_3 - Q_1$

interval estimate a range of values that contains the point estimate and is likely to contain the population parameter

inverse functions two functions f and g that "undo" each other; If you start with a value x, apply f, and then apply g, the result is the original value x: $(f \circ g)(x) = x$ and $(g \circ f)(x) = x$. The inverse of a function f is denoted by f^{-1} ("f inverse"). For every pair of inverse functions, if $f^{-1} = g$, then $g^{-1} = f$.

inverse of a function a relationship that interchanges the members of the ordered pairs of the original function; denoted by f^{-1}; The domain of the inverse function is the range of the original function. The range of the inverse function is the domain of the original function.

inverse of a relation a relationship that switches the x- and y-values of the ordered pairs of the original relation; The domain of the inverse relation is the range of the original relation. The range of the inverse relation is the domain of the original relation. The graph of the inverse of a relation is its reflection over the line $y = x$.

inverse tangent the angle that has a given value as its tangent ratio; abbreviated $\tan^{-1}$

invertible function a function f whose inverse is also a function

irrational number a real number that cannot be written in the form $\frac{a}{b}$ for any integers a and b

isometric transformation any transformation that results in an image that is congruent to the pre-image; also called an isometry

isosceles triangle a triangle that has at least two congruent sides

iterative rule a rule that can be used to find the nth term of a sequence without calculating previous terms of the sequence

lateral edges of a pyramid the edges of a pyramid that do not form the base; A lateral edge is formed when two lateral faces meet.

lateral side of an angle the ray from which the rotation of an angle starts

lateral surface the curved surface of a cylinder

law of detachment an argument that has two true premises and a valid conclusion; The premises and conclusion have the following form:

premise – If a, then b.
premise – a is true.
conclusion – Therefore, b is true.

law of syllogism a logical argument that always contains two premises and a conclusion; The premises and conclusion have the following form:

premise – If a, then b.
premise – If b, then c.
conclusion – Therefore, if a, then c.

leading coefficient of a polynomial in simplified form the coefficient of the first term

leaf the digits on the right side of a stem-and-leaf plot

least common denominator (LCD) the least common multiple of two or more denominators

least integer function a function that assigns the least integer greater than or equal to each real number in an interval; denoted by $f(x) = \lceil x \rceil$; also called the ceiling function

least squares regression line the line that makes the sum of the squares of the vertical distances from each data point to the line as small as possible

length of a line segment the distance between the endpoints of a line segment

like radicals two or more square root expressions that have the same radicand

like terms terms that contain the same variable factors taken to the same powers

line a collection of points arranged in a straight path

line of best fit a least squares regression equation

line of symmetry a line over which you can flip a given figure, leaving the figure unchanged; A line of symmetry divides a figure into two congruent (mirror-image) halves.

line segment a part of a line that consists of any two points on the line and all the points in between those two points

line symmetry a characteristic of a figure in which there is at least one line such that when the figure is folded over the line, the two halves are mirror images that match up perfectly; also called reflection symmetry

linear equation an equation whose graph in a coordinate plane is a line

linear inequality an inequality that has terms with degree zero or one and an inequality symbol to relate two variables

linear pair of angles two angles that have a common side and the same vertex with their other sides point in opposite directions

linear programming the process of maximizing or minimizing a linear function subject to a set of conditions, called constraints, that are linear inequalities

logarithm the exponent to which a base would have to be raised to result in a given value; The logarithm of a with base b, $\log_b a$, where $b > 0$, $b \neq 1$, and $a > 0$, is defined as $\log_b a = x$ if and only if $b^x = a$.

logistic growth function a function of the form $f(x) = \frac{C}{1 + Ae^{-Bx}}$ where A, B, and C are all positive constants

lower limit in sigma notation, the starting value for the index n; In $\sum_{n=1}^{n} a_n$, the lower limit is 1.

major arcs arcs larger than a semicircle

margin of error the greatest likely difference between the point estimate and the parameter

marginal frequency the ratio of the total for a particular column or row to the overall total in a two-way table

mean the statistical average of a data set

means of a proportion the middle variables of a proportion

median of a data set the middle value when the values are ordered; If the data set has an even number of values, the median is the mean of the two middle values.

median of a triangle a segment from the vertex of a triangle to the midpoint of its opposite side

midline of a sinusoidal function the horizontal line that is halfway between the maximum and the minimum; The equation of the midline of a sinusoidal function is $y = \frac{\text{maximum} + \text{minimum}}{2}$.

midpoint a point that divides a line segment into two congruent parts

minor arcs arcs smaller than a semicircle

mixed number a number consisting of both a whole number and a fraction or the opposite of such a number

mode the value that occurs most frequently

model parameter a value that is held constant for a specific model

model variable a variable that takes on different values for a particular model

modified box-and-whisker plot a box-and-whisker plot in which outliers are shown with dots and the whiskers extend to the least and greatest values in the data set that are not outliers

monomial a number, a variable, or the product of a number and one or more variables

multiplication counting principle if a task can be broken into two stages and there are m ways of doing the first stage and n ways of doing the second stage, then there are $m \bullet n$ ways of doing one thing and the other

multiplicity for a root a of $p(x) = 0$, the number of times the factor $x - a$ occurs in the factorization of any polynomial $p(x)$

nappe one of two equal pieces of a cone where the cone is divided at the vertex by a plane perpendicular to the axis

natural logarithm a logarithm with a base e; Natural logarithms, such as $\log_e x$, are often written using the notation $\ln x$.

natural logarithmic function with base *e* $g(x) = \ln x$ where x is a positive real number; The domain is $x > 0$, and the vertical asymptote is $x = 0$.

natural numbers the set of numbers $\mathbb{N} = \{1, 2, 3, \ldots\}$; also called counting numbers or positive integers

nearest integer function a function that assigns the nearest integer to each real number in an interval; denoted by $\text{nint}(x)$; also called the round function

negative association when comparing two data sets, as the data from one set increase, the data from the second set decrease; In a scatter plot, the data points decrease from left to right.

noncollinear points that do not lie on the same line

nonstrict inequality an inequality that uses $\leq$ or $\geq$

normal distribution a bell-shaped distribution, centered on the mean

n*th root of *b a when $a^n = b$, a and b are both real numbers, and n is a positive integer

number line a line with equally spaced intervals that are labeled with numbers

numerical expression an expression that consists of numbers, operations, and sometimes grouping symbols

objective function a linear function that models a quantity that is to be optimized in a linear programming problem

oblique cone a cone with an axis that is not an altitude

oblique cylinder a cylinder with an axis that is not an altitude

obtuse angles angles that measure greater than 90° and less than 180°

odd function a function in which $f(-x) = -f(x)$; The graph of an odd function is symmetric about the origin.

one-to-one function a function in which every element of the domain corresponds to exactly one element on the range

open half-plane a half plane in a strict inequality where the boundary line is dashed

open sentence an equation or inequality containing one or more variables

opposite side of an acute angle in a right triangle the side across from the given angle

ordered pair a pair of numbers on a coordinate plane, in which the first number is the x-coordinate the second is the y-coordinate

origin the intersection of the x- and y-axes

outcomes the results of an experiment

outlier a value far away from most other values in a data set

parabola a symmetric curve that is the graph of a quadratic function

parabola (conic section) a conic section formed when a plane intersects only one nappe, parallel to the generating line

parabola (locus of points) the set of all points in a plane that are equidistant from a fixed line (the directrix) and a fixed point (the focus)

paragraph proof a proof in the form of a paragraph

parallel lines coplanar lines that never intersect

parallelogram a quadrilateral with two pairs of parallel sides

parameter a measurement that describes a population

parent function the most basic function in a family of functions

partition a directed line segment to divide a directed line segment into segments based on a given ratio

percentile rank the percentage of data that falls below a particular value

perfect square a rational number with a square root that is also rational

perimeter the distance around a figure

period the length of each interval in a periodic function

period of a sinusoidal graph the interval over which a sinusoidal graph repeats itself

periodic function a function that repeats itself in regular intervals

perpendicular bisector a line, line segment, or ray that passes through the midpoint of a line segment and forms a right angle with the segment

perpendicular lines lines that meet at right angles

piecewise function a function defined using different rules for different intervals of the domain

plane a flat surface that has infinite length and width but no thickness

point references a location in space; It has no length, width, or depth.

point estimates statistics, such as $\hat{p}$ and $\hat{x}$, that are used to estimate population parameters

point of tangency a point where a circle and one of its tangents intersect

point-slope form of a linear equation an equation of the form $y - y_1 = m(x - x_1)$ where m is the slope and (x_1, y_1) is a point on the corresponding line

polygon a closed figure in a plane formed by three or more line segments, such that each line segment intersects exactly two other line segments at their endpoints only

polynomial a monomial or the sum of monomials

polynomial in *x* a polynomial of the form $a_n x^n + a_{n-1} x^{n-1} + \ldots + a_2 x^2 + a_1 x + a_0$ where the exponents are all whole numbers, the coefficients are all real numbers, and $a_n \neq 0$

population an entire set of members that you want to know something about

positive association when comparing two data sets, if the data from one set increase, the data from the second set also increase; In a scatter plot, data points increase from left to right.

postulates mathematical statements that are accepted as true without proof

power a number that is, or could be, represented by a base with an exponent

power function any function that can be written in the form $f(x) = ax^2 + b$ when n is a positive integer, a is any nonzero real number, and b is any real number

practical domain and range of a function the sets of all realistic inputs and outputs for a particular situation

pre-image the original figure before a transformation

premises statements that are presumed to be true in the course of a logical argument

prime polynomial a polynomial that cannot be factored

principal of a loan the amount of money actually borrowed

principal square root another name for a positive square root; indicated by the radical sign $\sqrt{}$

probability distribution table a frequency table where each frequency is replaced by the probability of the outcome

probability of an event a measure of the likelihood that an event will occur; Probability is always a number between 0 and 1 (inclusive) that can be written as a fraction, a decimal, or a percent.

product of the functions *f* and *g*
$(fg)(x) = f(x) \cdot g(x)$

proof a clear, logical structure of reasoning that begins from accepted ideas and proceeds through logic to reach a conclusion

proper fraction a fraction in which the numerator is less than the denominator

proportion an equation that states that two ratios are equal; often written as $a : b = c : d$ or $\frac{a}{b} = \frac{c}{d}$

pyramid a polyhedron with a polygonal base and lateral faces; The faces are triangles that meet at a common vertex.

Pythagorean identity for any angle θ, $\sin^2 \theta + \cos^2 \theta = 1$

quadrantal angles angles in standard position that have their terminal sides along the horizontal or vertical axis

quadrants the sections of a coordinate plane; The first quadrant is between the positive horizontal axis and the positive vertical axis. The second, third, and fourth quadrants are located counterclockwise from the first quadrant, respectively.

quadratic formula a formula for finding the solutions of a quadratic equation in the form $ax^2 + bx + c = 0$ where $a \neq 0$; $x = \frac{-b \pm \sqrt{b^2 - 4ac}}{2a}$

quadratic function a second-degree polynomial function

quadrilateral a four-sided polygon

quotient the number of times the divisor goes into the dividend evenly

quotient of the functions *f* and *g* $\frac{f}{g}(x) = \frac{f(x)}{g(x)}$, $g(x) \neq 0$

radian measure of a central angle of a circle the quotient of the angle's arc length and the circle's radius

radian measure of an angle the length of the arc on a unit circle subtended (intercepted) by the angle

radical equation an equation that contains at least one radical expression with a variable in the radicand

radical expression an expression that contains a radical sign $\sqrt{}$

radical function a function of the form $f(x) = a\sqrt{x - h} + k$ where n is an integer greater than 1

radicand the expression under a radical sign; For example, in the expression $\sqrt[n]{b}$, b is the radicand.

radius a line segment that connects the center of a circle to a point on the circle; also the length of all radii of a given circle

range of a data set the difference between its greatest value (maximum) and its least value (minimum)

range of a relation the set of possible outputs

rational expression a ratio with a numerator and a denominator that are polynomials and with a denominator that is nonzero

rational function any function that can be written as the quotient of two polynomials

rational number any number that can be expressed as a ratio $\frac{a}{b}$, where a and b are integers and $b \neq 0$; denoted $\mathbb{Q}$

raw score an original data value

ray part of a line that starts at an endpoint and extends infinitely in one direction

real axis the horizontal axis of a complex plane along which the real part of a complex number is graphed

real numbers the set of numbers that can be written as decimals; the combined set of the rational and irrational numbers; denoted $\mathbb{R}$

reciprocal power function a function that has the power of x in the denominator of a rational function; The functions $f(x) = \frac{1}{x}$, $g(x) = \frac{1}{x^2}$, and $h(x) = \frac{1}{x^3}$ are reciprocal power functions.

rectangle a parallelogram with four right angles

recursive rule a rule for generating terms of a sequence that depends on one or more previous terms of the sequence

reference angle for an acute angle x, the positive acute angle made by the terminal side of x and the horizontal axis

reflection an isometric transformation that flips a figure across a line or line segment, creating a mirror image of the figure

reflection symmetry when a figure that has at least one axis of symmetry; The figure can be folded along the axis of symmetry so that both halves match up.

regression line a line drawn through the points of a scatter plot to summarize the straight line pattern that the points fit

regular hexagon a six-sided polygon with congruent sides and congruent angles

regular polygon a polygon that is both equiangular and equilateral

regular pyramid a pyramid whose base is a regular polygon and whose lateral faces are congruent isosceles triangles

relation a mapping from one set, called the domain, to another set, called the range

relative frequency the ratio of the value of a subtotal to the value of the total

relative maximum point of a function a point that has a greater function value than all the points on the function that are close to it

relative minimum point a point that has a value that is less than all the points on the function that are close to it

remainder the amount left over after evenly dividing a dividend by a divisor

remote interior angles the angles that are inside the triangle and are not adjacent to a given exterior angle

repeating decimal a decimal that does not end but shows a repeating of digits (not made up of all zeros) that goes on forever after the decimal point

residual the difference between an observed value and the predicted value from a model; residual (e) = observed (y) − predicted $(\hat{y})$; the vertical distance between a point on the scatter plot and the point on the linear model directly above or below the point

residual plot a graph that shows the residual for each value of the explanatory variable

response variable the variable graphed along the vertical axis in a scatter plot; the independent variable(s) in a statistical analysis

rhombus a parallelogram with four congruent sides

right angle an angle that measures exactly 90°

right cone a cone with an axis that is also an altitude

right cylinder a cylinder with an axis that is also an altitude

rigid motion motion that relocates a figure while preserving its shape and size

roots of a polynomial the solutions to a polynomial equation in which one side of the equation is a factored polynomial and the other side of the equation is equal to zero

rotation an isometric transformation that turns a figure a certain number of degrees, called the angle of rotation, around a central point, called the center of rotation

rotation symmetry when a figure can be rotated around its center less than one full turn so that the rotated figure looks exactly like the original figure

round function another name for the nearest integer function

same-side interior angles angles in between the two lines that are not the transversal and are on the same side of the transversal

sample a subset of a population

sample space the set of all possible outcomes of an experiment

scale factor *t* of a dilation the ratio of the length of any side of on an image to the length of its corresponding side on the pre-image

scalene triangle a triangle that has no congruent sides

scatter plot a graph that displays a set of bivariate data

secant a line that intersects a circle in two points

second quartile, Q_2 the median of the entire data set that separates the ordered data set into a lower subset and an upper subset

sector a region whose boundaries are two radii and part of the circle

segment bisector a line, line segment, or ray that passes through the midpoint of a line segment

semicircle an arc with endpoints that are also the endpoints of a diameter

sequence a function whose domain is the set of natural numbers

series the sum of consecutive terms of a sequence

set a collection of objects

sides the line segments that form a polygon

sigma notation a way to write a sum as sum as $\sum_{i=1}^{n} a_i = a_1 + a_2 + a_3 + \ldots + a_n$; $\sum_{i=1}^{n} a_i$, read as "the sum from 1 to n of a_i," where i is the index, n is the upper limit, and 1 is the lower limit; The right side of the equation is the expanded form of the sum.

similar figures figures that are the same shape but are not necessarily the same size; The symbol $\sim$ means "is similar to."

similar solids solids that have the same shape and all the corresponding dimensions are proportional

similar triangles two triangles with congruent corresponding angles and proportional corresponding side lengths

simple event a single outcome of an experiment; a single element of a sample space

simplified form of a polynomial a polynomial that has no like terms, every term is in simplest form, and its terms are in order of decreasing degree with respect to a variable

simplified radical form of a square root expression a square root expression in which the radicand is not a fraction, there are no radicals in the denominator, and no factor is a perfect square other than 1

sine of an angle the ratio of the length of the leg opposite the angle to the length of the hypotenuse; abbreviated sin

sine function $\sin x = b$ is a trigonometric function of x when x is a radian measure of the angle that intercepts the unit circle at (a, b)

sinusoidal function a function that has the equation $f(x) = A \sin Bx + C$ or $f(x) = A \cos Bx + C$ where $A \neq 0$ and $B \neq 0$

skewed distribution one side has lower frequencies than the other side

slope a number that describes the steepness of a line; the ratio of the vertical change, or rise, to the horizontal change, or run, between any two points on a line

slope of a line the ratio of the vertical change, or rise, to the horizontal change, or run, between any two points on the line

slope-intercept form of a linear equation an equation of the form $y = mx + b$ where m is the slope and b is the y-intercept of the corresponding line

solution a value for the variable that makes the equation or open sentence a true statement

solve to find all the solutions for an equation

sphere the set of all points in space that are a given distance from a point called the center

square a parallelogram with four congruent sides and four right angles

square root a factor of a number that, when multiplied by itself, results in the number

standard deviation a measure of spread of a data set; the standard deviation $s = \sqrt{\frac{\Sigma(x - \overline{x})^2}{n - 1}}$ where x is a data value, $\overline{x}$ is the mean of the data set, and n is the number of data values in the set

standard form of a linear equation an equation of the form $Ax + By = C$ where A, B, and C are integers, and A and B are both nonzero

standard form of a polynomial the form of a polynomial in which every term is simplified and its terms are listed by decreasing degree

standard normal curve a probability distribution where the mean is 0, the standard deviation is 1, and the total area under the curve is 1

standard position of an angle an angle on coordinate plane that has its vertex is at the origin and its initial side along the positive horizontal axis

statement a sentence that is either true or false

statistic a measurement that describes a sample

stem leftmost digit of data values in a stem-and-leaf plot

stem-and-leaf plot a data display that lists the last digits (leaves) of the data values to the right of the earlier digits (stems)

step function a function defined using a rule that produces a constant value for each designated interval of the domain

straight angles angles that measure exactly 180°; A straight angle is a line.

strength of association how closely the data points on a scatter plot fit a straight line pattern

strict inequality inequality that uses $<$ or $>$

substitute to replace

sum of the functions *f* and *g* $(f + g)(x) = f(x) + g(x)$

supplementary angles angles with measures that sum to 180°

system of equations a group of two or more equations in the same variables

system of linear equations two or more linear equations with the same variables

system of linear inequalities a set of two or more linear inequalities using the same variables

tangent function $\tan x = \frac{\sin x}{\cos x}$; a trigonometric function of x in which x is the radian measure of the angle that intercepts the unit circle at (a, b); The value of x may not result in the cosine being zero.

tangent of an angle the ratio of the length of the leg opposite the angle to the length of the leg adjacent to the angle; abbreviated tan

tangent to a circle a line in the plane of the circle that intersects the circle in exactly one point

terminal side of angle the ray at which the rotation of an angle stops

terms the parts of an expression that are added or subtracted

terms of a sequence the values of a function whose domain is the set of natural numbers; the range of a sequence

theorem a mathematical statement that has been proven to be true

theoretical domain and range of a function the sets of all allowable inputs and outputs

third quartile, Q_3 the median of the upper subset

transformation a one-to-one mapping between two sets of points

translate (a figure) the sliding of a figure in a straight path without rotating or reflecting it

translation a transformation that slides a figure in a straight path without rotation or reflection

transversal a line that intersects two or more lines in a plane

trapezoid a quadrilateral with exactly one pair of parallel sides

triangle a three-sided polygon

trigonometric functions of angle θ $\sin \theta = \frac{b}{r}$, $\cos \theta = \frac{a}{r}$, $\tan \theta = \frac{b}{a}$ $(a \neq 0)$ where (a, b) is a point other than the origin on the terminal side of an angle θ in standard position, and r is the distance $\sqrt{a^2 + b^2}$ from the point to the origin

trigonometric identity an equation containing a trigonometric ratio that is true for all values of the variable

trigonometric ratio the ratio of two sides of a right triangle

trinomial a polynomial with three terms

two-column proof a proof shown in two columns; The first column sows the steps and the second column shows the justification for each step.

two-way table a table that shows data from one sample group as it relates to two different categories

unbounded interval the set of all real numbers on one side of a number, called an endpoint; The endpoint may or may not be included.

uniform distribution a type of symmetric distribution of data sets where all intervals have the same frequency

uniform probability distribution the probability distribution resulting when all values of a random variable X are equally likely to occur

unit circle circle with a radius of one unit

upper limit in sigma notation $\sum_{i=1}^{n} a_i$, the variable n, which indicates the maximum value for the index i

valid argument an argument in which, if the premises are all true, then the conclusion must also be true

variable a symbol that represents a value

variable expression a combination of variables, numbers, and operations

variance a measure of variability of a set relative to its mean; For a data set with values $x_1, x_2, \ldots, x_n$, the variance is $s^2 = \frac{\sum_{i=1}^{n} (x_i - \overline{x})^2}{n - 1}$ where each difference $x_i - \overline{x}$ is called a deviation and s is called the standard deviation

vertex form of a quadratic function $f(x) = a(x - h)^2 + k$ where $a \neq 0$

vertex of a double-napped cone the point where the axis and the generating line of a double-napped cone intersect

vertex of a parabola the highest or lowest point on a parabola that opens down or up

vertex of a polygon a point where the sides of a polygon meet

vertex of a pyramid the common vertex where the triangular faces of a pyramid meet

vertex of an angle the common endpoint of two rays that form an angle

vertex points corner points of the feasible region

vertical angles nonadjacent angles formed by intersecting lines; Vertical angles are congruent.

vertical asymptote the line $x = a$ of the graph of the function f if $f(x)$ approaches ∞ or $-\infty$ as x approaches a, either from the left or the right

vertical line test a test used to determine whether a graphed relation is a function; If the graph is a function, then there is no vertical line that passes through the graph more than once.

volume the measure of the space inside (or the space occupied by) a three-dimensional figure; expressed in cubed units

volume of rectangular prism the product of the rectangular prism's length, width, and height

whole number a number in the set $\{0, 1, 2, 3, \ldots\}$

x-coordinate the first number in an ordered pair

x-intercept the x-coordinate of a point where a graph intersects the x-axis

y-coordinate the second number in an ordered pair

y-intercept the y-coordinate of a point where a graph intersects the y-axis

zeros of a polynomial function $f(x)$ the roots (solutions) of the equation $f(x) = 0$

z-score the number of standard deviations that a data value is from the mean

Symbols

Symbol	Meaning
$\mid$	such that
$\in$	is an element of
$\varnothing$ or $\{\ \}$	null or empty set
$\subset$	is a proper subset of
$\subseteq$	is a subset of
$\cap$	intersection
$\cup$	union
$-a$	the opposite of a
∞	infinity
$\sqrt{\ }$	radical sign; the principal square root
$\sqrt[n]{x}$	nth root of x
i	imaginary unit
$\mathbb{N}$	the set of natural numbers
$\mathbb{Z}$	the set of integers
$\mathbb{Q}$	the set of rational numbers
$\mathbb{R}$	the set of real numbers
$\mathbb{I}$	the set of irrational numbers
$\mathbb{W}$	the set of whole numbers
$\mathbb{C}$	the set of complex numbers
e	base of the natural logarithm
$\ln x$	logarithm with base e; natural logarithm
$\log x$	logarithm with base 10
$\log_b a$	log base b of a
a_n	nth element of a sequence
π	pi
σ	standard deviation of a population
S_n	the sum of the first n terms of a series
$\sum_{i=1}^{n} a_i$	the sum from 1 to n of a_i
$n!$	factorial of a nonnegative integer n
$\overline{x}$	sample mean
$\approx$	is approximately equal to
$=$	is equal to
$\neq$	is not equal to
$<$	is less than
$>$	is greater than
$\leq$	is less than or equal to
$\geq$	is greater than or equal to
$f(x)$	f is a function of x
$\lfloor x \rfloor$	greatest integer function; floor function
$\lceil x \rceil$	least integer function; ceiling function
$\text{nint}(x)$	nearest integer function; round function
$f \circ g$	the composition of function f with function g
f^{-1}	inverse of a function f
$\lvert x \rvert$	absolute value of x
$\{\ldots\}$	description or list of all elements in a set; roster notation

$\{x \mid \text{condition}\}$	the set of all x that satisfy the given condition; set-builder notation
$P(A)$	the probability of event A
$P(A \mid B)$	the conditional probability of A given B
ϕ	phi; the golden ratio
$'$	prime
$^\circ$	degree
$\ldots$	continues
$\sim$	is similar to
$\cong$	is congruent to
$\parallel$	is parallel to
$\perp$	is perpendicular to
$\therefore$	therefore
$\angle$	angle
$\triangle$	triangle
$\overleftrightarrow{AB}$	line AB
$\overline{AB}$	line segment AB
$\overrightarrow{AB}$	ray AB
$m\angle CAB$	measure of angle CAB
$\overset{\frown}{AB}$	arc AB
$m\overset{\frown}{AB}$	measure of arc AB

Properties

Real Number Properties

Let a, b, and c be any real numbers.

Addition Property of Equality	If $a = b$, then $a + c = b + c$ and $c + a = c + b$.	
Addition Property: Addends with Like Signs	For all $a > 0$ and $b > 0$, $a + b = \|a\| + \|b\|$. For all $a < 0$ and $b < 0$, $a + b = -\|a\| + \|b\|$.	
Addition Property: Addends with Unlike Signs	For all $a > 0$ and $b < 0$, If $\|a\| > \|b\|$, then $a + b = \|a\| - \|b\|$. If $\|a\| < \|b\|$, then $a + b = -\|b\| - \|a\|$.	
Subtraction Property of Equality	If $a = b$, then $a - c = b - c$.	
Substitution Property of Equality	If $a = b$, then a may be replaced with b in any expression or equation.	
Multiplication Property of Equality	If $a = b$, then $c \bullet a = c \bullet b$ and $a \bullet c = b \bullet c$.	
Division Property of Equality	If $a = b$ and $c \neq 0$, then $\frac{a}{c} = \frac{b}{c}$.	
Distributive Property	$a(b + c) = ab + ac$	
	Addition	Multiplication
Commutative Properties	$a + b = b + a$	$a \bullet b = b \bullet a$
Associative Properties	$(a + b) + c = a + (b + c)$	$(a \bullet b) \bullet c = a \bullet (b \bullet c)$
Inverse Properties	$a + (-a) = 0$ and $(-a) + a = 0$	$a \bullet \frac{1}{a} = 1$ and $\frac{1}{a} \bullet a = 1, a \neq 0$
Identity Properties	$a + 0 = a$ and $0 + a = a$	$a \bullet 1 = a$ and $1 \bullet a = a$

Absolute Value Equations

If $|x| = a$ for some positive number a, then $x = a$ or $x = -a$.

Properties of Exponents

Let a and b be nonzero real numbers. Let m and n be integers.

If n is a positive integer, then $a^n = a \bullet a \bullet a \bullet \ldots \bullet a$ (n factors).

Zero Exponent Property	$a^0 = 1, a \neq 0$
Negative Exponent Property	$a^{-m} = \frac{1}{a^m}, a \neq 0$
Product of Powers Property	$a^m \bullet a^n = a^{m+n}$

Square Root Properties

For nonnegative values of m, n, and p, if $m < n < p$, then $\sqrt{m} < \sqrt{n} < \sqrt{p}$.

Product Property	For real numbers a and b, $\sqrt{ab} = \sqrt{a} \bullet \sqrt{b}$ and $\sqrt{a} \bullet \sqrt{b} = \sqrt{ab}$.
Quotient Property	For real numbers a and b with $b \neq 0$, $\sqrt{\frac{a}{b}} = \frac{\sqrt{a}}{\sqrt{b}}$.

Reciprocal Properties

Reciprocal Property of Multiplication	For any nonzero real number a, $a \bullet \frac{1}{a} = 1$.

For all nonzero real numbers a and b, the reciprocal of $\frac{a}{b}$ is $\frac{b}{a}$.

For any nonzero real number a, $\frac{1}{-a} = \frac{-1}{a} = -\frac{1}{a}$.

For all nonzero real numbers a and b, $\frac{1}{ab} = \frac{1}{a} \bullet \frac{1}{b}$.

Division Properties

For any real number a and nonzero real number b, $a \div b = a \bullet \frac{1}{b}$.

For all real numbers a and b and nonzero real number c, $a + \frac{b}{c} = \frac{a}{c} + \frac{b}{c}$.

For all $a > 0$ and $b > 0$, $a \div b > 0$.

For all $a < 0$ and $b < 0$, $a \div b > 0$.

For all $a < 0$ and $b > 0$, $a \div b < 0$.

Properties of Order

Comparison Property of Order	If $a > b$, then $b < a$. If $a < b$, then $b > a$.
Transitive Property of Order	If $a > b$ and $b > c$, then $a > c$. If $a < b$ and $b < c$, then $a < c$.
Addition Property of Order	If $a > b$, then $a + c > b + c$. If $a < b$, then $a + c < b + c$.
Subtraction Property of Order	If $a > b$, then $a - c > b - c$. If $a < b$, then $a - c < b - c$.
Multiplication Property of Order, Positive Multiplier	If $a > b$ and $c > 0$, then $ca > cb$ and $ac > bc$. If $a < b$ and $c > 0$, then $ca < cb$ and $ac < bc$.
Multiplication Property of Order, Negative Multiplier	If $a > b$ and $c < 0$, then $ca < cb$ and $ac < bc$. If $a < b$ and $c < 0$, then $ca > cb$ and $ac > bc$.
Division Property of Order, Positive Multiplier	If $a > b$ and $c > 0$, then $\frac{a}{c} > \frac{b}{c}$. If $a < b$ and $c > 0$, then $\frac{a}{c} < \frac{b}{c}$.
Division Property of Order, Negative Multiplier	If $a > b$ and $c < 0$, then $\frac{a}{c} < \frac{b}{c}$. If $a < b$ and $c < 0$, then $\frac{a}{c} > \frac{b}{c}$.

Comparison Property of Rational Numbers

For nonzero integers a and c and positive integers b and d,

$\frac{a}{b} > \frac{c}{d}$ if, and only if, $ad > bc$.

$\frac{a}{b} < \frac{c}{d}$ if, and only if, $ad < bc$.

Properties of Proportions

Let a, b, c, and d be real numbers.

Means-Extremes Product Property	$\frac{a}{b} = \frac{c}{d}$ if, and only if, $ad = bc$, given that b and d are not 0.
Reciprocal Property	If $\frac{a}{b} = \frac{c}{d}$, then $\frac{b}{a} = \frac{d}{c}$, given that a, b, c, and d are all nonzero.

Formulary

Real, Imaginary, and Complex Numbers

RATIONAL EXPONENTS

$$x^{\frac{a}{b}} = \sqrt[b]{x^a}$$

POWERS OF i

$$i = \sqrt{-1}$$

$$i^2 = -1$$

$$i^3 = -i$$

$$i^4 = 1$$

ADDING COMPLEX NUMBERS

For any real a, b, c, and d, if $w = a + bi$ and $z = c + di$, then $w + z = (a + c) + (b + d)i$.

Factoring Patterns

PERFECT SQUARE TRINOMIAL PATTERNS

$$a^2 + 2ab + b^2 = (a + b)^2$$

DIFFERENCE OF SQUARES PATTERNS

$$a^2 - b^2 = (a + b)(a - b)$$

SUM OF CUBES

$$a^3 + b^3 = (a + b)(a^2 - ab + b^2)$$

DIFFERENCE OF CUBES

$$a^3 - b^3 = (a - b)(a^2 + ab + b^2)$$

Plane Geometry

CIRCLE

circumference $C = \pi d = 2\pi r$

area $A = \pi r^2$

length of an arc with degree measure m $L = \left(\frac{m}{360^\circ}\right)2\pi r$

equation with center (h, k) on a coordinate plane $(x - h)^2 + (y - k)^2 = r^2$

PARALLOGRAM

area $A = bh$

REGULAR POLYGON WITH n SIDES

sum of interior angles $I = (n - 2)180^\circ$

interior angle of regular polygon $i = \frac{(n - 2)180^\circ}{n}$

perimeter of regular polygon $P = ns$

area of regular polygon $A = \frac{1}{2}aP$

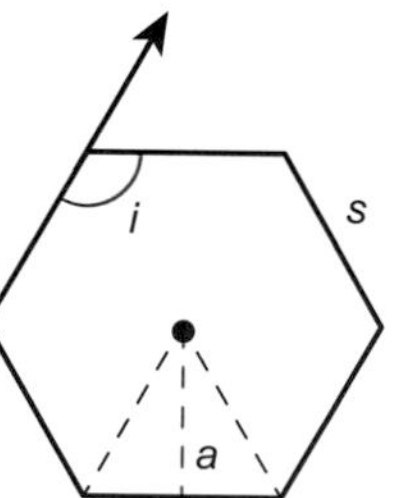

RECTANGLE

area $A = lw$

perimeter $P = 2l + 2w$

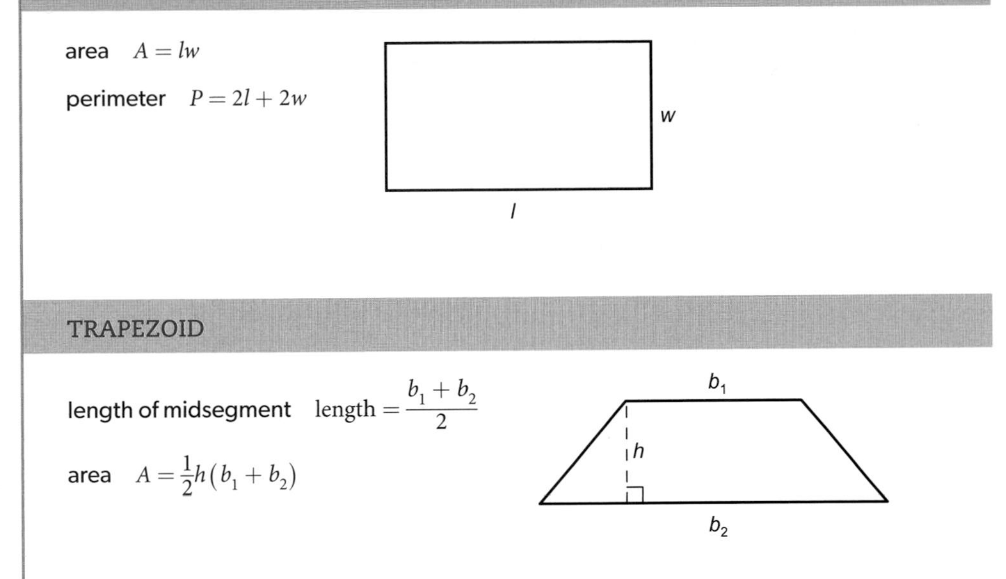

TRAPEZOID

length of midsegment $\text{length} = \dfrac{b_1 + b_2}{2}$

area $A = \frac{1}{2}h(b_1 + b_2)$

TRIANGLE: GENERAL

sum of interior angles $m\angle A + m\angle B + m\angle C = 180°$

area $A = \frac{1}{2}bh$

length of midsegment $\text{length} = \frac{1}{2}\text{ length of parallel side}$

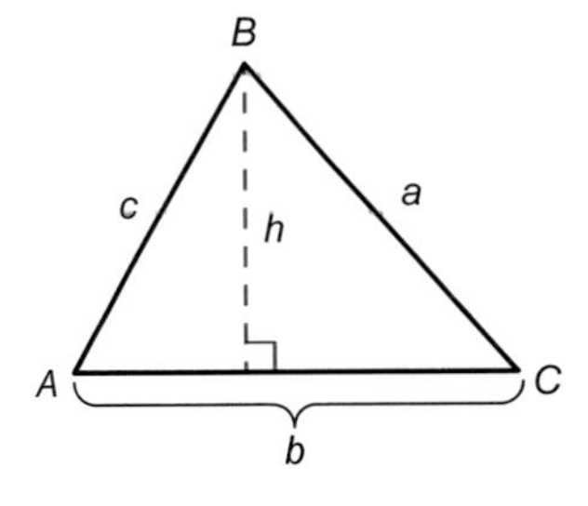

TRIANGLE: RIGHT

Pythagorean theorem $a^2 + b^2 = c^2$

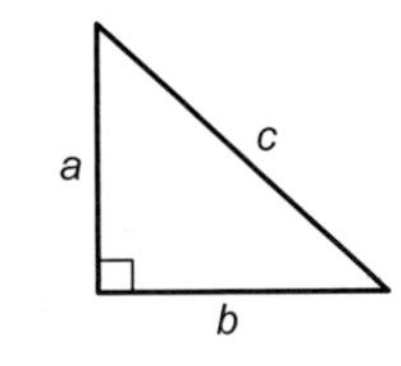

Solid Geometry

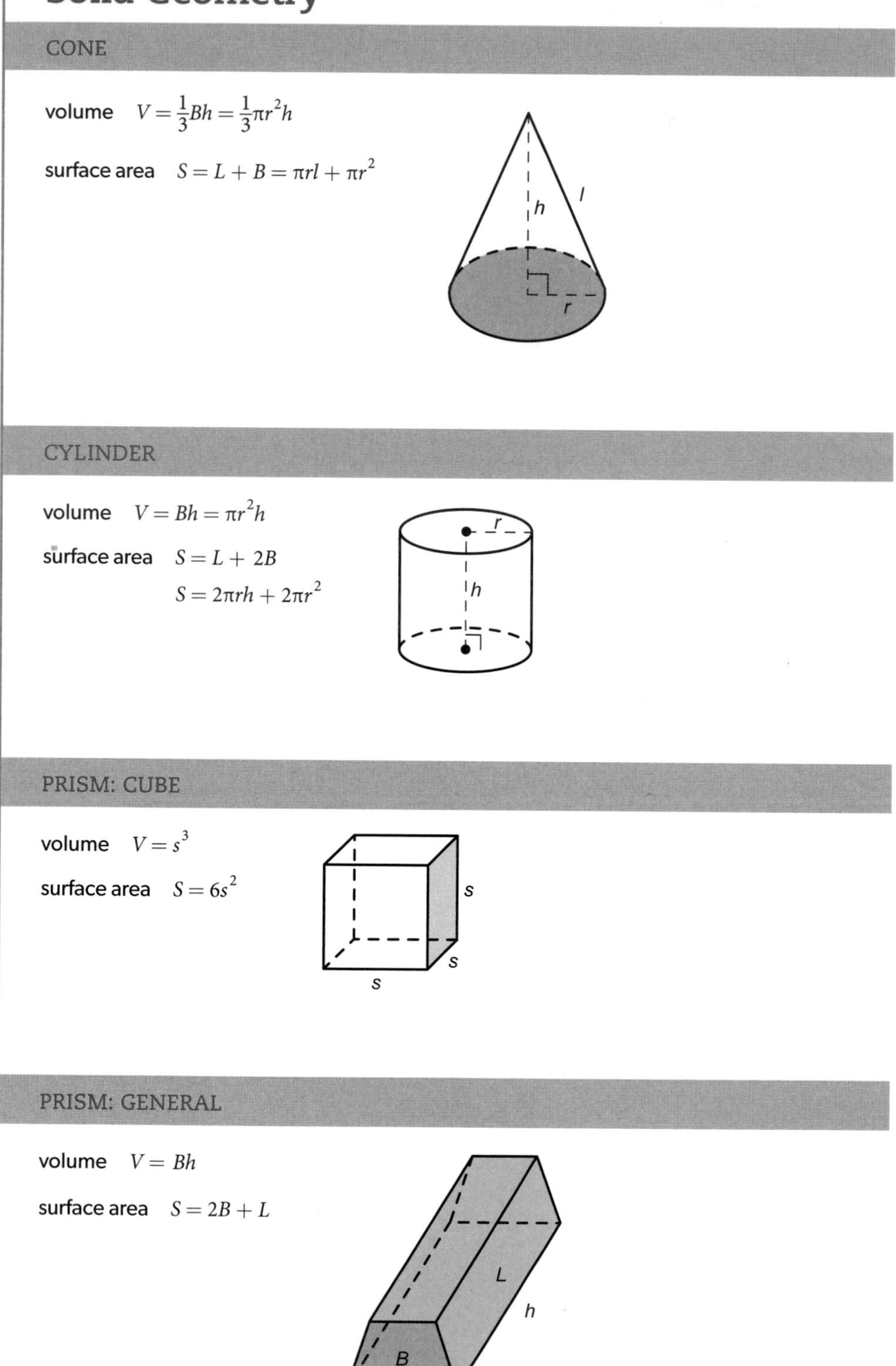

CONE

volume $V = \frac{1}{3}Bh = \frac{1}{3}\pi r^2 h$

surface area $S = L + B = \pi rl + \pi r^2$

CYLINDER

volume $V = Bh = \pi r^2 h$

surface area $S = L + 2B$

$S = 2\pi rh + 2\pi r^2$

PRISM: CUBE

volume $V = s^3$

surface area $S = 6s^2$

PRISM: GENERAL

volume $V = Bh$

surface area $S = 2B + L$

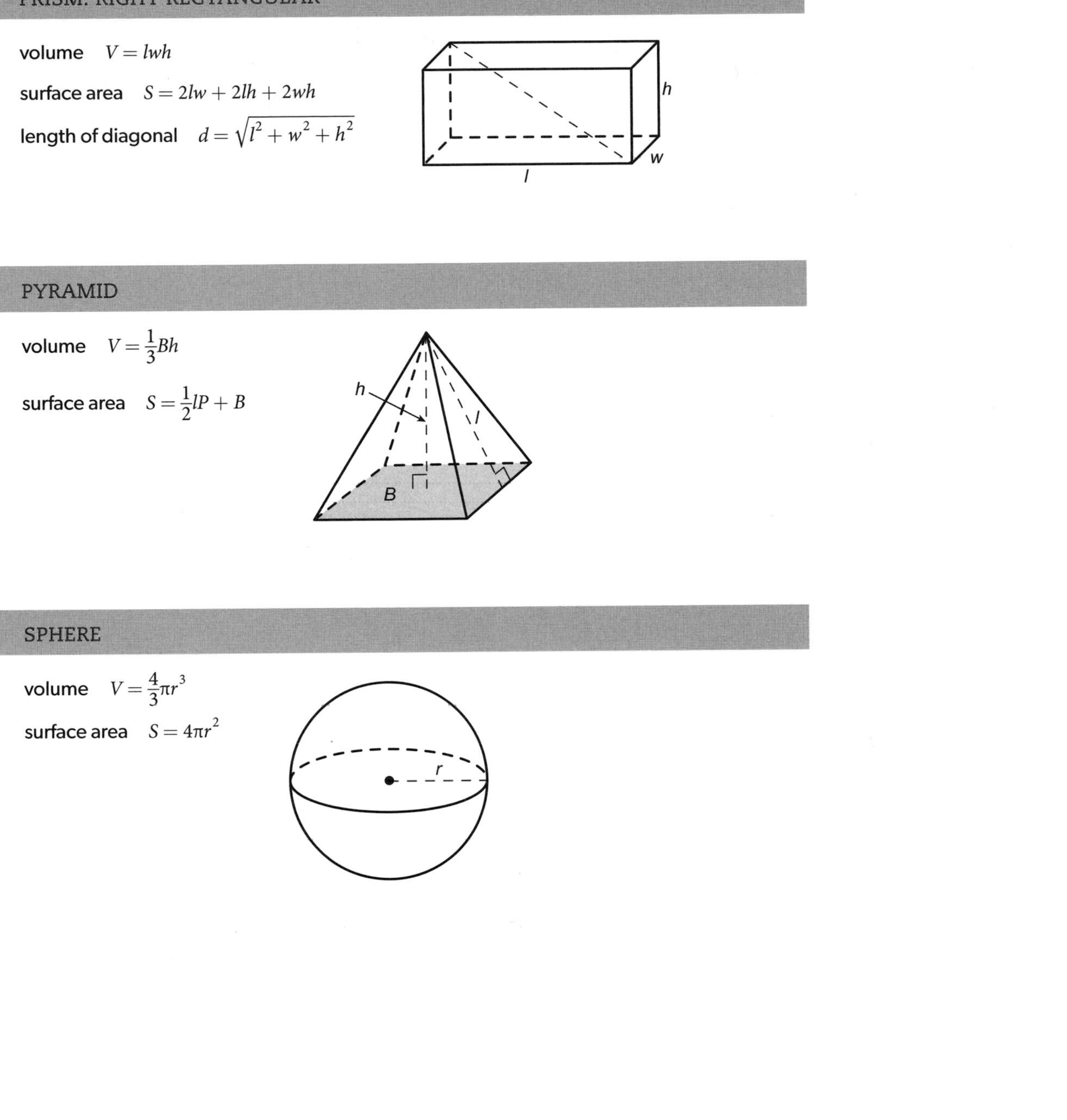

PRISM: RIGHT RECTANGULAR
volume $V = lwh$
surface area $S = 2lw + 2lh + 2wh$
length of diagonal $d = \sqrt{l^2 + w^2 + h^2}$
h
w
l
PYRAMID
volume $V = \frac{1}{3}Bh$
surface area $S = \frac{1}{2}lP + B$
h
l
B
SPHERE
volume $V = \frac{4}{3}\pi r^3$
surface area $S = 4\pi r^2$
r

Coordinate Geometry

LINE AND SEGMENT

slope $m = \frac{\text{rise}}{\text{run}} = \frac{y_2 - y_1}{x_2 - x_1}$

coordinates of midpoint $M = \left(\frac{x_1 + x_2}{2}, \frac{y_1 + y_2}{2}\right)$

distance $d = \sqrt{(x_2 - x_1)^2 + (y_2 - y_1)^2}$

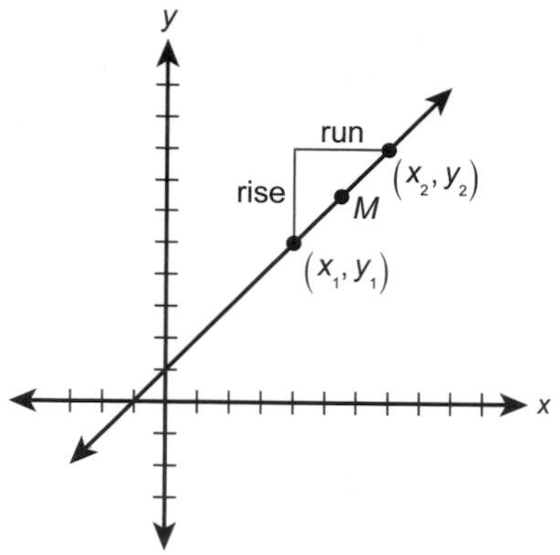

y
run
rise
(x_2, y_2)
M
(x_1, y_1)
x

LINEAR EQUATION FORMS

standard $Ax + By = C$

slope-intercept $y = mx + b$

point-slope $y - y_1 = m(x - x_1)$

CIRCLE

equation in graphing form $(x - h)^2 + (y - k)^2 = r^2$

center (h, k) and radius r

PARABOLA GRAPHING FORMS

vertical axis of symmetry
$y - k = a(x - h)^2$ (axis of symmetry $x = h$)

horizontal axis of symmetry
$x - h = a(y - k)^2$ (axis of symmetry $y = k$)

vertex (h, k)

focal distance $f = \frac{1}{4a}$

eccentricity $e = 1$

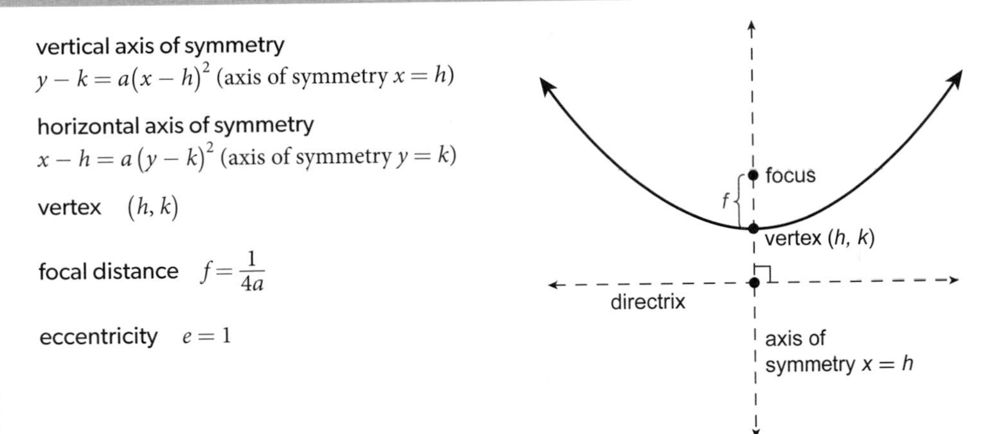

THREE-DIMENSIONAL SPACE

distance between points $d = \sqrt{(x_2 - x_1)^2 + (y_2 - y_1)^2 + (z_2 - z_1)^2}$

coordinates of midpoint $\left(\frac{x_1 + x_2}{2}, \frac{y_1 + y_2}{2}, \frac{z_1 + z_2}{2}\right)$

general equation of a line $Ax + By + Cz = D$

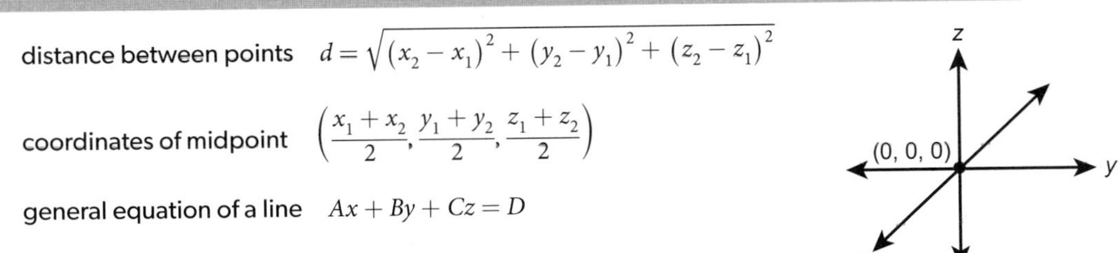

FUNCTIONS

average rate of change $\frac{f(b) - f(a)}{b - a}$

axis of symmetry for $f(x) = ax^2 + bx + c$ $x = -\frac{b}{2a}$

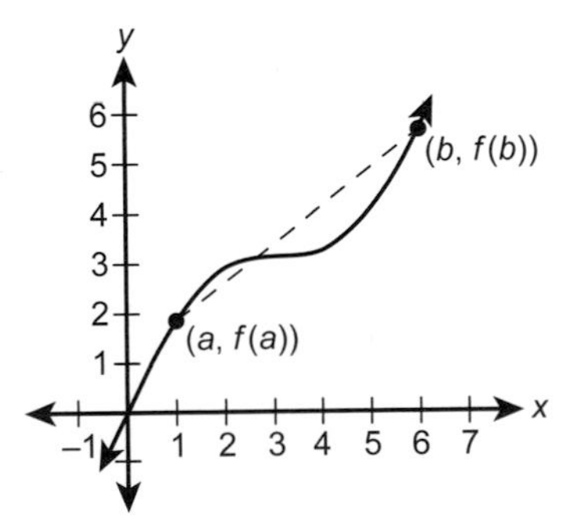

Solving Equations

SOLVING QUADRATICS

completing the square Given the equation $ax^2 + bx = c$, add $\left(\frac{b}{2a}\right)^2$ to both sides.

discriminant Given the equation $ax^2 + bx + c = 0$, the discriminant is $b^2 - 4ac$.

quadratic formula The solutions of the equation $ax^2 + bx + c = 0$, where $a \neq 0$, are $x = \dfrac{-b \pm \sqrt{b^2 - 4ac}}{2a}$.

EXPONENTS AND LOGARITHMS

$$x^a \bullet x^b = x^{a+b}$$

$$\frac{x^a}{x^b} = x^{a-b}$$

$$x^0 = 1$$

$$x^1 = x$$

For any $a > 0$ and $b > 0$, $b \neq 1$: $\log_b a = x$ if and only if $b^x = a$.

$$\log mn = \log m + \log n$$

$$\log\left(\frac{m}{n}\right) = \log m - \log n$$

$$\log m^a = a \log m$$

Counting and Probability

FACTORIAL

$n! = n \bullet (n-1) \bullet (n-2) \bullet \ldots \bullet 1$ (n factors)

$0! = 1$

SIMPLE THEORETICAL PROBABILITY

$$P(E) = \frac{\text{number of outcomes in event } E}{\text{total number of outcomes in sample space } S} = \frac{n(E)}{n(S)}$$

PROBABILITY OF DEPENDENT EVENTS

$$P(A \text{ and } B) = P(A) \bullet P(B|A)$$

PROBABILITY OF INDEPENDENT EVENTS

$$P(A \text{ and } B) = P(A) \bullet P(B)$$

PROBABILITY OF MUTUALLY EXCLUSIVE EVENTS

$$P(A \text{ or } B) = P(A) + P(B)$$

PROBABILITY OF COMPLEMENTARY EVENTS

$$P(A) = 1 - P(B)$$

EXPERIMENTAL PROBABILITY OF EVENT E

$$P(E) = \frac{\text{number of times event } E \text{ has occurred}}{n}$$

Statistics

MEAN

For a data set with n elements, the mean is

$$\overline{x} = \frac{x_1 + x_1 + \ldots + x_n}{n}.$$

MEDIAN

Arrange the values in order from least to greatest. For an

Odd number of values, use the middle value.

Even number of values, use the average of the middle two values.

MODE

The mode is the value that occurs most often in a set of data. If no one value occurs most often, then there is no mode for the set.

STANDARD DEVIATION

To find the standard deviation s of a data set with n values, where x is the data value and $\overline{x}$ is the mean, use the formula

$$s = \sqrt{\frac{\Sigma(x - \overline{x})^2}{n - 1}}.$$

z-SCORE

If x is a raw data value from a normally distributed data set with mean μ and standard deviation σ, then

$$z = \frac{x - \mu}{\sigma}$$

is the number of standard deviations x is from the mean.

SAMPLING STANDARD DEVIATION

If random samples of size n are taken from a distribution with poplation standard deviation σ, then the sampling distribution will have standard deviation approximately equal to

$$\frac{\sigma}{\sqrt{n}}.$$

STANDARD DEVIATION OF A SAMPLING DISTRIBUTION OF A PROPORTION

If a sample of size n is drawn from a population with proportion p, then the sampling distribution of the proportion will have standard deviation approximately equal to

$$\sqrt{\frac{p(1 - p)}{n}}.$$

Sequences and Series

SEQUENCES: ARITHMETIC

common difference of an arithmetic sequence $d = a_n - a_{n-1}$

iterative rule for an arithmetic sequence $a_n = a_1 + (n-1)d$

recursive rule for an arithmetic sequence $a_n = a_{n-1} + d$

SEQUENCES: GEOMETRIC

common ratio of a geometric sequence $r = \frac{a_n}{a_{n-1}}$

iterative rule for a geometric sequence $a_n = a_1 \cdot r^{n-1}$

recursive rule for a geometric sequence $a_n = r \cdot a_{n-1}$

GENERAL FORMULA FOR THE SUM OF A SERIES

sigma notation The sum of the first n terms of a sequence can be written as

$$S_n = \sum_{i=0}^{n} a_i = a_1 + a_2 + a_3 + \ldots + a_n$$

where i is the index, 1 is the lower limit, and n is the upper limit.

arithmetic series The nth partial sum of an arithmetic series a with common difference d is

$$S_n = \frac{n}{2}(a_1 + a_2) \text{ or } S_n = \frac{n}{2}(2a_1 + (n-1)d).$$

geometric series The nth partial sum of a geometric series a with common ratio r is

$$S_n = \frac{a_1(1 - r^n)}{1 - r}, \text{ or } S_n = \frac{a_1 - a_n r}{1 - r} \text{ where } r \neq 1.$$

Exponential Growth and Decay

EXPONENTIAL DECAY FORMULA

If a quantity is decaying exponentially from initial amount b and with decay rate r, then the amount y remaining after t time periods is

$$y = b(1 - r)^t.$$

EXPONENTIAL GROWTH FORMULA

If a quantity is growing exponentially from the initial amount b where r is the fixed percent expressed as a decimal, then the total amount y after t time periods is

$$y = b(1 + r)^t.$$

COMPOUND INTEREST FORMULA

The total amount A of an investment with initial principal P, earning compound interest at an annual interest rate r and compounded n times per year for t years, is

$$A = P\left(1 + \frac{r}{n}\right)^{nt}.$$

HALF-LIFE FORMULA

The amount y of a radioactive substance after t time periods, where b is the initial amount and h is the half-life, is

$$y = b\left(\frac{1}{2}\right)^{\frac{t}{h}}.$$

Trigonometry

RIGHT TRIANGLE RATIOS

tangent: $\tan A = \dfrac{\text{opposite}}{\text{adjacent}} = \dfrac{a}{b}$

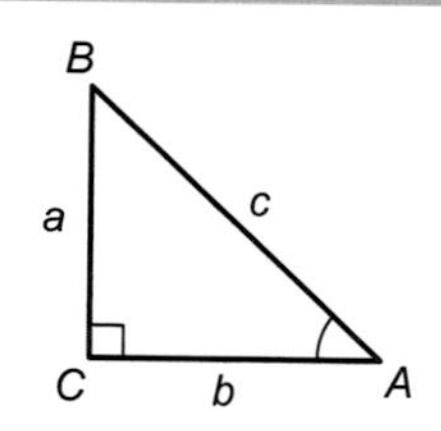

cosine: $\cos A = \dfrac{\text{opposite}}{\text{hypotenuse}} = \dfrac{a}{c}$

sine: $\sin A = \dfrac{\text{adjacent}}{\text{hypotenuse}} = \dfrac{b}{c}$

SPECIAL RIGHT TRIANGLES

Angle measure	Sine	Cosine	Tangent
30°	$\frac{1}{2}$	$\frac{\sqrt{3}}{2}$	$\frac{\sqrt{3}}{3}$
45°	$\frac{\sqrt{2}}{2}$	$\frac{\sqrt{2}}{2}$	1
60°	$\frac{\sqrt{3}}{2}$	$\frac{1}{2}$	$\sqrt{3}$

UNIT CIRCLE ON THE COORDINATE PLANE

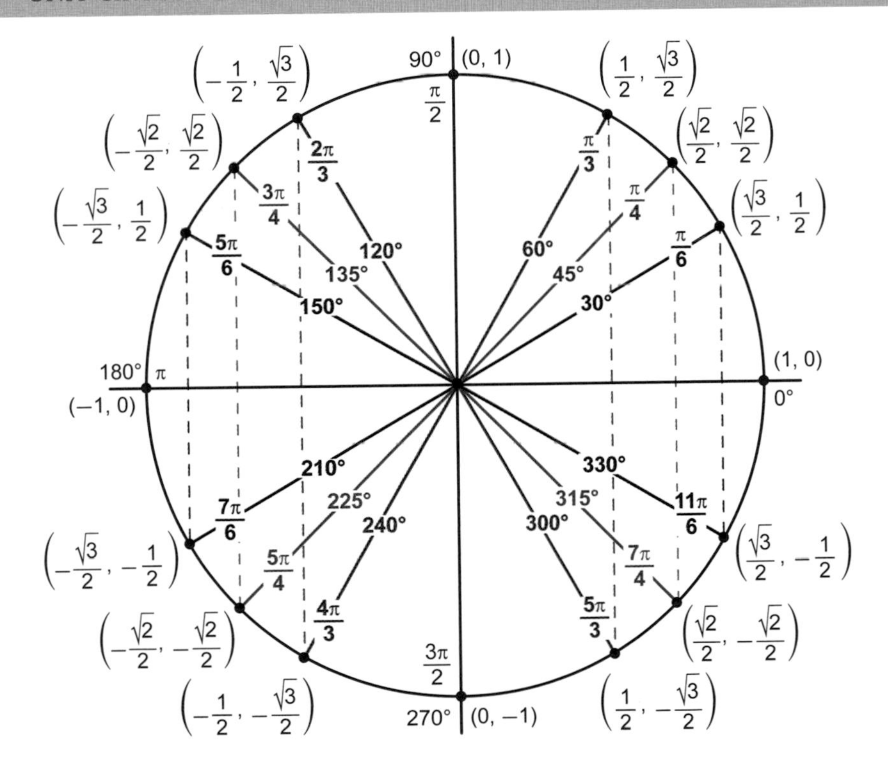

TRIGONOMETRIC IDENTITIES

$$\sin^2 x + \cos^2 x = 1$$

$$\tan x = \frac{\sin x}{\cos x}$$

$$\sin x = \cos(90° - x)$$

$$\cos x = \sin(90° - x)$$

General Applications

DISTANCE

For uniform motion, where d is distance, r is rate, and t is time,

$$d = rt.$$

PROJECTILE MOTION

The height of an object, in meters, after t seconds, with initial vertical velocity v_0 and initial height h_0, is given by

$$h(t) = -4.9t^2 + v_0 t + h_0.$$

The height of an object, in feet, after t seconds, with initial vertical velocity v_0 and initial height h_0, is given by

$$h(t) = -16t^2 + v_0 t + h_0.$$

SIMPLE INTEREST

The amount of simple interest I earned, where P is the principal (amount borrowed, deposited, or invested), r is the annual interest rate, and t is the time in years, is given by

$$I = Prt.$$

TEMPERATURE CONVERSION

$$F = \frac{9}{5}C + 32$$

where F is degrees Fahrenheit and C is degrees Celsius.

Postulates and Theorems

Euclid's Postulates

POSTULATE EUC-1

Any two points can be connected with a line segment.

POSTULATE EUC-2

Any line segment can be extended indefinitely in two directions to make a line.

POSTULATE EUC-3

Given any line segment, a circle can be drawn that has the segment as its radius and one endpoint as its center.

POSTULATE EUC-4

All right angles are equivalent to each other.

POSTULATE EUC-5

Given any straight line and a point not on the line, there is exactly one line through the point that is parallel to the line.

General

POSTULATE GEN-1

Two points determine a line.

POSTULATE GEN-2

Three noncollinear points determine a plane.

Measurement

POSTULATE MEAS-1

Ruler Postulate The points on a line can be numbered so that positive number differences measure distances.

POSTULATE MEAS-2

Segment Addition Postulate If B is between A and C, then $AB + BC = AC$. Also, if $AB + BC = AC$ and A, B, and C are collinear, then B is between A and C.

POSTULATE MEAS-3

Segment Congruence Postulate If two segments have the same length as measured by a fair ruler, then the segments are congruent ($\cong$). Also, if two segments are congruent, then they have the same length as measured by a fair ruler.

POSTULATE MEAS-4

Angle Addition Postulate If point D lies in the interior of $\angle ABC$, then $m\angle ABD + m\angle DBC = m\angle ABC$.

POSTULATE MEAS-5

Angle Congruence Postulate If two angles have the same measure as measured by a protractor, then the angles are congruent. Also, if two angles are congruent, then they have the same measure as measured by a protractor.

POSTULATE MEAS-6

Linear Pair Postulate If two angles form a linear pair, then they are supplementary angles.

THEOREM MEAS-1

Vertical Angles Theorem If two angles form a pair of vertical angles, then they are congruent.

Parallels

POSTULATE PAR-1

Corresponding Angles Postulate If two parallel lines are intersected by a transversal, then corresponding angles are congruent.

POSTULATE PAR-2

Converse of the Corresponding Angles Postulate If two coplanar lines are intersected by a transversal and the corresponding angles are congruent, then the lines are parallel.

THEOREM PAR-1

Alternate Interior Angles Theorem If two parallel lines are intersected by a transversal, then the alternate interior angles are congruent.

THEOREM PAR-2

Alternate Exterior Angles Theorem If two parallel lines are intersected by a transversal, then the alternate exterior angles are congruent.

THEOREM PAR-3

Same-Side Interior Angles Theorem If two parallel lines are intersected by a transversal, then the same-side interior angles are supplementary.

THEOREM PAR-4

Converse of the Alternate Interior Angles Theorem If two coplanar lines are intersected by a transversal and the alternate interior angles are congruent, then the lines are parallel.

THEOREM PAR-5

Converse of the Alternate Exterior Angles Theorem If two coplanar lines are intersected by a transversal and the alternate exterior angles are congruent, then the lines are parallel.

THEOREM PAR-6

Converse of the Same-Side Interior Angles Theorem If two coplanar lines are intersected by a transversal and the same-side interior angles are supplementary, then the lines are parallel.

Lines

POSTULATE LINES-1

Parallel Postulate Given a line and a point not on the line, there is one and only one line that contains the given point and is parallel to the given line.

THEOREM LINES-1

If two coplanar lines are perpendicular to ($\perp$) the same line, then the two lines are parallel.

THEOREM LINES-2

If two coplanar lines are parallel to the same line, then the two lines are parallel.

Coordinate

THEOREM COORD-1

Parallel Lines Theorem Two coplanar nonvertical lines are parallel if and only if they have the same slope. Any two vertical lines are parallel.

THEOREM COORD-2

Perpendicular Lines Theorem Two coplanar nonvertical lines are perpendicular if and only if the product of their slopes equals -1. Any vertical line is perpendicular to any horizontal line.

Congruence

POSTULATE CONG-1

Polygon Congruence Postulate Two polygons are congruent if and only if there is a correspondence between their sides and angles so that all pairs of corresponding angles are congruent and all pairs of corresponding sides are congruent.

POSTULATE CONG-2

Side-Side-Side (SSS) Congruence Postulate If the three sides of one triangle are congruent to the three sides of another triangle, then the two triangles are congruent.

POSTULATE CONG-3

Side-Angle-Side (SAS) Congruence Postulate If two sides and the included angle in one triangle are congruent to two sides and the included angle in another triangle, then the two triangles are congruent.

POSTULATE CONG-4

Angle-Side-Angle (ASA) Congruence Postulate If two angles and the included side in one triangle are congruent to two angles and the included side in another triangle, then the two triangles are congruent.

THEOREM CONG-1

Hypotenuse-Leg (HL) Congruence Theorem If the hypotenuse and a leg of one right triangle are congruent to the hypotenuse and corresponding leg of another right triangle, then the two triangles are congruent.

Triangles

THEOREM TRI-1

Triangle Sum Theorem The sum of the measures of the interior angles of a triangle is 180°.

THEOREM TRI-2

Exterior Angle Theorem The measure of an exterior angle of a triangle is equal to the sum of the measures of the remote interior angles.

THEOREM TRI-3

Isosceles Triangle Theorem If two sides of a triangle are congruent, then the angles opposite those sides are congruent.

THEOREM TRI-4

Converse of the Isosceles Triangle Theorem If two angles of a triangle are congruent, then the sides opposite those angles are congruent.

Quadrilaterals

THEOREM QUAD-1

In a parallelogram, the opposite sides are congruent.

THEOREM QUAD-2

In a rectangle, the diagonals are congruent.

THEOREM QUAD-3

If two pairs of opposite sides of a quadrilateral are congruent, then the quadrilateral is a parallelogram.

THEOREM QUAD-4

If two opposite sides of a quadrilateral are parallel and congruent, then the quadrilateral is a parallelogram.

THEOREM QUAD-5

If the diagonals of a quadrilateral bisect each other, then the quadrilateral is a parallelogram.

THEOREM QUAD-6

If the diagonals of a parallelogram are congruent, then the parallelogram is a rectangle.

THEOREM QUAD-7

If the diagonals of a parallelogram are perpendicular, then the parallelogram is a rhombus.

THEOREM QUAD-8

If two adjacent sides of a parallelogram are congruent, then the parallelogram is a rhombus.

THEOREM QUAD-9

If the diagonals of a parallelogram bisect the angles of the parallelogram, then the parallelogram is a rhombus.

THEOREM QUAD-10

If one angle of a parallelogram is a right angle, then the parallelogram is a rectangle.

Right Triangles

THEOREM RIGHT-1

Pythagorean Theorem For all right triangles, the square of the length of the hypotenuse c equals the sum of the squares of the lengths of the legs a and b.

$$c^2 = a^2 + b^2$$

THEOREM RIGHT-2

Converse of the Pythagorean Theorem If the square of the length of the longest side of a triangle equals the sum of the squares of the lengths of the other two sides, then the triangle is a right triangle.

THEOREM RIGHT-3

45°-45°-90° Triangle Theorem In any 45°-45°-90° triangle, the length of the hypotenuse is $\sqrt{2}$ times the length of a leg.

THEOREM RIGHT-4

30°-60°-90° Triangle Theorem In any 30°-60°-90° triangle, the length of the hypotenuse is 2 times the length of the shorter leg, and the length of the longer leg is $\sqrt{3}$ times the length of the shorter leg.

Similarity

POSTULATE SIM-1

Polygon Similarity Postulate Two polygons are similar if and only if there is a correspondence between their angles and their sides so that all corresponding angles are congruent and all corresponding sides are proportional.

POSTULATE SIM-2

Angle-Angle (AA) Similarity Postulate If two angles of a triangle are congruent to two angles of another triangle, then the triangles are similar.

COROLLARY SIM-1

Two-Transversal Proportionality Corollary Three or more parallel lines divide two intersecting transversals proportionally.

THEOREM SIM-1

Side-Side-Side (SSS) Similarity Theorem If the three sides of a triangle are proportional to the three sides of another triangle, then the triangles are similar.

THEOREM SIM-2

Side-Angle-Side (SAS) Similarity Theorem If two sides of a triangle are proportional to two sides of another triangle and if their included angles are congruent, then the triangles are similar.

THEOREM SIM-3

Triangle Proportionality Theorem A line parallel to one side of a triangle divides the other two sides proportionally.

THEOREM SIM-4

Angle Bisector Theorem An angle bisector of an angle of a triangle divides the opposite side in two segments that are proportional to the other two sides of the triangle.

Circles

COROLLARY CIRC-1

Right-Angle Corollary An angle that is inscribed in a semicircle is a right angle.

COROLLARY CIRC-2

Arc-Intercept Corollary Two inscribed angles that intercept the same arc have the same measure.

COROLLARY CIRC-3

Converse of the Right-Angle Corollary If an inscribed angle is a right angle, then the intercepted arc is a semicircle.

THEOREM CIRC-1

Chords and Arcs Theorem In a circle or in congruent circles, the arcs of congruent chords are congruent.

THEOREM CIRC-2

Converse of the Chords and Arcs Theorem In a circle or in congruent circles, the chords of congruent arcs are congruent.

THEOREM CIRC-3

Tangent Theorem A line that is tangent to a circle is perpendicular to a radius of the circle at the point of tangency.

THEOREM CIRC-4

Converse of the Tangent Theorem A line that is perpendicular to a radius of a circle at its endpoint on the circle is tangent to the circle.

THEOREM CIRC-5

Radius and Chord Theorem A radius that is perpendicular to a chord of a circle bisects the chord.

THEOREM CIRC-6

Inscribed Angle Theorem An angle inscribed in a circle has a measure that equals one-half the measure of its intercepted arc.

THEOREM CIRC-7

Inscribed Quadrilateral Theorem If a quadrilateral is inscribed in a semicircle, then the opposite angles are supplementary.

THEOREM CIRC-8

If a tangent and a secant or chord intersect on a circle at the point of tangency, then the measure of the angle formed equals one-half the measure of the intercepted arc.

THEOREM CIRC-9

The measure of a secant-tangent angle with its vertex outside the circle equals one-half of the difference of the measures of the intercepted arcs.

THEOREM CIRC-10

The measure of an angle that is formed by two secants that intersect in the exterior of a circle equals one-half of the difference of the measures of the intercepted arcs.

THEOREM CIRC-11

The measure of a tangent-tangent angle with its vertex outside the circle equals one-half of the difference of the measures of the intercepted arcs, or the measure of the major arc minus 180°.

THEOREM CIRC-12

The measure of an angle that is formed by two secants or chords that intersect in the interior of a circle equals one-half the sum of the measures of the arcs intercepted by the angle and its vertical angle.

Illustrations Credits

All illustrations © K12 Inc. unless otherwise noted

Front cover Sea turtle. © Dobrynina Elena/Shutterstock.com

Back cover Blue watercolor illustration. © Dobrynina Elena/Shutterstock

K[12] Summit Curriculum Computer monitor. © antpkr/Shutterstock; Tablet and phone. © Radu Bercan/Shutterstock

Expressions and Problem Solving Barber pole. © Lost Mountain Studio/Shutterstock.com

Solving Linear Equations and Inequalities The Parthenon. © extravagantni/Thinkstock

Two-Variable Linear Equations and Inequalities Heavy traffic at dusk. © Olesia Bilkei/Shutterstock.com

Introduction to Functions Solar panels and sunflowers. © Henglein/Steets/Media Bakery

Radicals and Exponents Amonite fossil on beach. © Alan Copson/Getty Images

Exponential Functions *Staphylococcus aureus*. © iLexx/iStockphoto.com

Sequences and Modeling with Functions Computer chip on finger tip. © Roger Du Buisson/Corbis

Systems of Equations Crisscross railroads at cargo train platform. © Shutterstock

Polynomials Mondrian-style stained glass. © Paul Cummings/Shutterstock

Quadratic Equations Fountain. © Andrew Howson/Dreamstime.com

Quadratic Functions The Masia Freixa in Barcelona, Spain. © Paco Calvino/Getty Images

Univariate Data Shanghai skyline at night. © Iakov Kalinin/Shutterstock.com

Bivariate Data Vineyards against the backdrop of mountains. © Jeffrey Banke/Dreamstime.com

Data Sources

TWO-VARIABLE LINEAR EQUATIONS AND INEQUALITIES

U.S. Bureau of Labor Statistics. 2015. "Databases, Tables & Calculators by Subject." Accessed January 19, 2015. http://www.bls.gov/data/.

WORKING WITH FUNCTIONS

U.S. Census Bureau. 2015. "Resident Population and Apportionment of the U.S. House of Representatives." Accessed January 16, 2015. http://www.census.gov/dmd/www/resapport/states/northcarolina.pdf.

UNIVARIATE DATA

DOT (U.S. Department of Transportation) FHWA (Federal Highway Administration) Office of Highway Policy Information. 2012a. "Highway Statistics Series: Buses." Accessed April 22, 2013. http://www.google.com/publicdata/explore?ds=gb66jodhlsaab_#!ctype=l&strail=false&bcs=d&nselm=h&met_y=Buses&scale_y=lin&ind_y=false&rdim=state&ifdim=state&tdim=true&hl=en_US&dl=en_US&ind=false.

———. 2012b. "Highway Statistics Series: Automobiles per licensed driver." Accessed April 22, 2013. http://www.google.com/publicdata/explore?ds=gb66jodhlsaab_#!ctype=l&strail=false&bcs=d&nselm=h&met_y=Autos_driver&scale_y=lin&ind_y=false&rdim=state&ifdim=state&tdim=true&hl=en_US&dl=en_US&ind=false.

———. 2012c. "Highway Statistics Series: Trucks." Accessed April 23, 2013. http://www.google.com/publicdata/explore?ds=gb66jodhlsaab_#!ctype=l&strail=false&bcs=d&nselm=h&met_y=Trucks&scale_y=lin&ind_y=false&rdim=state&ifdim=state&tdim=true&hl=en_US&dl=en_US&ind=false.

NCAA. 2016. "Women's Soccer Championship History." Accessed May 3, 2016. http://www.ncaa.com/history/soccer-women/d1.

Peterson's CollegeQuest. 2010. "Does Education Pay? 2010 Bureau of Labor Statistics Research: Unemployment and Salary." Accessed January 21, 2015. http://www.collegequest.com/bls-research-education-pays-2010.aspx.

Tax Foundation. 2015a. "State Individual Income Tax Rates, 2000–2014." Accessed March 3, 2015. http://taxfoundation .org/article/state-individual-income-tax-rates.

———. 2015b. "State Sales, Gasoline, Cigarette, and Alcohol Tax Rates by State, 2000–2014." Accessed March 3, 2015. http://taxfoundation.org/article/state-sales-gasolinecigaretteand-alcohol-tax-rates.

TreasuryDirect. 2014. "Historical Debt Outstanding – Annual 2000–2014." Accessed January 21, 2015. http://www.treasurydirect.gov/govt/reports/pd/histdebt/histdebt_histo5.htm.

www.fueleconomy.gov (U.S. Department of Energy, Energy Efficiency & Renewable Energy and U.S. Environmental Protection Agency, Office of Transportation & Air Quality). 2013. "Fueleconomy Top Ten." Accessed April 16, 2013. http://www.fueleconomy.gov/feg/topten.jsp.